HOW TO BUILD

A Better Home

HOW TO BUILD A BETTER HOME

by

HOWARD H. MORRIS

An Illustrated Guide Book for Prospective Home Owners

SECOND EDITION
FIRST IMPRESSION

THE WESTPORT PUBLISHING COMPANY

WESTPORT, CONNECTICUT

FOREWORD

THE acquisition of a home is a very important step in the life of the average family. Unfortunately, however, it is too often a step taken in the dark, and with unhappy results. For, although such a family may recognize and discount the normal risks involved, such as loss of job by the head of the family, unforeseen sickness, etc., they fail (through lack of popular knowledge on the subject) to recognize other risks involved, among which are the following: Faulty design—undesirable location—faulty materials and workmanship—rapid depreciation and obsolescence —high maintenance costs.

It is the purpose of this Guide, therefore, to make available to prospective home owners complete, *unbiased,* up-to-date, boiled-down, *basic information,* and *definite recommendations*, relative to the broad field of home ownership, and to thereby materially increase their chances of acquiring a worthwhile home. No attempt has been made to include in this Guide house plans, or pictures and descriptions of home interiors, special home gadgets and equipment, or the like; for such information is readily available in the form of house plan books, magazines and periodicals for the home owner, and literature published by the manufacturers of equipment for the home.

This Guide does not endeavor to point out ways and means for obtaining something-for-nothing; nor does it advocate "cheap", temporary types of construction for those who want *permanent* homes. On the contrary, this Guide outlines only good, sound, permanent construction methods and materials, inasmuch as the experience of other home owners proves that it is far better to own a small, well-constructed house than to own a large, poorly constructed one; for the poorly constructed house will quickly, and surely, become a burden to the owner, from a standpoint of repair bills, alone.

It is hoped that this Guide may help the prospective home owner to acquire a house that is suitably located, of good design and construction, and priced within his means—a house which, above all, will be truly a *home.*

—H. H. M.

ACKNOWLEDGMENTS

THE Author wishes to express his sincere appreciation to the architects, engineers, practical builders, and the others, who contributed to this Guide with their advice or criticism; and to the many associations, organizations and other concerns, that comprise our building industry, for their generous permission to reprint portions of their printed data.

The Author desires to particularly acknowledge the assistance rendered by Charles E. Heath, Jr., Edward H. A. Schnitker, and the late T. W. O'Briant in the preparation of the 23 page-size Plates contained in this book. These Plates are based principally on the standard homebuilding practices recommended by various U. S. Government agencies in their printed literature, the Copper and Brass Research Association, National Board of Fire Underwriters, National Lumber Manufacturers Association, National Slate Association, Portland Cement Association, Structural Clay Products Association, Weyerhaeuser Forest Products, and Messrs. Ramsey's and Sleeper's "Architectural Graphic Standards."

—H. H. M.

CONTENTS

QUICK REFERENCE INDEX TO SPECIAL, PAGE-SIZE PLATES (ILLUSTRATIONS)
ITEMS ILLUSTRATED BY PLATE

GETTING STARTED

1. Careful Planning Necessary—If you are considering owning a home of your own, don't rush into the affair, but study the matter carefully from all angles, for the experience of others has shown that the acquisition of a worthwhile home requires careful, intelligent, and deliberate planning.

The average home-seeker who starts along the road to home ownership has only a vague idea about the whole matter, and often builds or buys a home perhaps more blindly than he purchases an automobile. It is inevitable, therefore, that many home-seekers of this type should, in the end, find themselves bound by legal ties to an undesirable house which can never be a "home", but only a burden upon which they must squander their life savings.

2. Be Guided by Knowledge—Many organizations and individuals, with the interest of the prospective home owner at heart, have studied ways and means of assisting him to acquire a worthwhile home. They have all reached the same conclusion, which is this: *Every prospective home owner, before acquiring a home, should get the basic facts relative to home ownership; and should especially know the difference between good and bad construction.*

This Guide will provide you with the home-building facts you will need; and whether you propose to spend $2,000.00 or $20,000.00 for a home; use traditonal, modern or prefabricated design; employ an architect or use stock plans; or buy a house instead of building, this Guide will help you.

USING THIS GUIDE BOOK

3. Suggested Procedure—Although this Guide can be used in various ways to assist you in planning and building your home, it is believed that the following suggestions and explanations in regard to certain portions of the Guide will help you to derive the maximum benefits from its use:

(1) Read Guide over once so as to become familiar with its general contents.

(2) Use Sections 2 to 6 to assist you in deciding upon the basic matters discussed in these Sections, such as "Deciding Upon Home Ownership", "Selecting Professional Service", "Financing Your Home", etc.

It is assumed that, by the time you have decided upon the matters covered by Sections 2 to 6, you will also have determined the type of home that you wish to build, and will either have decided to have an architect make the necessary drawings and write the specifications, or have obtained a set of drawings and specifications from other sources. (Par. 22 to 24, P. 27.)

(3) Use Sections 7 to 35 to assist you in selecting and specifying suitable materials, mechanical equipment, and construction details for your new home.

If you decide to employ an architect to make the drawings and write the specifications for your home, Sections 7 to 35 will assist you in preparing for the architect a condensed outline of the types of material, mechanical equipment, and construction details that you desire him to incorporate in your new home. This procedure will be advantageous to both you and the architect, as it will reduce to a minimum the number of changes that will have to be made to the working drawings and specifications after they are completed.

If you decide not to employ an architect, and procure working drawings and specifications from other sources (Pars. 22 to 24, P. 27), Sections 7 to 35 will assist you to make such changes to the specifications (and drawings too, if necessary,) as are advisable to insure that your new home incorporates the types of material, mechanical equipment, and construction details that you desire.

4. Use of "Special" Information—It will be noted that several Sections of this Guide contain a certain amount of information in regard to methods of determining the sizes of foundation wall footings, girders, columns, joists, etc. Such information, which is given in simplified, readily understood form, can be used to particularly good advantage by the prospective home owner who procures drawings and specifications of a house that was designed to meet conditions different from those which exist in his locality. For example, the drawings may specify footings that are of ample size for a locality where they will rest on hard clay, but which are too small for use on the prospective home owner's lot where they will rest on soft clay; or the sizes specified for wood girders, columns, joists, etc., may be based on the use of a species of wood stronger than that which is available locally, and thereby necessitate that the sizes of these framing members be increased.

5. Abbreviations — The following abbreviations, where they appear in the text or on the drawings contained in this Guide, should be interpreted as follows:

' = Feet (Example: 1' = one foot).

" = Inches (Example: 1" = one inch).

@ = At.

A. I. A. = American Institute of Architects.

Approx. = Approximate.

C. to C. = Center to center.

CL = Center line.

D., or Diam. = Diameter.

—Do.— = Ditto; "Similar to above".

Fig. = Figure.

Ga. = Gauge.

Lb. = Pound.

Matl. = Material.

Max. = Maximum.

Min. = Minimum.

No. = Number.

O. C. = On center.

P. = Page.

Par. = Paragraph.

Pc. = Piece.

Pl. = Plate (Page-size illustration, P. 42 to 64).

Ref. = Reference (for further reading).

Reqd. = Required.

Sec. = Section (of Guide).

Specs. = Specifications.

DECIDING UPON HOME OWNERSHIP

1. Before Deciding Upon Home Ownership—A person's judgement can be no better than his information. Therefore, both the good and the bad features of home ownership are outlined in this Section. This will allow you to weigh the good points against the bad, when deciding upon home ownership; and, as you take steps to acquire a home, you will be better able to take precautions against the things or conditions that tend to make home ownership a burden, and strive for conditions that make for a real home.

IMPORTANT POINTS TO CONSIDER

2. General—The following discussion in regard to possible expenses and losses involved in the ownership of a home, and the possible difficulties of selling, is not intended to discourage home ownership, but is inserted here to call the attention of the prospective home owner to certain facts that he should take into consideration.

3. Recurring Expenses of Home Ownership—These are expenses that usually require a periodic outlay of cash, in *addition* to any monies paid on the principal, and include the following:

Taxes—As real estate is tangible property that cannot be moved or concealed, it has been, in many cases, greatly overtaxed; and, no doubt, the future may bring even higher taxes.

Insurance—This is a continuous expense during the life of a house.

Interest Charges on Unpaid Balance—These may amount to as much as 6% per year.

Maintenance and Repair Costs—These will be high for a poorly constructed house.

Improvement Assessments (If Any)—These are especially likely to occur in a suburban locality.

Improvements and Additions (If Any)—These might consist of screening the porch; adding an additional room; building a garage; etc.

4. Indirect Expenses of Home Ownership—These are expenses that require no outlay of money, but are in the nature of losses to which the home owner may be subject. Some of these are:

Loss of Interest on Money Already Invested in Property—This assumes that all monies that the owner has paid on the property could have been invested in bonds, first mortgages, etc., and thereby be producing an income for the owner.

Loss Due to Depreciation—This loss is caused by the physical deterioration of the house over a period of years (Par. 2, P. 172).

Loss Due to Obsolescence—This loss is caused by changing styles of architecture; change in nature of neighborhood; etc. (Par. 2, P. 172).

Probable Loss When Selling—Your selling price, if and when you sell, will probably be less than your purchase price, unless you acquire a home when the cost of real estate is low, and sell when prices are relatively high. Reasons: (1) The value of your house will actually be less, due to depreciation and obsolescence. (2) You will probably require the services of a real estate agent in order to sell your house, and his fee will be about 5% of the selling price.

5. Possible Difficulties of Selling—Unlike a stock or bond, a home is not always readily negotiable. Its sale, during normal times, may be limited to a few people in your locality who are interested in buying a ready-built home in your particular neighborhood. Even then, your home must compete with other homes on the market in the matter of general appearance, arrangement, price, etc.

THE CASE FOR HOME OWNERSHIP

6. Benefits to the Home Owner—Like most of the really worthwhile things in life, the greatest benefits to be derived from home ownership are intangible, and cannot be measured in terms of money. A few of such benefits, as pointed out by Ref. R7-5, Sec. 38, are as follows:

Credit—Home ownership gives financial and credit rating in the business world because it is everywhere recognized as a fundamental principle of stability.

Social Background—The children of home-owning parents somehow seem to have a greater stake in the community.

Environment for Children—Your sons and daughters have the privilege of playing and spending recreation periods within the confines of land which is owned by the family and in which they have a personal interest. Improvements and additions can be made with no fear that your work will be wasted as is often the case when the family moves from a rented house.

Development of Responsibility—The home owner always feels a greater sense of responsibility for the preservation of his property; and, in any neighborhood where home ownership predominates, building values and the appearance of the community are always much better than in a rental area.

Expression of Individuality—The opportunity to express on the interior and exterior of your home those personal ideas of yours which individualize your property as having been developed according to your own taste is worth much in personal contentment and satisfaction.

Permanence of Environment—Old friends are always best, and it is pretty difficult to develop life-long attachments which make living more pleasant, when we move from rented house to rented house in many different communities.

Character Development—The responsibilities of home ownership have contributed greatly to the development of good business judgment and trading acumen on the part of many home owners.

Independence—It is certainly a pleasure for the home owner to know that no one can raise his rent, order him to move, tell him how many pets he can have, restrict the size of his family, or comment in any way upon the development of the home.

Savings Habit—Most of our actions being habitual, it is easy for the home owner who has completed the purchase of his dwelling to continue systematic monthly saving.

Peace of Mind—We always live better when we know that come-what-may the paid-for house means always a roof over the family.

7. You Might Own as Cheaply as Renting—As the owner of a good home, you might at least break even over a period of years in balancing the amount that your home cost you in relation to what rent would have cost, and at the same time enjoy the benefits of home ownership outlined in Par. 6. This could be possible due to a lower maintenance cost and a smaller depreciation and obsolescence devaluation for your house as compared to the average house, and also to the saving of moving costs, as well.

8. Possibility of Losing Home May Be Small—If you buy a home *within your means,* and finance it by the use of an FHA insured loan, you should have no more difficulty in making the monthly payments than you would otherwise have paying rent. Furthermore, the national trend is toward more protection for the home owner by the establishment of longer-term loans and lower interest rates, the creation of more jobs, and the payment of unemployment insurance.

9. Depreciation and Obsolescence May Be Curtailed—A knowledge of the causes of rapid depreciation and obsolescence will enable you to acquire a home that will be in style and retain its value during your lifetime, and longer.

SHOULD I OWN MY HOME?

10. When the Answer Should Be "No"—The answer to the question "Should I Own My Home?" should definitely be "No" under the following circumstances:

When the House is Undesirable Type—If the house that you are considering is poorly built, is located in an undesirable neighborhood, is architecturally a monstrosity, is unreasonably priced in relation to its sound value, or if it embodies other highly undesirable features, then it certainly is not worth buying. Even a good house cannot always be considered a sound financial investment. Therefore, for you to acquire a house handicapped by poor construction, undesirable location, or other fundamental ailments, would be unfortunate. Such a house will almost surely be worthless as an investment—either financially or spiritually—and will very likely be only a worry, responsibility, and definite handicap to you.

If You Must Overreach—If you must pay more for a home than you can afford, it is sure to be a burden to you, regardless of how fine a home it may be; and, when a home becomes a burden, it is certainly not worthwhile.

When Financing Charges are Excessive—When the purchase of a home is financed in such a manner that the carrying charges are excessive, home ownership is definitely not worthwhile.

11. The Answer May Be "No" for a Young, Newly-Married Couple—Although it is popularly *assumed* that young, newly-married couples should acquire a home of their own at the very earliest possible moment, this assumption is not always true, especially in regard to those who are "on their own" in the matter of earning a living. Sometimes the acquisition of a home by them early in their married life would be a distinct handicap, and most unwise. For the benefit of all the young married couples who read this Guide, we quote as follows from Mr. Horace Davis' book entitled "Money Sense":[1]

"The first and gravest mistake you may make is in the purchase of a home. This, the lot upon which it is to be built, or the furniture which is to go into it, may be presented to you in terms of 'investment', 'a lifetime purchase', 'happiness in its possession'. Guard yourself against being deceived by such expressions. Let no one persuade you that any purchase is an investment in commercial terms where there is not a probability of your being able to realize at least the full amount of the principal whenever you desire to convert that investment into money. Only a financial miracle would permit such a recovery from any one of these purchases. Not only would a home purchased at that time probably present a definite financial burden without any compensating financial return, but would also work as a positive financial deterrent to your removal to some other locality if, later, business or other reasons dictated you should move."

12. The Answer Is "Yes" for a Real Home—If the home that you are considering is of sound construction, is well designed and architecturally pleasing, is located in a good neighborhood into which it properly blends, is reasonably priced in relation to its sound values, and has no undesirable physical fea-

tures of fundamental importance, then this Guide's answer to the question "Should I Own My Home?" is "Yes", subject to the following conditions:

(1) You do not pay more for the home than you can afford.

(2) Your plan of financing is sound.

(3) You are settled enough to feel reasonably sure that you will spend quite a few years in the particular locality that you have selected.

(4) You are reasonably certain of continuous employment in your locality, at a salary that will enable you to make the necessary payments on your home.

(5) *You do not build or buy your home during a period when real estate prices are excessively inflated.*[2]

---

[1] Published by McGraw-Hill Book Co., Inc.

[2] As this Guide goes to press, home-building costs have, on an average, risen more than 85% above prewar costs. Economists are, therefore, urging prospective home owners not to build or buy a house during this period of inflation, *except in cases of the most urgent necessity.* During this period of waiting, however, one should carefully plan the home he hopes to eventually own.

SELECTING PROFESSIONAL SERVICE

1. Need for Expert Advice and Service—As you take positive action toward the acquisition of a home, you will need expert local advice and service before deciding upon any of the important phases of home ownership.

2. The Service You Will Need—You will probably need a bank or other lending institution to finance your home; a real estate dealer to sell you the lot (or house and lot); a lawyer to advise you before you sign any papers or pay out any money; an architect to tender advice, or render service in connection with the planning or construction of your house; and a contractor to build your house (if you build instead of buying.)

3. Selecting Your Bank—Such a bank (or lending institution) should have a reputation of being well managed, both financially and otherwise. Also, it should have reasonable interest rates, and a minimum of so-called fees and service charges.

4. Selecting a Lawyer—Due to the complications, variations, and technicalities involved in the laws in force in various parts of this country, it is difficult for the average home seeker to protect his interests without the aid of a lawyer.

The time to seek advice from a lawyer is *before* signing papers or making initial payments. (An initial payment, however small, serves to make a contract binding.)

You should endeavor to select a lawyer who is particularly well versed in laws pertaining to real estate transactions; and who has earned a reputation for being reliable, and reasonable in regard to his fees.

5. Selecting a Real Estate Dealer—You should select your real estate dealer by his reputation, just as you do your banker or lawyer. Such a person (or persons) should have the following qualifications:

(a) He should have a reputation for fair dealing.

(b) He should endeavor to maintain this good reputation through the goodwill of his clients.

(c) He should endeavor to obtain a square deal for both the seller and buyer of any proprety that he sells, by arriving at a fair selling price through the use of the latest accepted appraisal methods and his own knowledge of local real estate values.

(d) He should be of the type that will not try to rush you into a deal.

(e) He should be a genuine supporter of local building restrictions and zoning laws that will promote and protect civic beauty and real estate values.

6. Architectural Service for the Average Home Seeker—It is not always possible for the home seeker to avail himself of complete architectural service when he acquires a home. However, it is possible, and advisable, for the average home seeker to get a competent architect's opinion and advice concerning any home that he contemplates buying or building. It is especially important to let an architect check over your plans and specifications for soundness of design, suitability of materials and construction methods, and suitability of design in relation to the proposed building lot and neighborhood.

7. Selecting an Architect—Select an architect who has a reputation for being a *good* architect. Make inquiries about his abilities from people whom he has served. If the architect whom you select is to design your home, and supervise its construction, he should have the following minimum qualities:

(a) He should, of course, be thoroughly reliable.

(b) He should combine good, sound design and at least a reasonable amount of beauty in his houses.

(c) He should furnish *complete* working drawings and specifications for the houses that he designs.

(d) He should advocate only good material and workmanship.

(e) He should solicit only competent contractors to bid on his jobs.

(f) He should supervise his jobs in a fair, but competent, manner.

8. Selecting a Contractor—You cannot be too careful about the selection of your contractor. You may have the best architect, plans, and specifications obtainable, but without a *good* contractor you will surely come to grief—in one way or another. *The quality of any house is dependent upon the contractor who builds it.*

In order to receive competitive bids for the construction of your home, you should obtain the names of at least three contractors who have a reputation for being thoroughly reliable; who use only good material and workmanship; and who are financially responsible. Such names may be obtained from your friends or acquaintances (or even strangers), who have built good homes. You may also make inquiries at one or more *good* lumber mills, as they are in constant contact with most of the better class of contractors.

9. Selecting Subcontractors — Practically all portions of a house, except the carpentry and millwork, are executed by subcontractors, under the supervision of the general contractor. It is, therefore, apparent that they should be selected with great care so as to be sure of their reliability and efficiency. When you employ a *good* general contractor, you have little to worry about on this score, because such contractors usually sublet their work only to responsible subcontractors. Nevertheless, before accepting the bid submitted by any general contractor, you are advised to ascertain the names of his various subcontractors and check their qualifications.

10. Selecting a Lumber and Planing Mill — The *good* mills handle a good grade of well-seasoned lumber, and they keep their woodworking equipment in good shape so as to enable them to turn out smooth, first-class millwork. Your dealings with them are likely to be entirely satisfactory.

As in the case of subcontractors, you may expect a good general contractor to select only a good, reputable mill. But, here again, you should make a check before accepting the contractor's submitted proposal.

FINANCING YOUR HOME

1. Total Amount to Spend for House and Lot— This amount may vary from 1½ to 2½ times a person's income, depending on individual desires and on circumstances. The average person should spend *not more* than 2 times his annual income.

It should be borne in mind that many of the current or recurring expenses of home ownership, such as interest on money invested, taxes, and fire insurance *are almost in direct proportion to the original cost of a home*. Also, the more expensive a house is, the fewer the prospective buyers in case you ever wish to sell it.

2. Amount to Spend for Lot— The lot should be obtained for as reasonable a price as is possible, without sacrificing any essential qualities. The less expensive the lot, the more money that will be left for the house itself; and a well-constructed house on a cheap lot is far more desirable than an unsatisfactory house on an expensive lot—in fact, a cheap house may add nothing to the sale of an expensive lot. The actual amount to spend for a lot depends to a great extent on whether or not it is "improved", and its proportionate cost should be about as follows:

Unimproved Lot—Where streets, curbing, sidewalks, water, electricity, gas, and sewerage improvements have *not* been made, a lot may sometimes be acquired for less than 5% of the total cost of the house and lot, and 10% should be the upper limit.

Improved Lot—If the lot has all of the improvements listed above, the cost of such lot may be as high as 20% of the total cost of the house and lot, but 25% should be the limit.

3. Method of Financing— Unless you pay cash for your home, you are advised to make use of an amortized, first mortgage loan. By following this plan of financing, the loan will be paid off in easy, but definite, monthly installments. For the average home-seeker this will mean obtaining an FHA insured loan.

4. Essential Features of FHA Loans[1]—An FHA loan is a special, amortized, first mortgage loan having the following features:

[1]The Servicemen's Readjustment Act ("G. I. Bill of Rights") entitles veterans to certain special privileges in regard to the purchase and financing of a home. Veterans who are unfamiliar with their specific rights under this law may obtain the desired information from a reliable, local lending institution.

Who makes the Loan—An approved, local lending institution makes the loan. The FHA merely insures the loan.

Amount Loaned—The lending agency may loan up to a *maximum* of 90% of the FHA appraised value of the house and lot for new home construction, and up to 80% of the appraised value for the purchase of an existing house.

Duration of Loan—A loan may be obtained for a maximum period of 25 years for new home construction, and for a maximum period of 20 years for the purchase of an existing house. At the end of the loan period the house will be yours free of liens.

Maximum Interest Rate—The maximum interest rate is 4½%, plus ½ of 1 percent mortgage insurance premium on diminishing balances.

Methods of Making Payments—Payments must be made monthly, like rent, until the loan is paid off. Such monthly payments include payments on principal, interest, mortgage insurance premium, taxes, fire insurance, and special assessments, if any.

No Refinancing Necessary—The initial financing expense is the last.

5. FHA Loans for New Home Construction— These are of three classes, as follows:

Small Loans—These are loans that do not exceed $5,400. These cases are eligible for loans:

(a) Up to 90% of value.

(b) Up to 25 years amortization period.

(c) At a mortgage insurance premium rate of ½% per annum on declining balances.

Medium Loans—These are loans that exceed $5,400 but do not exceed $8,600. These cases are eligible for loans:

(a) Up to 90% of the first $6,000 of value plus 80% of the next $4,000 of value.

(b) Up to 20 years amortization period.

(c) At a mortgage insurance premium rate of ½% per annum on declining balances.

Large Loans—These are loans that exceed $8,600 but do not exceed $16,000. These cases are eligible for loans:

(a) Up to 80% of value.

(b) Up to 20 years amortization periods.

(c) At a mortgage insurance premium rate of ½% per annum on declining balances.

TABLE 1.—*Monthly Payments (Principal and Interest) Required to Pay Off A $1,000 Loan in Various Periods and at Various Interest Rates.*

LOAN PERIOD (YEARS)	INTEREST RATES		
	4 PERCENT	4½ PERCENT	5 PERCENT
	MONTHLY PAYMENTS		
10	$10.13	$10.37	$10.61
11	9.38	9.62	9.87
12	8.76	9.01	9.25
13	8.24	8.48	8.74
14	7.79	8.04	8.29
15	7.40	7.65	7.91
16	7.06	7.32	7.58
17	6.77	7.03	7.29
18	6.51	6.77	7.04
19	6.27	6.54	6.81
20	6.06	6.33	6.60
21	5.88	6.15	6.42
22	5.71	5.98	6.26
23	5.55	5.83	6.11
24	5.41	5.69	5.97
25	5.28	5.56	5.85

6. Monthly Payments — These should not exceed 25% of your monthly income, and should preferably be less. For the average home seeker this may mean obtaining an FHA loan for a 20-year period, or longer.

Estimating Monthly Payments for FHA Loans— The total monthly payments on an FHA loan may be estimated in the manner indicated below. For typical examples, see Table 2.

(1) Knowing the period of years for which the loan will be required and the rate of interest that will be charged, the monthly payments necessary for repaying the principal and paying the interest charges may be ascertained by use of Table 1. *Example:* If a loan of $4,000 is to be paid off in 25 years, and the rate of interest is 4½%, the monthly payments (for principal repayment and interest charges) will be: 4 x $5.56 = $22.24.

(2) To the monthly payments computed in Par. (1) above, must be added the following additional monthly payments:

(a) 1/12 of ½%, on *unpaid balance* of loan, for mortgage insurance premium.

(b) 1/12 of estimated annual fire insurance costs. (Annual fire insurance rates for your locality may be obtained from a lending institution or an insurance agency.)

(c) 1/12 of estimated annual taxes. (Tax rates for your community may be obtained from the local tax collector. Annual taxes may vary, in different communities, from 1% to 5% of the purchase price of a home. A tax rate greater than 3% should be considered excessive.)

7. Some Final Pointers—Before availing yourself of any method of financing, be sure of the following:

(a) It is safe, conservative, and economical.

(b) The interest charges per annum do not exceed 4½% (4% preferably) of the *remaining* unpaid balance at any time during the life of the loan.

(c) It will be unnecessary for you to ever have to refinance the loan.

(d) You thoroughly *understand* the proposed method.

TABLE 2.—*Approximate Monthly Payments Required for FHA Loans*

APPROXIMATE MONTHLY PAYMENTS REQUIRED UNDER 15-YEAR PLAN

Appraised value of house and lot..........................	$ 2,000	$ 2,500	$ 3,000	$ 3,500	$ 4,000	$ 4,500	$ 5,000
Maximum loan possible (90%)[1]...........................	1,800	2,250	2,700	3,100*	3,600	4,000*	4,500
Principal and 4½ % interest, Plus ½ % Mortgage insurance[2]	$ 14.24	$ 17.80	$ 21.36	$ 24.52	$ 28.48	$ 31.64	$ 35.60
Fire insurance (estimated)[3].............................	.27	.34	.40	.47	.53	.60	.67
Taxes (estimated)[3]......................................	2.48	3.10	3.72	4.34	4.96	5.58	6.20
Total Cost Per Month..................................	**$ 16.99**	**$ 21.24**	**$ 25.48**	**$ 29.33**	**$ 33.97**	**$ 37.82**	**$ 42.47**

APPROXIMATE MONTHLY PAYMENTS REQUIRED UNDER 20-YEAR PLAN

Appraised value of house and lot..........................	$ 2,000	$ 2,500	$ 3,000	$ 3,500	$ 4,000	$ 4,500	$ 5,000
Maximum loan possible (90%)[1]...........................	1,800	2,250	2,700	3,100*	3,600	4,000*	4,500
Principal and 4½ % interest, Plus ½ % Mortgage insurance[2]	$ 11.88	$ 14.85	$ 17.82	$ 20.46	$ 23.76	$ 26.40	$ 29.70
Fire insurance (estimated)[3].............................	.27	.34	.40	.47	.53	.60	.67
Taxes (estimated)[3]......................................	2.48	3.10	3.72	4.34	4.96	5.58	6.20
Total Cost Per Month..................................	**$ 14.63**	**$ 18.29**	**$ 21.94**	**$ 25.27**	**$ 29.25**	**$ 32.58**	**$ 36.57**

APPROXIMATE MONTHLY PAYMENTS REQUIRED UNDER 25-YEAR PLAN

Appraised value of house and lot..........................	$ 2,000	$ 2,500	$ 3,000	$ 3,500	$ 4,000	$ 4,500	$ 5,000
Maximum loan possible (90%)[1]...........................	1,800	2,250	2,700	3,100*	3,600	4,000*	4,500
Principal and 4½ % interest, Plus ½ % Mortgage insurance[2]	$ 10.53	$ 13.17	$ 15.80	$ 18.13	$ 21.06	$ 23.40	$ 26.33
Fire insurance (estimated)[3].............................	.27	.34	.40	.47	.53	.60	.67
Taxes (estimated)[3]......................................	2.48	3.10	3.72	4.34	4.96	5.58	6.20
Total Cost Per Month..................................	**$ 13.28**	**$ 16.61**	**$ 19.92**	**$ 22.94**	**$ 26.55**	**$ 29.58**	**$ 33.20**

---

[1] If you already own a lot, or if you purchase a lot which represents 10 percent of the total value of your house, your 90 percent loan will cover the full cost of your house. If your lot is less than 10 percent of the value of the whole you must make up the difference in cash.

[2] You pay ½ of 1 % mortgage insurance premium only on the **unpaid balance** of loan.

[3] Fire insurance and Taxes shown are only estimated averages.

*Mortgages are insurable only in multiples of $100.

SELECTING A BUILDING LOT

1. Location of Lot—This is of the greatest importance, for it determines the neighborhood in which you and your family may spend many years, if not a lifetime. The location also determines to a great extent, the rate of obsolescence of your property. The following is quoted from FHA booklet entitled "Property Standards," in regard to the location of your lot:

(a) "The property should be located in a neighborhood homogeneous in character, or promising of an harmonious development. It should, through zoning, deed restrictions, or otherwise, offer security against decline in desirability for residential purposes due to the encroachment of inharmonious land uses. The presence or imminent danger of the intrusion of buildings or other uses detrimental to residential neighborhoods; the presence of objectionable smoke, odor, noise, unsightly features, or similar nuisances creates hazardous conditions which should be avoided in selecting a property.

(b) "The property should be so located as to be free from unusual danger from conflagrations, flood, subsidence, erosion, and similar conditions which might damage or destroy land and buildings.

(c) "The property should be accessible to suitable employment areas, market centers, schools, and recreational facilities. Adequate and convenient means of transportation at reasonable cost should be available.

(d) "The property should be located preferably on a minor street rather than on a major thoroughfore with heavy traffic."

2. Size of Lot—If you have selected the house you propose to build, this will help determine the minimum size of the lot. Most lending institutions making FHA loans require a minimum space of 8 feet between the house and boundary of lot, on each side.

The very minimum width of lot should be 40 feet; a *safe* minimum width is 50 feet; and a *desirable* minimum width is 60 feet. This latter width allows you a fairly wide latitude in the choice of a house, and also assures you an ample yard or lawn.

The minimum length of lot should in no case be *less* than 100 feet, and should preferably be not less than 150 feet.

3. Borings and Soil Tests—Before deciding upon a lot, it may be advisable to have several holes made in the lot by means of a post-hole digger. This will reveal the following:

Nature of Soil—Borings will indicate: (1) Whether or not the lot is composed of "filled" land; (2) whether or not the soil is of a type that drains well (sandy) or of a type that retains water (clay); (3) whether or not the footings for the house will have to be relatively large or small (Sec. 15, P. 91); and, (4) whether or not the soil will be suitable for the growth of plants and trees when the lot is landscaped.

Suitability for Basement—Borings (especially if made during the rainy season of any particular locality) will reveal the depth of the ground-water level below the surface, and will thus indicate what trouble may be experienced with a basement (Sec. 18, P. 97).

4. Other Important Items to Consider—These are:

(a) Does the selling price include payment of all assessments or other similar fees?

(b) Is the title to the property clear?

(c) Are there any back taxes on the property?

(d) Are there any easements in the title which grant special privileges to an individual or company, such as permission for a telephone company to run its poles on, or near, the property, etc.?

(e) Are the boundaries of the lot correct as represented?

To be sure in regard to the above questions, you should have a competent lawyer search the court records relative to the lot, and present his findings in a brief paper known as an Abstract of Title.

5. Option to Buy—If it happens that you are satisfied with a building lot, but are not *sure* that you want to buy it, you may be able to purchase an option on the lot for a few dollars. An option, when properly written (Form No. 2, P. 176) gives you the privilege of purchasing the property for a certain specified sum, at any time during a specified time; but it does not obligate you to buy. An option usually is not legally binding unless something has been paid for it.

6. Sales Contract (for Purchase of Lot)—See Form No. 1, P. 175.

TABLE 1.—*Check List for the Selection of a Building Lot.*

MISCELLANEOUS ITEMS TO BE CHECKED

LAND	OWNER'S REMARKS	SERVICE	OWNER'S REMARKS	UTILITY	OWNER'S REMARKS	CONDITIONS	OWNER'S REMARKS
Width		Water		Schools		Kind of Neighborhood	
Depth		Electricity		Churches		Traffic Conditions	
Shape		Gas		Distance to Transportation		Zoning	
Topography		Sewer		Distance to Work		Restrictions	
Natural or "Filled" Land		Telephone		Neighborhood Shopping		Easements	
Alleys		Mail Service		Main Shopping		Percent Developed	
Corner Lot		Removal of Garbage, Ashes, and Rubbish		Recreational Facilities		Exposure	
Drainage		Transportation				Taxes	
Suitability for Basement		Street Lighting				Assessments	
Nature of Soil		Paving (Roads)				Trend of Values	
Floods		Sidewalks				Dust, Smoke, etc.	
Erosion		Fire Protection				Noise	
Street Width		Police Protection				Odors	

PLANNING THE HOME

TYPES OF HOUSE CONSTRUCTION

1. Comparative Costs—A contractor can furnish you with fairly accurate data in regard to comparative *local* costs for the various types of construction. Tables 1 and 2 will serve as a general guide, only.

TABLE 1.—*Approximate Comparative Costs for Various Types of Construction**

(Based on cost of a $5,000 frame house, with side walls of wood siding, being 100%)

FRAME CONSTRUCTION	COST	MASONRY CONSTRUCTION[1]	COST
Sidewalls of: Wood Siding	100%	Sidewalls of: 8″ Concrete Block	106%
Stucco	102%		
Wood Shingles	103%	12″ Rubble Stone	110%
Asbestos Siding	106%	8″ Tile or Concrete Block, Stuccoed	112%
Asbestos Shingles	108%		
Brick Veneer	110%	8″ Solid Brick[2]	120%

[1]Interior surfaces of outer walls furred.
[2]Selected common brick exterior.

TABLE 2.—*Average Disposition of Funds on a Typical 6-Room Frame House**

Excavation accounts for	2%
Concrete floors and walls	6
Carpentry including lumber	50
Brickwork	1
Roofing	1½
Sheet Metal	1½
Plastering	9
Plumbing	8
Heating	8
Electrical	3
Tile Work	2
Hardware	1½
Painting and decorating	6½
	100

*NOTE: Tables 1 and 2 are based on pre-war costs, and are given here as an approximate guide, only. At the present time, due to current post-war conditions, no accurate cost figures are available that will apply to the country as a whole.

2. Dwellings of Frame Construction—Such a dwelling consists of a house having a wooden frame, and exterior walls of wood siding or shingles.

Advantages—These should be: (1) Low first cost. (2) Dry interior. (3) Pleasing, home-like appearance. (4) Readily remodeled. (5) Good insulation (Tables 4 and 5, P. 136).

Disadvantages—Such houses must be painted periodically (about once every 3 or 4 years).

Comments—Approximately 80% of all residences and 98% of all farm structures in the United States are built of wood. Due to its abundance, prevalence, comparative cheapness, ease of fabrication, and many other meritorious features, the present proportionate use of wood is likely to continue indefinitely. If good design, materials, and workmanship are used when constructing a frame house, it will probably be a desirable home for many years. However, if poor design, materials, and workmanship are used, its rate of obsolescence and depreciation may be rapid.

In regard to the necessity of painting wooden houses periodically, it should be noted that the exterior trim, windows, and other woodwork of every type of house must also be painted periodically; and, inasmuch as these items require the greatest proportionate amount of the painter's time, it will be seen that the expense of painting a frame house is only proportionately more than the expense of painting houses of masonry, etc.

It should also be noted that it is possible to substitute cement-asbestos shingles or siding for those of wood, and obtain an attractive house having fireproof exterior, and requiring low maintenance costs. Such shingles or siding have the following disadvantages, however: (1) Prevent the house from being readily remodeled. (2) More subject to damage than is wood, due to their brittleness. (3) Poorer insulating properties than wood (Table 4, P. 136).

3. Dwellings of Brick Veneer and Frame Construction—Such a dwelling consists of a frame (wooden) house, having brick exterior walls that are 4″ thick (Pl. 7, Fig. 4).

Advantages—These should be: (1) Moderate first cost. (2) Low maintenance costs. (3) Fireproof exterior. (4) Dry interior. (5) Good insulation (Tables 4 and 5, P. 136).

Disadvantages—Unsuitable for remodeling.

Comments—Brick veneer construction has become quite popular in recent years, and has much to recommend it, if it is properly designed and constructed.

However, the *average* brick veneering will usually leak when exposed to a prolonged, driving rain. Therefore, good design, materials, and workmanship are essential for this type of construction. Otherwise, the inner (hidden) structure of the house may be progressively disintegrated due to leaks, termites, and decay.

4. Dwellings of Masonry Construction — Such a dwelling (Pl. 7, Figs. 1 to 3) is constructed, in general, as follows: (1) Exterior walls are of solid or hollow brickwork (Pl. 5, Figs. 16 to 24); or, of hollow masonry units (structural clay tile, concrete blocks, etc.) with a facing of brick or stucco (Pl. 5, Figs. 25 to 41). (2) Floor joists are of wood or steel, with outer ends resting in exterior masonry walls. (3) Floors are of wood. (4) Partitions are of wood, metal, or masonry. (5) Roof rafters and roof sheathing are of wood.

Advantages—These should be: (1) Low maintenance costs. (2) Fireproof. (This is a relative term, only, as there is usually enough combustible material, such as wood beams, floors, furniture, etc., inside most masonry houses to feed a fire of sufficient proportions as to cause disintegration of the exterior walls.) (3) Fair to good insulation (Tables 4 and 5, P. 136).

Disadvantages—(1) Possibility of damp walls. (The interior faces of the masonry walls are apt to sweat, due to humid air coming in contact with the cold walls.) (2) Unsuitable for remodeling.

Comments—When properly designed and constructed, masonry houses may be very beautiful, and may have a useful life of many years. Without good architectural design, however, such a dwelling may be devoid of architectural appeal; and, unless good design, materials, and workmanship are employed, the exterior walls may leak during prolonged, driving rains, and thereby allow the wooden interior portions to deteriorate due to rot and termite infestation.

5. Dwellings of Concrete Construction — Such a dwelling is constructed, in general, as follows: (1) Exterior walls are of monolithic (one-piece) concrete *or* concrete masonry. (2) Floors are of monolithic, reinforced concrete. (3) Partitions are of monolithic concrete or concrete masonry. (4) Roof rafters and roof sheathing are of wood.

Advantages—These should be: (1) Low maintenance costs. (2) Strong. (It can be reinforced with steel bars to obtain practically any desired strength.) (3) Termite and rat proof. (4) Fireproof. (This is a relative term, for, when exposed to heat of 1800° F., concrete will dehydrate and disintegrate.)

Disadvantages—(1) Possibility of damp walls. (The interior faces of concrete walls may sweat, due to humid air coming in contact with the cold walls.) (2) "Hard" floors. (Bare concrete floors have a tiring effect, and tend to conduct heat from one's body.) (3) Unsuited for remodeling. (4) Relatively poor insulation (Table 4, P. 136).

Comments—Concrete homes are best suited to dry, temperate climates; and they often have stucco exteriors, and tile roofs.

When considering this type of house, you should consult an architect as to whether or not it will harmonize with the other buildings in your prospective neighborhood.

Such dwellings should be carefully designed by a competent architect, and should be erected only by a contractor who is properly experienced and equipped for this type of construction. Otherwise, the dwelling may cost decidedly more than it is worth, and may be of an inferior quality and have a rapid physical depreciation.

6. Dwellings With Exterior Walls of Stucco —As regards this discussion, such a dwelling consists of a masonry or frame house with the outermost portion of the sidewalls plastered with Portland cement stucco.

Advantages—These should be: (1) Low maintenance costs. (2) Fireproof exterior.

Disadvantages—(1) Possibility of cracks. (Stucco is very susceptible to cracks.) (2) Unsuitable for remodeling.

Comments—Stucco side walls, due to the poor design and construction of such walls in the past, have come into disrepute in some localities. There is no doubt, however, concerning the possibility of building satisfactory and enduring stucco dwellings, if the proper methods and materials are used.

Although stucco dwellings are suited to, and used in, all parts of this country, such dwellings are more popular in some sections—such as California and Florida—than in others.

DISCUSSION OF HOUSE DESIGN

7. Modern Design—Modern design, as pointed out by Ref. R1-5, Sec. 38, is based on the following motives: (1)—"to create a floor plan which will provide a functional relation between rooms arranged to suit present day modes of living, to facilitate efficient housekeeping, and to permit an economical use of materials; (2) to permit the exterior treatment to be dictated primarily by the plan, and to be the expression thereof, with little or no regard to traditional concepts; (3) to use materials efficiently, economically, and directly, boldly eliminating decorative features, and relying upon texture and color of materials together with *skillful* arrangement of masses and openings to produce an esthetic effect."

Although much that has been written about the house of the future is obviously ballyhoo, modern design is more than a fad, and sooner or later a large proportion of our houses will embody its characteristics. However, inasmuch as the customs and habits of people change very slowly, it seems safe to say that such an evolution in house construction will require many years, in spite of the present trend towards patio and one-story ranch styles, lower roof lines, and large glass areas for homes.

It should be noted by those prospective home owners who are considering building homes of modern design, however, that the home building art has progressed to the point where present-day design, materials, and construction methods may be so employed as to produce a house having practically every worthwhile feature now envisioned for homes of the future. Further improvements will, of course, continue to be made in the design and construction of homes in the same way that improvements are made in the design and construction of automobiles, radios, and other present-day necessities—a few at a time, year after year, for an infinite period of time. It is apparent, therefore, that those who postpone building their homes until the *ultimate* is reached in house design and construction will never build. (For more detailed discussions of modern design, see Ref. R1-5 and R1-12, Sec. 38.)

8. Traditional Design

—Many present-day examples of traditional house design may be described as being the employment of a combination of outmoded practices, rather than design. However, because the customs and habits of people change very slowly, and most people still prefer traditional styles of architecture, it is safe to estimate that the *better* examples of traditional house design will meet with popular approval many years hence.

It appears safe to assume, therefore, that most of the 13,000,000, or more, single-unit post-war homes that it is estimated will be constructed during the next 10 years will embody, to a great extent, traditional designs and materials. If properly planned, however, such homes may also embody most of the really worthwhile features of houses of modern design, such as convenient kitchens and better lighting, heating, ventilation, soundproofing, etc.

9. Prefabricated Houses

— Housing experts look to the prefabricated house as the ultimate answer to the *low-cost* housing problem, inasmuch as it will be produced by mass-production methods, with a resultant reduction in cost. Although the prefabricated house has been the subject of much discussion in recent years, it is still in the experimental stage.

A few of the present obstacles to the success of such houses are the following: (1) The cost of transporting large sections of such houses any appreciable distance is too high. (2) There is a lack of public enthusiasm for the modern style of architecture frequently used in the prefabricated houses. (3) The labor organizations of the building trades are questioning the introduction of methods which will reduce the amount of job labor. (4) The building codes of many towns and cities lack uniformity, and in many cases are unjustifiably rigid in regard to some items.

However, a number of large companies[1] are now concentrating on this problem; and within a reasonable time they may make available complete prefabricated houses, and prefabricated units (roofs, walls, etc.) for conventional types of houses, that will be better and cheaper than some of those now produced by custom-built methods. Many prefabricated units for home construction, such as complete window and door assemblies, kitchen units, interior stairways, etc., are, of course, already available. (For more detailed discussion of prefabricated houses, see Ref. R11-5 and R11-11, Sec. 38.)

The prospective home owner who is considering the purchase of a prefabricated house should preferably obtain *unbiased* professional advice in regard to the house under consideration before closing the deal.

10. Bungalows

— Bungalows are generally most popular in the suburban sections of a town or city.

---

[1]Well-known companies in the prefabrication field include: Allied Housing Associates, Inc., Langhorne, Pa.; American Houses, Inc., 570 Lexington Ave., New York, N. Y.; E. F. Hodgson Co., 730 Fifth Ave., New York, N. Y.; Fuller Houses (Beech Aircraft), Wichita, Kan.; Gunnison Homes, Inc., New Albany, Indiana; John A. Johnson, Lumber and Millwork Co., Pemberton, N. J.; National Homes Corp., Lafayette, Indiana; and The Pease Woodwork Co., Cincinnati, Ohio. (Names of other prefabricators are listed in Ref. R11-5, Sec. 38.)

Advantages—(1) No stairs to climb. (2) Convenient. (3) Housework made easier. (4) The problem of shrinkage of framing members is partially eliminated (Par. 10, P. 104, and Sec. 23, P. 114).

Disadvantages—(1) Lacks the privacy of a two-story house. (2) The floor plan is usually large, and tends to spread the house out more on the lot. (3) The foundation and roof areas generally exceed those of a comparable two-story house, thereby increasing the cost of these two items. (4) The cost per square foot of the available living space usually exceeds that of a two-story house of comparable quality.

11. Two-Story Houses — This type of house predominates in most sections of the country.

Advantages—(1) Privacy (provided it is properly located on a lot of reasonable width). (2) Utilizes the lot area more economically than does a bungalow. (3) The cost per square foot of the available living space is usually less than that of a one-story house of comparable quality.

Disadvantages—The problem of eliminating or equalizing the shrinkage of the wooden framework is usually present when designing and building a two-story house. (Par. 10, P. 104, and Sec. 23, P. 114.)

12. Dormers—The use of dormers is one of the building practices borrowed from the past.

Advantages—(1) Tend to improve appearance of some types of houses. (2) Provide a limited amount of light and ventilation under the roof areas (attics) of a house.

Disadvantages — (1) Costly. (2) Weaken roof construction. (3) Require careful flashing. (4) Present a potential source of leaks. (5) The light and ventilation afforded is limited. (6) Dormers are generally associated with low, sloping walls. (7) The sloping walls of rooms provided with dormers are formed by the roof, thus careful insulation is necessary to prevent the room from being uncomfortably hot in summer and cold in winter.

USUAL MISTAKES OF HOME PLANNING

13. Poor Location—Due to haste or lack of foresight in selecting their lot, many present day home owners find themselves living in a depreciated neighborhood.

14. Poor Architecture—Such architecture may be the result of the following: (1) "Home-made" house plans. (2) Inexpert alteration of good plans, by the owner or contractor. (3) The use of artificial effects, such as is illustrated by the present-day imitations of Dutch Colonial construction. (4) The misconception that a small house should be a reduced copy of a large house, etc. (5) The use of too many materials in combination.

15. Miscellaneous Defects—Among such defects are the following: (1) Poor orientation in regard to light and ventilation. (2) Lack of cross ventilation. (3) Inconvenient arrangement of rooms. (4) Lack of privacy, due to nearness of other houses. (5) Lack of sufficient closets.

16. Results—The obvious results of some of these mistakes and defects are a very high rate of depreciation and obsolescence (Par. 2, P. 172).

SUGGESTIONS FOR HOME PLANNING

17. General—The home should be planned to provided as fully as possible the following fundamental requisites of a real home: Privacy, convenience, efficiency, roominess, light and air, facilities for recreation, facilities for study, facilities for hobbies, quiet, repose, comfort, security, cheerfulness, beauty, and *permanent value*. (For a more detailed discussion of planning than is given in this Guide, see Ref. R1-10 and R1-11, Sec. 38.)

18. Selecting Type of Construction—The type of construction (frame, brick, stucco, etc.) should be selected in accordance with the desires and the budget of the prospective home owner, the style of architecture used, the climate and geographic location, and the neighborhood. Due regard should be given to the characteristics of each type (Pars. 1 to 6).

19. Selecting Style of Architecture—The style of architecture selected should, to a great extent, be governed by the desires and budget of the prospective home owner, the climate and geographic location, and the neighborhood in which the house will be located. However, careful consideration should also be given to the trends in house styles, otherwise such a house may soon become obsolete.

There is no doubt that the art of home design and construction is now at the cross-roads; and, as a result, many prospective home owners are somewhat confused as to the style of architecture to select for their homes. Therefore, it is believed that the following summary in regard to modern and traditional styles of architecture will be helpful:

Modern Styles of Architecture—(1) All houses will, eventually, embody the **characteristics of** "modern" design; but such an evolution will come slowly, not overnight. (2) The present trend is towards patio and one-story ranch styles, lower roof lines, and large glass areas. (3) The "know how" and the materials are available today to design and build practically any so-called "house of the future" that has, so far, been envisioned. (See Fig. 1.)

Traditional Styles of Architecture—(1) Conservative, traditional styles of architecture are still preferred by most people. (2) The *better* examples of traditional architecture will be in style for many years to come. (3) Houses embodying traditional styles can, with proper planning, have most of the desirable features of modern-style houses.

Those readers considering building a new home embodying conservative, traditional design should give consideration to the general *types* of architecture shown by Figs. 2 and 3, for the following reasons: (1) Good design, from both an architectural and structural standpoint. (2) Simple and economical to construct. (3) The lack of dormers and cut-up

type of roof reduces the first-cost, adds to the structural strength of the house, and reduces the possibilities of leaks. (4) The location of the chimney within the house increases its efficiency, adds to the structural strength of the house, reduces the possibilities of leaks, and reduces cost of chimney. (5) A full basement for recreational purposes, and space in attic for storage or other purposes, are readily practicable. (6) Such houses will be in style for an indefinitely long period. (7) Such houses, if constructed of wood, are readily adapted to remodeling, and to the addition of rooms, if these are ever necessary or desirable.

20. A Few Architectural "Don'ts"—To insure that your home will remain in style, and thus minimize its rate of obsolescence, the following "don'ts" should be observed: (1) Don't use freakish designs. (2) Don't attempt to alter existing designs without consulting a competent architect. (3) Don't use more than two combinations of material (such as combination brick-and-wood sidewalls) for the exterior of the house. (4) Don't employ artificial "imitations"

FIG. 1.—*House Embodying Modern Design*
(*Courtesy of the California Redwood Association*)

FIG. 2–*One Story House Embodying Traditional Design*   EZRA STOLLER

FIG. 3–*Two Story House Embodying Traditional Design With Some Modern Features*   EZRA STOLLER

in striving for effect. (5) Don't use a conglomeration of fancy and useless decorative effects.

21. Selection of House Plan—Even though one may expect eventually to have an architect draw up the plans for his house, it is well to decide on what is wanted by examining the plans and pictures of houses that have been constructed. For sources of house plans, see Pars. 22 to 24. The house selected should fulfill all of the requirements of Par. 17, in so far as possible. The following additional suggestions are also offered:

Orientation—Particular attention should be paid to the direction of the sun and the prevailing winds in relation to the building site, so that a house plan may be selected that will insure proper lighting and ventilation the year-round. Most house plans may be obtained "reversed", if so desired.

Size and Arrangement of Rooms — The rooms should be conveniently arranged in relation to each other, and should be of sufficient size, with enough *unbroken* wall space, to accommodate the necessary furniture. It is well to check this latter requirement by making simple outline drawings of the necessary furniture to the same scale as the house plans, and cutting out such furniture drawings to serve as paper models. These models can then be shifted around over the house plans, until they are satisfactorily located, in which position they may be suitably attached to the house plans.

Closets—The following *minimum* number of closets are recommended: (1) At least one closet in each bedroom. (2) A coat closet in the downstairs entrance hall or other convenient location. (3) A roomy closet adjoining the kitchen to serve as a pantry, storage for brooms, mops, vacuum cleaners, etc. (4) A closet in the bathroom for towels and miscellaneous items. (5) Adequate linen and storage closets in, or adjoining, the upstairs hallway.

Cross-Ventilation—Each bedroom, and all other rooms where practicable, should be provided with at least two windows suitably located to provide cross-ventilation.

Bathroom—Many modern houses of even moderate cost are provided with two bathrooms—one adjoining the master bedroom, and one for general use. The modern trend is towards larger bathrooms, with the different fixtures separated by suitable partitions, so as to allow several members of the family to use the bathroom simultaneously. Consideration should also be given to the provision of a servant's toilet in the basement or heater room.

Convenient Kitchen—Special attention should be given to the kitchen. The present trend is toward small, oblong kitchens having a floor area of from 90 to 108 square feet; and toward the use of "packaged" utility cores containing automatic, time saving equipment such as a mixing machine, dishwasher, garbage disposal unit, etc. (Helpful information for planning a kitchen will be found in Ref. R1-9, Sec. 38.)

Built-In Items—Consideration should be given to having the following built-in, stock items installed in your new home: Kitchen cabinets; ironing board; breakfast unit; broom closet; mantel; bookcase; telephone cabinet; and medicine cabinet.

Porches—In most climates a porch is indispensible for a real home. Proper thought should also be given to the screening of porches.

Basement—See Par. 1, P. 97, for advantages of a basement.

SOURCES OF HOUSE PLANS

22. Magazines—Many well-known popular magazines feature homes that are well-designed architecturally, and publish the names of the designing architects. Working drawings (blueprints) and specifications for such homes may usually be obtained from the architect who designed the home, for a reasonable sum.

23. Lumber Mills—Most lumber mills have books of "stock" house plans on hand which they are generally glad to loan or give to interested parties. Plans and specifications for any of the houses listed in these books are usually available at a reasonable cost.

24. Miscellaneous Sources—House plan books are available at a very reasonable cost from the various sources listed below. Plans and specifications for the houses listed in most of these books may also be obtained at reasonable prices.

Architects Small House Service Bureau, Inc.,
101 Park Avenue, New York City, or
1200 Second Avenue, South Minneapolis, Minnesota.

Arkansas Soft Pine Bureau,
Boyce Building,
Little Rock, Arkansas.

American Builder and Building Age,
30 Church St.,
New York 7, N. Y.

Better Homes and Gardens Plan Service,
Meredith Publishing Co.,
Des Moines, Iowa.

Federal Home Loan Bank Administration,
Federal Home Building Service Plan,
101 Indiana Ave., N. W.,
Washington 25, D. C.

Franklin Watts, Inc.,
285 Madison Ave.,
New York, N. Y.

Garden City Publishing Co., Inc.
Garden City, N. Y.

Home Builders' Service,
405 South Hill, Suite 807,
Los Angeles, California.

Ladies Home Journal,
Curtis Publishing Co.,
Philadelphia, Pennsylvania.

National Homebuilders' Bureau,
140 Nassau St.,
New York, N. Y.

National Lumber Manufacturers Association,
1319 18th St., N. W.
Washington, D. C.

Portland Cement Association,
33 West Grand Avenue,
Chicago, Ill.

Southern Pine Association,
520 Canal Building,
New Orleans, La.

Standard Homes Company,
Colorado Building,
Washington, D. C.

Structural Clay Products Institute, Inc.,
1756 K St., N. W.,
Washington, D. C.

U. S. Department of Agriculture,
Bureau of Agricultural Engineering,
Washington, D. C.

Western Pine Association,
510 Yeon Building,
Portland, Oregon

25. Obtaining House Plans—Before sending away for any house plans, the opinion of a reputable contractor should be sought as to the probable cost of building the particular house under consideration, for it is a waste of time to buy the plans and obtain bids on a house that will cost too much to build. Also, all plans should preferably be purchased with the understanding that they may be returned in good condition prepaid, within a reasonable time after they are received if, for any reason, they are found to be unsuited to the purchaser's needs.

CONTRACT DOCUMENTS FOR HOUSE CONSTRUCTION

1. Documents That Are Required—The most careful planning will be of little or no avail if complete and proper contract documents are not used. The prospective home owner is therefore urged to use adequate contract documents consisting of (1) a good Agreement, (2) a good set of General Conditions of the Contract, (3) a good set of Specifications, and (4) a good set of Contract Drawings.

2. Usual Defects of Contract Documents — Many prospective home owners, who conduct their usual business deals in an intelligent, exacting, and businesslike manner, display a childlike trustfulness when building their home; and readily sign loose, irregular contractural agreements, which afford them little or no protection. A summary of such defects and their results are listed below.

The Agreement—This often consists of a half-baked document that assures the contractor his money, but assures the prospective home owner nothing.

The General Conditions of the Contract—Such General Conditions are often omitted, due to the prospective home owner's ignorance of the need for such a contractural document, with the result that the contractor is practically at liberty, if he so desires, to run the job as he pleases without regard for the best interests of the prospective home owner.

The Specifications—Most specifications are woefully inadequate; and, in combination with inadequate drawings, are the chief reason for the existence of so many present-day, shoddily built homes. For, when indefinite specifications are used, the good contractor will submit a bid that is based on at least a fair quality of material and workmanship, while the low-grade contractor will submit a *low* bid, which though it is *apparently* based on the same quality of material and workmanship as the other bids, is really based on material and workmanship of an inferior grade.

The Contract (Working) Drawings—Such drawings are often inadequate, and allow the contractor to construct the house practically as he pleases.

3. Number of Documents Required—A *minimum* of three complete sets of contract documents are generally required for a contract, and are distributed as follows: One set for the owner, one set for the contractor, and one set for the institution making the loan. Additional sets of drawings and specifications are a good investment, as they will make it possible for more contractors to bid in a given time and will also facilitate the work, if placed at the disposal of the various subcontractors after actual construction is begun.

4. Check With Local Ordinances—Before actually using any contract document for the construction of a house, such documents should be checked carefully to make sure that they meet all of the requirements of local and state laws, and that they will be legally binding.

THE AGREEMENT

5. Definition—The Agreement used should not only constitute a legal contract, but should specify the following important items: (1) Scope of work. (2) Time of completion. (3) The contract sum. (4) Progress payments (if any). (5) Conditions of acceptance, and final payment. (6) Enumeration of the contract documents.

6. Type of Agreement—It is recommended that the contract be let on the basis of the contractor completing the entire job for a stipulated sum. Contracts based on the 'Percentage Basis" or "Cost Plus Fee Basis" usually result in a higher cost to the owner than he had anticipated.

7. Recommended A g r e e m e n t (Architect Employed)—Where an architect is employed, the [1]A.I.A. Agreement, Form A1, is recommended (Ref. R5-4, Sec. 38).

8. Recommended Agreement (No Architect) — Where an architect is not employed, it is recommended that the Agreement embodied in the [1]A.I.A.

---

[1]The various A.I.A. forms referred to in this Section are for sale at book and stationery stores at reasonable cost.

Short Form for Small Construction Contracts be considered for use (Ref. R5-2, Sec. 38). A sample copy of the document is shown on P. 32 and is also contained in Ref. R5-1, Sec. 38.

9. Specifying Time for Completion of House — Three to four months is usually sufficient time to allow a contractor to build a house, inasmuch as a competent contractor should be able to complete the average six-room frame house in 75 working days, assuming that good weather conditions prevail. The approximate time required for the various building operations are as follows:

OPERATION[1]	DAYS
Layout and excavation	3
Footings and foundation	5
Framing to ridge pole	9
Sheathing and cornice	6
Roofing and flashing	3
Siding and window frames	4
Plaster and drying period	15
Laying finish floor	3
Interior trim	15
Interior paint	5
Sand and finish floor	2
Grade yard	5
TOTAL	75

10. Arrangement of Payments—It is recommended that, *where practicable,* no progress payments be made during the course of construction, but that the full amount be paid within, say, 10 days *after the completion and acceptance of the work.* This method (sometimes termed a "turnkey job") has the following advantages for the owner: (1) The contractor will have more incentive to complete the job by the stipulated time. (2) There will be less danger of the contractor pulling the men off the job at periodic intervals, as is sometimes done when periodic payments are made. (3) The contractor will have more incentive to do good work, as he will be at the owner's mercy more so than will the owner be at the contractor's mercy. (4) The owner will be protected in case the contractor fails to carry out the terms of the contract.

In any case, the terms of payment should be such that the Owner may withhold a rather substantial amount to be paid only after the work is completed in full accordance with the terms of the contract.

---

[1]The heating, plumbing, and electrical wiring should be carried on simultaneously with the structural work.

THE GENERAL CONDITIONS OF THE CONTRACT

11. Definition — The General Conditions should cover every important phase of the contractural relationship that is to exist between the contractor and owner during the construction of the house. Among the things to be covered are provisions for the correction of work improperly done, provision for the arbitration of disputes, provision for insurance, etc.

12. Recommended General Conditions (Architect Employed)—Where an architect is employed, the Standard Form of the A.I.A. General Conditions of the Contract for the Construction of Buildings, Form A2, should be used (Ref. R5-3, Sec. 38).

13. Recommended General Conditions (No Architect) — Where an architect is not employed, it is recommended that the General Conditions embodied in the A.I.A. Short Form for Small Construction Contracts (Par. 8) be considered. However, inasmuch as the aforementioned Short Form was designed to be used for work that is of a simple nature and low in cost, it is recommended that if it, or a similar type of document, is used for house construction (and no architect is employed), the prospective home owner consult with his lawyer concerning his individual contract; for only by such action can the prospective home owner be reasonably sure that he is fully protected in regard to every phase of such contract that is peculiar to his own special requirements and to the existing local conditions. A few suggestions as to how the aforementioned Short Form, or a similar type of document, might be made suitable for use between a contractor and owner for the construction of a house, when no architect is employed, are as follows:

*(a) Deletion—*Delete any "Article" relating to "The Architect's Status".

*(b) Addenda—*Below the last printed "Article" listed in the General Conditions, add any additional articles as may be deemed necessary, such as the following:

ARTICLE..... *Superintendence—*The Contractor or a competent superintendent shall remain on the work at all times during its progress. The superintendent shall be familiar with the Drawings and Specifications, and shall fully represent the Contractor during his absence.

ARTICLE ..... *Assignment—*This Contract shall not be assigned or sublet as a whole by the Contractor.

ARTICLE .... *Subcontracts—*The Contractor shall furnish the Owner with a list of all subcontractors for the Owner's

approval prior to the signing of the Contract, and no substitutions of subcontractors shall be made thereafter without the written consent of the Owner. The term "subcontractor" shall include those who furnish the following material, even though they do no work: ....
....
....

The Contractor shall be responsible to the Owner for the acts or omissions of all subcontractors employed by him; and nothing in the Contract Documents shall be construed as establishing a contractural relation between the Owner and any subcontractor.

ARTICLE .... *Substitutions, Alternates*—No substitution or change in materials or construction shall be made without the written order of the Owner; and such order shall state the agreed addition or deductions from the Contract Sum, if any. Changes made prior to the signing of the Contract shall be listed on one or more sheets entitled "The Addenda to the Specifications"; and such sheets shall be signed by the Contractor and Owner, and attached to the Specifications. Where alternates are called for, the Contractor shall state in his Bid which is included.

ARTICLE .... *Bond*—The Owner shall have the right to require the Contractor to furnish bond covering the complete and faithful performance of the Contract and the payment of all obligations arising thereunder, in such form and with such sureties as the Owner may approve. The premium for the Bond, if required, will be paid by the Owner. Bond shall remain in force until completion of the Contract and the acceptance of the work by the Owner.

ARTICLE .... *Local Building Requirements*—Local building requirements shall be followed where such requirements require a quality of material or workmanship in excess of that specified by the Contract Drawings or Specifications. After the signing of the Contract, all extra costs due to following such local building requirements shall be borne by the Contractor.

ARTICLE .... *Progress of Work*—Upon the signing of the Contract by both parties, the Contractor shall commence work at once or otherwise on date agreed upon. All work shall be carried on with reasonable and proper speed and in such a manner that the residence and all other attached or detached structures shall be closed in, and all wooden portions protected from the weather, in the shortest time consistent with good workmanship.

ARTICLE .... *When Drawings and Specifications Conflict*—When the requirements of the Drawings and Specifications do not agree, the Owner shall decide which of such requirements shall be binding.

ARTICLE .... *Toilet Facilities*—The Contractor shall provide and properly maintain suitable screened toilet facilities for the use of the workmen, and shall not permit misuse of the toilet or premises. Before final payment is made, the Contractor shall clean up and remove the toilet from the premises.

ARTICLE .... *Copies of Commercial Specifications or Printed Instructions*—Where any work is specified to be in accordance with the requirements of Commercial Specifications or printed Instructions of any kind, a copy of all such Specifications or printed Instructions shall be made available on the job by the Contractor at such times as the work covered by such Specifications or Instructions is being performed.

ARTICLE .... *Temporary Heat*—If artificial heat is required in the building, the Contractor may use salamanders or, at the option of the Owner, he may use the main heating system provided that he furnishes and pays for a suitable attendant, removes all ashes from the premises, and assumes full responsibility for all damage to the heating system. All necessary fuel shall be provided by the Contractor.

ARTICLE .... *Bids*—The Owner reserves the right to accept or reject any or all bids.

(c) Supplementary Contract Drawings — When any of the Plates shown on P. 42 to 64 are used as supplementary contract drawings (Par. 21), it is recommended that such Plates be listed under the Article of the Agreement entitled "Contract Documents", and that the following additional Article be listed under the General Conditions:

ARTICLE .... *Supplementary Contract Drawings*—The *undeleted* portions of the Plates enumerated under Article ......, entitled "Contract Documents", shall be considered Contract Drawings *only* to the extent specified in the Specifications; or otherwise to the extent that they illustrate the requirements of the Specifications. All Plates shall, in general, serve only as a typical illustration of the type of construction details required. However, all *undeleted* dimensions and notes on these Plates, that are applicable to the work required by the Specifications, shall be binding and shall supersede any corresponding notes and dimensions of the other Contract Drawings included under this Contract.

14. Bond—Where doubt exists as to the willingness or ability of the contractor to fulfill his part of the contract, he should be bonded. Also, in every case where partial payments are made to the contractor before completion of the house, he should preferably be bonded; for the owner would be very poorly protected without such bond if the contractor should fail financially and become bankrupt before the completion of the house.

THE A. I. A. SHORT FORM
for
SMALL CONSTRUCTION CONTRACTS[1]

AGREEMENT AND GENERAL CONDITIONS
BETWEEN CONTRACTOR AND OWNER

ISSUED BY THE AMERICAN INSTITUTE OF ARCHITECTS FOR USE ONLY WHEN THE PRO-
POSED WORK IS SIMPLE IN CHARACTER, SMALL IN COST, AND WHEN A STIPULATED SUM
FORMS THE BASIS OF PAYMENT. FOR OTHER CONTRACTS THE INSTITUTE ISSUES THE
STANDARD FORM OF AGREEMENT BETWEEN CONTRACTOR AND OWNER FOR CONSTRUC-
TION OF BUILDINGS AND THE STANDARD GENERAL CONDITIONS IN CONNECTION THERE-
WITH FOR USE WHEN A STIPULATED SUM FORMS THE BASIS FOR PAYMENT.

FIRST EDITION, COPYRIGHT, 1936, BY THE AMERICAN INSTITUTE OF ARCHITECTS, THE OCTAGON, WASHINGTON, D. C.

THIS AGREEMENT made the...day of

....in the year Nineteen Hundred and..,

by and between...

hereinafter called the Contractor, and...

....hereinafter called the Owner.

WITNESSETH, that the Contractor and the Owner for the considerations hereinafter named agree as follows :

Article 1. Scope of the Work—The Contractor shall furnish all of the material and perform all of the work

for ....as shown

(Caption indicating the portion or portions of work covered)

on the drawings and described in the specifications entitled

prepared by.. Architect

all in accordance with the terms of the contract documents.

Article 2. Time of Completion—The work shall be substantially completed...

Article 3. Contract Sum—The Owner shall pay the Contractor for the performance of the contract subject to

the additions and deductions provided therein in current funds, the sum of...

....dollars. ($..)

Article 4. Progress Payments—The Owner shall make payments on account of the contract, upon requisition
by the contractor, as follows:

Article 5. Acceptance and Final Payment—Final payment shall be due..days
after completion of the work, provided the contract be then fully performed, subject to the provisions of
Article 16 of the General Conditions.

Article 6. Contract Documents—Contract documents are as noted in Article 1 of the General Conditions. The following is an enumeration of the drawings and specifications:

GENERAL CONDITIONS

Article 1. Contract Documents—The contract includes the **Agreement** and its **General Conditions**, the **Drawings**, and the **Specifications**. Two or more copies of each, as required, shall be signed by both parties and one signed copy of each retained by each party.

The intent of these documents is to include all labor, materials, appliances and services of every kind necessary for the proper execution of the work, and the terms and conditions of payment therefor.

The documents are to be considered as one, and whatever is called for by any one of the documents shall be as binding as if called for by all.

Article 2. Samples—The Contractor shall furnish for approval all samples as directed. The work shall be in accordance with approved samples.

Article 3. Materials, Appliances, Employees—Except as otherwise noted, the Contractor shall provide and pay for all materials, labor, tools, water, power and other items necessary to complete the work.

Unless otherwise specified, all materials shall be new, and both workmanship and materials shall be of good quality.

All workmen and sub-contractors shall be skilled in their trades.

Article 4. Royalties and Patents—The Contractor shall pay all royalties and license fees. He shall defend all suits or claims for infringement of any patent rights and shall save the Owner harmless from loss on account thereof.

Article 5. Surveys, Permits, and Regulations—The Owner shall furnish an adequate survey of the property. The Contractor shall obtain and pay for all permits necessary for the prosecution of the work. He shall comply with all laws and regulations bearing on the conduct of the work and shall notify the Owner if the drawings and specifications are at variance therewith.

Article 6. Protection of Work, Property, and Persons—The Contractor shall adequately protect the work, adjacent property and the public and shall be responsible for any damage or injury due to his act or neglect.

Article 7. Inspection of Work—The Contractor shall permit and facilitate inspection of the work by the Owner and his agents and public authorities at all times.

Article 8. Changes in the Work—The Owner may order changes in the work, the Contract Sum being adjusted accordingly. All such orders and adjustments shall be in writing. Claims by the Contractor for extra cost must be made in writing before executing the work involved.

Article 9. Correction of Work—The Contractor shall re-execute any work that fails to conform to the requirements of the contract and that appears during the progress of the work, and shall remedy any defects due to faulty materials or workmanship which appear within a period of one year from the date of completion of the contract. The provisions of this article apply to work done by sub-contractors as well as to work by direct employees of the Contractor.

Article 10. Owner's Right to Terminate the Contract—Should the Contractor neglect to prosecute the work properly, or fail to perform any provision of the contract, the Owner, after seven days' written notice to the Contractor, may, without prejudice to any other remedy he may have, make good the deficiencies and may deduct the cost thereof from the payment then or thereafter due the Contractor or, at his option, may terminate the contract and take possession of all materials, tools, and appliances and finish the work by such means as he sees fit, and if the unpaid balance of the contract price exceeds the expense of finishing the work, such excess shall be paid to the Contractor, but if such expense exceeds such unpaid balance, the Contractor shall pay the difference to the Owner.

Article 11. Contractor's Right to Terminate Contract—Should the work be stopped by any public authority for a period of thirty days or more, through no fault of the Contractor, or should the work be stopped through act or neglect of the Owner for a period of seven days, or should the Owner fail to pay the Contractor any payment within seven days after it is due, then the Contractor upon seven days' written notice to the Owner, may stop work or terminate the contract and recover from the Owner payment for all work executed and any loss sustained and reasonable profit and damages.

Article 12. Payments—Payments shall be made as provided in the Agreement. The making and acceptance of the final payment shall constitute a waiver of all claims by the Owner, other than those arising from unsettled liens or from faulty work appearing thereafter, as provided for in Article 9, and of all claims by the Contractor except any previously made and still unsettled. Payments otherwise due may be withheld on account of defective work not remedied, liens filed, damage by the Contractor to others not adjusted, or failure to make payments properly to sub-contractors or for material or labor.

Article 13. Contractor's Liability Insurance—The Contractor shall maintain such insurance as will protect him from claims under Workmen's Compensation Acts and from any other claims for damages for personal injury, including death, which may arise from operations under this contract. Certificates of such insurance shall be filed with the Owner, if he so require, and shall be subject to his approval for adequacy of protection.

Article 14. Owner's Liability Insurance—The Owner shall be responsible for and at his option may maintain such insurance as will protect him from his contingent liability for damages for personal injury, including death, which may arise from operations under this contract.

Article 15. Fire Insurance—The Owner shall effect and maintain fire insurance upon the entire structure on which the work of this contract is to be done and upon all materials, in or adjacent thereto and intended for use thereon, to at least eighty per cent of the insurable value thereof. The loss, if any, is to be made adjustable with and payable to the Owner as Trustee for whom it may concern, except in such cases as may require payment of all or a proportion of said insurance to be made to a mortgagee as his interests may appear.

The insurance shall cover the following items and labor connected therewith whether in or adjacent to the structure insured:—materials in place or to be used as part of the permanent construction including surplus materials, shanties or temporary structures, scaffoldings, and stagings, protective fences, bridges, forms, and miscellaneous materials and supplies necessary to the work.

The insurance shall not cover any tools owned by mechanics or any tools or equipment owned or rented by the Contractor, and the Owner shall not be responsible for any loss on such property.

Article 16. Liens—The final payment shall not be due until the Contractor has delivered to the Owner a complete release of all liens arising out of this contract, or receipts in full covering all labor and materials for which a lien could be filed, or a bond satisfactory to the Owner indemnifying him against any lien.

Article 17. Separate Contracts—The Owner has the right to let other contracts in connection with the work and the Contractor shall properly cooperate with any such other contractors.

Article 18. The Architect's Status—The Architect shall have general supervision of the work. He has authority to stop the work if necessary to insure its proper execution. He shall certify to the Owner when payments under the contract are due and the amounts to be paid. He shall make decisions on all claims of the Owner or Contractor. All his decisions are subject to arbitration.

Article 19. Arbitration—Any disagreement arising out of this contract or for the breach thereof, shall be submitted to arbitration and this agreement shall be specifically enforceable under the prevailing arbitration law, and judgment upon the award rendered may be entered in the highest court of the forum, state or federal, having jurisdiction. It is mutually agreed that the decision of the arbitrators shall be a condition precedent to any right of legal action that either party may have against the other.

The parties may agree upon one arbitrator; otherwise there shall be three, one named in writing by each party of this contract within five days after notice of arbitration is served by either party upon the other, and a third arbitrator selected by these two arbitrators within five days thereafter. No one shall serve as an arbitrator who is in any way financially interested in this contract or in the affairs of either party thereto.

At the written request of either party, at any time prior to the complete appointment of arbitrators, as provided above, or in the event of any default or lapse in the proceeding, the arbitration shall be held under the Standard Form of Arbitration Procedure of The American Institute of Architects or of the Rules of the American Arbitration Association.

Article 20. Cleaning Up—The Contractor shall keep the premises free from accumulation of waste material and rubbish and at the completion of the work he shall remove from the premises all rubbish, implements and surplus materials and leave the building broom clean.

IN WITNESS WHEREOF the parties hereto executed this Agreement, the day and year first above written.

629326

SPECIFICATIONS

15. General—The specifications are one of the most important of the contract documents. Quoting from Ref. R5-1, Sec. 38: "Specifications should amplify the plans or working drawings, and should describe fully all process of the work, the quality of the materials, and the quality of workmanship to be required . . . The specifications proper should outline in detail the kind and quality of materials and equipment and the method and quality of construction used in the dwelling."

16. What Should Be Included in Specifications—The following detailed descriptions of what should be contained in an adequate set of specifications for the construction of a house are reprinted from Ref. R5-1, Sec. 38. As pointed out by this reference, "The description of the work desired should describe the finished result together with only the necessary features that are essential to secure good quality of materials and workmanship. A full description of the way in which a particular job is actually to be done is unnecessary."

Clearing Site.—The exact extent of clearing to be done should be specified and definite provision made for the preservation and protection of such trees, shrubs, and other natural features as may be agreed upon between Contractor and Owner.

Excavation.—Describe the quality of excavation work desired, listing all items including that for the cellar, footings, piers, plumbing lines, dry wells, septic tanks, drains, etc., and giving the minimum depths below finish grade for each item, if it is not shown on the drawings. State by whom each item of excavation shall be done. State also the method of paying with unit price for excavation in the case of unforeseen circumstances which may arise, such as the need to dynamite large boulders or rock.

Backfill and Grading.—State the extent of backfilling to be done and the materials to be used, and by whom extra material shall be furnished, if needed. State what disposition is to be made of the topsoil removed and the depth to which it shall be removed. State what shall be done with surplus excavated material.

Specify exactly what other grading, if any, is to be included in the contract; and if additional materials are required, specify the quality of the workmanship and of the materials and by whom they shall be supplied.

Footings.—Describe the construction of footings and the materials to be used and give the sizes, if not shown on drawings, for each class of footing (under walls, piers, chimneys, etc.).

Foundation Walls.—Describe the foundation walls, piers, etc., giving the materials and methods of construction to be used. If there is to be a portion of the house under which no cellar is to be built, describe the method of ventilation of this portion and the distance from the first floor joists to the ground level.

Cellar Floors.—Describe the cellar floor, its composition, including sub-base and finish, thickness, reinforcement, if any, method of drainage, etc.

Chimneys.—State the materials to be used in the construction of the chimney; how flues, cap, fireplace, and hearths are to be built; what thimbles, cleanouts, etc., are to be incorporated. If the frame of the house is of wood, describe under Framing how the frame will be formed around the masonry of the chimney.

Outside Steps, Porches, Terraces, and Walls.—Describe the construction of any outside steps, masonry, porches, terraces, and retaining walls to be included.

Walks and Driveways.—State what walks and driveways are included in the contract and describe their construction.

Framing.—State what material is to be used in framing. If wood is to be used, give the kinds, grades, and sizes to be used for sills, plates, girders, joists, studs, corner posts, wind-bracing, bridging, fire stops, rafters, ridge pole, sheathing, subflooring, etc., and describe the manner of erection. Describe the manner in which all openings in floors, walls, and partitions shall be framed. The requirement that lumber shall be grade-marked will provide protection as to the quality of material furnished.

Exterior Walls.—Describe the materials to be used for exterior wall finishes, stating quality, sizes, and methods of erection.

Roof.—State the kind of roofing to be used, giving the grade and, if a trade-marked product is to be used, the manufacturer's name, and describe the method of laying.

Sheet Metal.—State what kind and weight of metal is to be used for flashing chimneys, dormers, vents, window and door heads, valleys, intersections of roofs with walls, etc., and describe the method of installation. State where counter flashing is to be installed and describe the methods and materials to be used. Describe leaders and gutters and how and by whom they are to be connected to the drains.

Ornamental and Structural Iron and Steel.—State where iron and steel lintels, beams, columns, anchor bolts, etc., are to be used and give the sizes and method of installation. Describe any ornamental iron railings, grills, etc., required.

Interior Wall and Ceiling Finishes.—State the kinds of wall and ceiling finishes to be used and describe fully.

Trim.—State the kind and quality of materials to be used for exterior and interior trim, such as baseboards, mouldings, cornices, etc. If detailed drawings are to be furnished or stock items are to be used, it should be stated. All stock item numbers should be listed. Describe the mantels to be used. Describe the construction of all stairways, giving the quality and kind of materials used for each part.

Windows and Doors.—Give the style, material, quality, thickness, and sizes of windows, and exterior and interior doors and frames if not shown on drawings. Where double hung windows are to be installed, describe how they are to be controlled. Where patented devices are to be used, give the manufacturer's name and the style and number of the devices.

Rough Hardware.—State by whom the rough hardware is to be furnished.

Screens and Storm Sash.—State what openings are to be screened and describe the types to be used, giving the kinds of materials for frames and screen cloth, and the methods of operation.

If storm sash are to be supplied, enumerate the openings to be protected, and describe the construction, quality, and means of installation of the sash.

Closets.—Describe the interior fittings of clothes closets, linen closets, broom closets, and any other closets that may be included.

Built-In Accessories.—Describe fully, kitchen cabinets, bookcases, medicine cabinets, and other built-in accessories, giving the sizes, kinds, and quality of materials for each. If stock items, give manufacturer's name and item number. If they are specially designed, drawings should be furnished.

Finish Floors.—State the kinds or materials of finished floors to be installed, giving the quality, sizes, and method of laying and finishing for each room.

Painting.—State the mixture of paint materials to be used, giving the qualities and manufacturer's name. If ready mixed paints are used, state manufacturer's name and trade-mark name. State the number of coats to be applied on the various parts of the work, and colors, or the method of determining colors to be used.

Glazing.—State the quality and thickness of glass to be used and describe its installation.

Finish Hardware.—State the amount to be allowed for the purchase of finish hardware and the types to be installed, or list the different items to be used and give the manufacturers' name and catalog numbers of each item.

State by whom finish hardware is to be installed.

Plumbing.—Give the sizes and materials of all soil lines, vents, drains, hot and cold water lines, gas lines, and any other piping to be installed. Describe the fittings and methods of installation. State what excavating is to be done by the plumber and whether or not he is to do his cutting and patching. State also who is to make connection with public water supply and sewage systems.

List all fixtures and give the manufacturers' name and catalog numbers of each item.

Describe the system of hot water supply.

Heating.—Describe the heating system. Give the names of the manufacturers and the catalog numbers of the heater and other manufactured parts of the system.

If not shown on the plans, list the amount of radiation or the sizes of registers and their location for each room.

Electric Work.—Describe the type of wiring to be used. State the number of circuits to be installed and the number of outlets per circuit. State the allowance for lighting fixtures, and by whom they are to be installed. Describe the way in which connection is to be made to service lines.

If not shown on the plans, list all outlets and switches and where they are to be located.

Equipment.—List all equipment, not otherwise specified, that is to be installed, giving the manufacturers' name and catalog numbers, and state by whom each item is to be supplied and by whom installed.

Miscellaneous. — Weather stripping, insulation, waterproofing, or any other items of work not specifically covered here shall be fully described.

Garage.—If a separate garage is to be included in the work, describe fully all items of work and special equipment and hardware necessary.

17. Some Pointers on Specification Writing—The first requisite of specifications is that they are *reasonable, accurate,* and *complete.* Other pointers are given below:

Make Mandatory—The word "shall" should be used instead of "will", "must be", "to be", "should be", etc.

Style and Language—Specifications should be written in a simple, clear, brief style. It is important that the punctuation is correct to the extent that a sentence or clause does not have several meanings. No abbreviations should be used unless properly defined. No attempt should be made to use fancy legal terms or phrases.

The Phrase "Except as Otherwise Noted"—Instead of saying, "except as otherwise noted" and thus requiring everyone to search through the specifications for these "otherwise" items, it is better, *where possible,* to state where and what the exceptions are. For instance, instead of saying, "All finish floors throughout the residence shall be clear, plain sawed, white oak, except as noted otherwise", it would be better to say, "All finish floors throughout the residence shall be clear, plain sawed, white oak, except the kitchen floor, which shall be B and Better Edge Grain yellow pine."

The Phrase "Or Equal"—The phrases "or equal", "or approved equal", etc., should preferably not be used when specifying materials, as such phrases may not serve the best interests of the prospective home owner. The material should be specified as to quality and *alternate* source of manufacture, where possible; and a substitution clause should be used, specifying that "No substitutions of material shall be made without the written order of the owner".

"Guarantees" in Specifications—Do not specify that the contractor shall "guarantee" certain things. For the specifications to be legally correct, the contractor shall "warrant" these certain things. It should also be noted here that, as the General Conditions recommended in Pars. 12 and 13 already contain a blanket warranty for all the work done under the contract, it becomes dangerous to promiscuously insert other warranties throughout the specifications. This is true because a court might allow that, due to the specific warranty clauses, the general warranty clause (of the General Conditions) is waived for all but the specific cases. Therefore, when inserting additional warranty clauses in the specifications, you are cautioned to qualify such insertions by stating that they "shall supplement, but not nullify, the General Conditions".

Specifying Contractor—If you are contracting the entire job out to a general contractor, be sure to use only the phrase "the contractor" throughout your specifications and not such phrases as "this contractor", "the plumbing contractor", etc. This is necessary because your contract is with the general contractor, and not with the subcontractor. Therefore, you should expect the general contractor to be fully responsible for all materials and workmanship.

"Duplication" Between Specifications and Drawings—When something is shown and described in a sufficient manner on the drawings, it should preferably not be repeated in the specifications. In other words, duplications between the drawings and specifications should be avoided as much as possible for the sake of brevity.

"Grandfather Clauses"—This type of clause is one which incompetent architects or specification writers resort to, in order to protect themselves from their own incompetence. An example of such a clause is as follows: "The contractor shall provide and install everything necessary for the full and complete equipment of the building, whether such equipment is shown or specified, or not". Such clauses are also known as "murder" clauses because they allow the architect or owner to "get away with murder" in their demands upon the contractor. These clauses should be avoided because they make for high bids; are a cause of much wrangling and hard feelings on the job; and will not be legally binding in court.

Arrangement of Trade Groups—Although the general contractor is usually made responsible for furnishing all material and labor, etc., called for by the drawings and specifications, it is customary to specify, under *separate headings,* such as Carpentry, Masonry, Plumbing, etc., the scope of the work that is to be provided under each *separate trade.* This method works out to the advantage of everyone concerned. It is especially advantageous for the general contractor, as it permits him to obtain bids from subcontractors of each trade with a minimum of time and effort. One possible arrangement of trade groups is as follows:

1. Demolition, Excavating, and Grading.
2. Monolithic Concrete Work and Membrane Waterproofing.
3. Masonry and Exterior Waterproofing.
4. Miscellaneous Steel and Iron.
5. Carpentry and Millwork; Thermal Insulation; and Glazing.
6. Sheet Metal Work.
7. Roofing.
8. Exterior Stucco.
9. Interior Lathing and Plastering.
10. Painting.
11. Tile Work.
12. Electrical Work.
13. Plumbing, Sewering, and Gas Supply.
14. Heating.
15. Weather Stripping.
16. Caulking.

CONTRACT (WORKING) DRAWINGS

18. General—The contract drawings are the basic contract documents and are, therefore, of extreme importance. Such drawings should be *accurate* and *complete.*

19. Requirements of FHA—The following sample drawings entitled Sheets Nos. 1, 2, 3, 4, and 6, are reprinted from Ref. R5-1, Sec. 38, and indicate the data which should be included on drawings submitted to the FHA for approval. Quoting from Ref. R5-1: "These drawings should consist of a plot plan, showing the location of the house on the lot; a section through the exterior wall showing the foundation construction, and the construction of eaves or coping; a basement plan; a first floor plan; and, if finished off, the second and third floor plans; together with elevations of each side of the dwelling. Plans and elevations of the garage, if any, should be included. Where stock items of millwork or cabinets are not used, detailed drawings should be provided for these items.

"The working drawings should include a layout of the heating system. This may be shown on separate drawings, or the size and location of the heater and arrangement and sizes of all piping may be shown on the basement plan, and the sizes and location of radiators or registers and the heat losses for each room may be shown on the floor plans of other floors.

"If a private sewage disposal system is used, the drawings should contain a complete layout of the system. If a septic tank is to be built by the contractor, its construction details should be included in the drawings, as well as a layout and details of the method of disposing of the effluent, whether subsurface or otherwise."

20. Additional Requirements—It should be borne in mind that the requirements indicated by the sample drawings entitled Sheets Nos. 1, 2, 3, 4, and 6 (P. 39 to 41) are *minimum* FHA requirements, and fall far short of indicating the detail construction of the house. A really *complete* set of drawings should include detail working drawings for the framework of the house, and for the construction of stairs, chimneys, fireplaces, steps, walks, and other miscellaneous items. Instead of furnishing drawings that will merely get by a FHA approval (where such approval is required), you should preferably furnish the contractor with drawings so complete that no important construction detail will be left to chance.

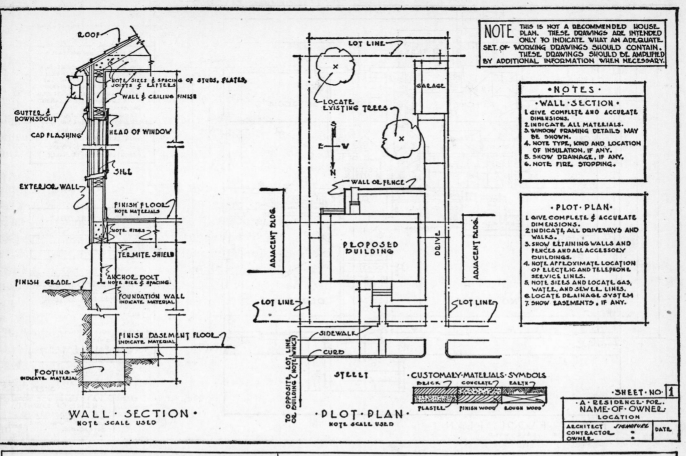

NOTE THIS IS NOT A RECOMMENDED HOUSE PLAN. THESE DRAWINGS ARE INTENDED ONLY TO INDICATE WHAT AN ADEQUATE SET OF WORKING DRAWINGS SHOULD CONTAIN. THESE DRAWINGS SHOULD BE AMPLIFIED BY ADDITIONAL INFORMATION WHEN NECESSARY.

Wall Section labels:
- ROOF
- NOTE SIZES & SPACING OF STUDS, PLATES, JOISTS & RAFTERS
- WALL & CEILING FINISH
- GUTTER & DOWNSPOUT
- CAP FLASHING
- HEAD OF WINDOW
- EXTERIOR WALL
- SILL
- FINISH FLOOR NOTE MATERIALS
- NOTE SIZES
- TERMITE SHIELD
- FINISH GRADE
- ANCHOR BOLT NOTE SIZE & SPACING
- FOUNDATION WALL INDICATE MATERIAL
- FINISH BASEMENT FLOOR INDICATE MATERIAL
- FOOTING INDICATE MATERIAL

WALL · SECTION ·
NOTE SCALE USED

Plot Plan labels:
- LOT LINE
- LOCATE EXISTING TREES
- GARAGE
- WALL OR FENCE
- ADJACENT BLDG.
- PROPOSED BUILDING
- DRIVE
- ADJACENT BLDG.
- LOT LINE
- LOT LINE
- TO OPPOSITE LOT LINE OR BUILDING (NOTE WHICH)
- SIDEWALK
- CURB
- STREET

· PLOT · PLAN ·
NOTE SCALE USED

· CUSTOMARY · MATERIALS · SYMBOLS ·
BRICK   CONCRETE   EARTH
PLASTER   FINISH WOOD   ROUGH WOOD

· NOTES ·
· WALL · SECTION ·
1. GIVE COMPLETE AND ACCURATE DIMENSIONS.
2. INDICATE ALL MATERIALS.
3. WINDOW FRAMING DETAILS MAY BE SHOWN.
4. NOTE TYPE, KIND AND LOCATION OF INSULATION, IF ANY.
5. SHOW DRAINAGE, IF ANY.
6. NOTE FIRE STOPPING.

· PLOT · PLAN ·
1. GIVE COMPLETE & ACCURATE DIMENSIONS.
2. INDICATE ALL DRIVEWAYS AND WALKS.
3. SHOW RETAINING WALLS AND FENCES AND ALL ACCESSORY BUILDINGS.
4. NOTE APPROXIMATE LOCATION OF ELECTRIC AND TELEPHONE SERVICE LINES.
5. NOTE SIZES AND LOCATE GAS, WATER, AND SEWER LINES.
6. LOCATE DRAINAGE SYSTEM
7. SHOW EASEMENTS, IF ANY.

· SHEET · NO. 1
· A · RESIDENCE · FOR ·
NAME · OF · OWNER
LOCATION
ARCHITECT   SIGNATURE   DATE
CONTRACTOR
OWNER

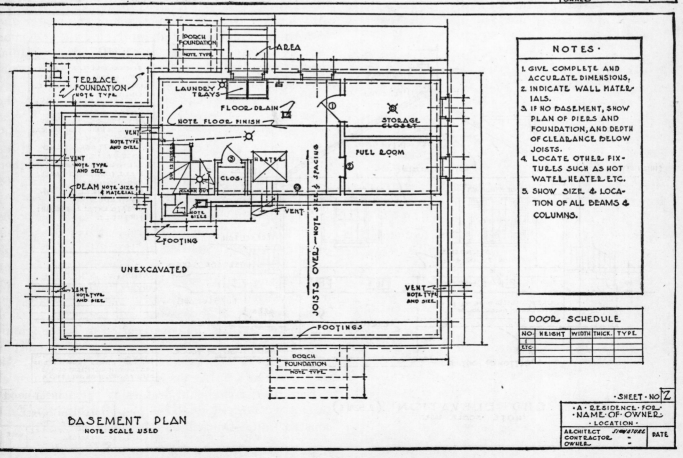

Basement Plan labels:
- PORCH FOUNDATION NOTE TYPE
- AREA
- TERRACE FOUNDATION NOTE TYPE
- LAUNDRY TRAYS
- FLOOR DRAIN
- NOTE FLOOR FINISH
- STORAGE CLOSET
- VENT NOTE TYPE AND SIZE
- VENT NOTE TYPE AND SIZE
- BEAM NOTE SIZE & MATERIAL
- HEATER
- FUEL ROOM
- CLOS.
- CLEAN OUT
- NOTE SIZES
- VENT
- FOOTING
- JOISTS OVER — NOTE SIZE & SPACING
- UNEXCAVATED
- VENT NOTE TYPE AND SIZE
- VENT NOTE TYPE AND SIZE
- FOOTINGS
- PORCH FOUNDATION NOTE TYPE

BASEMENT PLAN
NOTE SCALE USED

NOTES ·
1. GIVE COMPLETE AND ACCURATE DIMENSIONS.
2. INDICATE WALL MATERIALS.
3. IF NO BASEMENT, SHOW PLAN OF PIERS AND FOUNDATION, AND DEPTH OF CLEARANCE BELOW JOISTS.
4. LOCATE OTHER FIXTURES SUCH AS HOT WATER HEATER ETC.
5. SHOW SIZE & LOCATION OF ALL BEAMS & COLUMNS.

DOOR SCHEDULE

NO.	HEIGHT	WIDTH	THICK.	TYPE
ETC.				

· SHEET · NO. 2
· A · RESIDENCE · FOR ·
NAME · OF · OWNER
· LOCATION ·
ARCHITECT   SIGNATURE   DATE
CONTRACTOR
OWNER

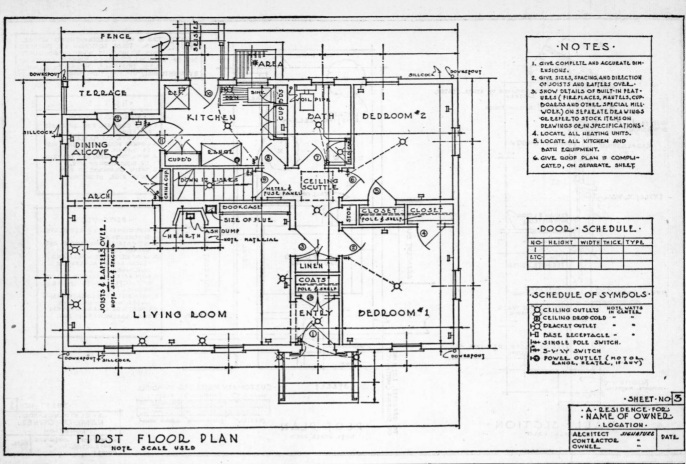

FIRST FLOOR PLAN
NOTE SCALE USED

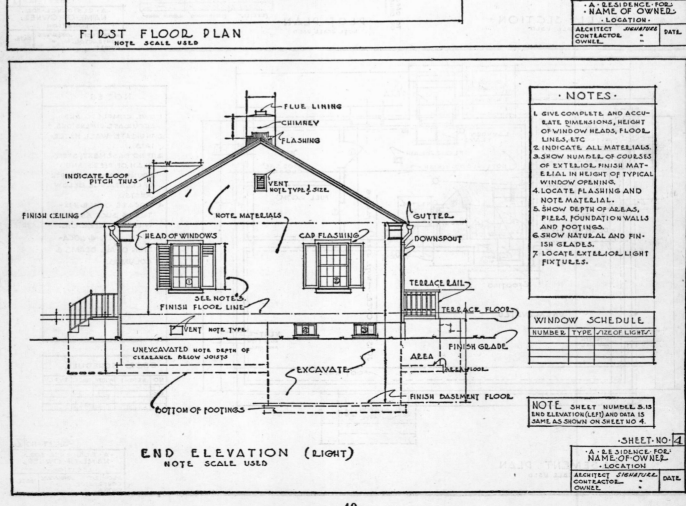

END ELEVATION (RIGHT)
NOTE SCALE USED

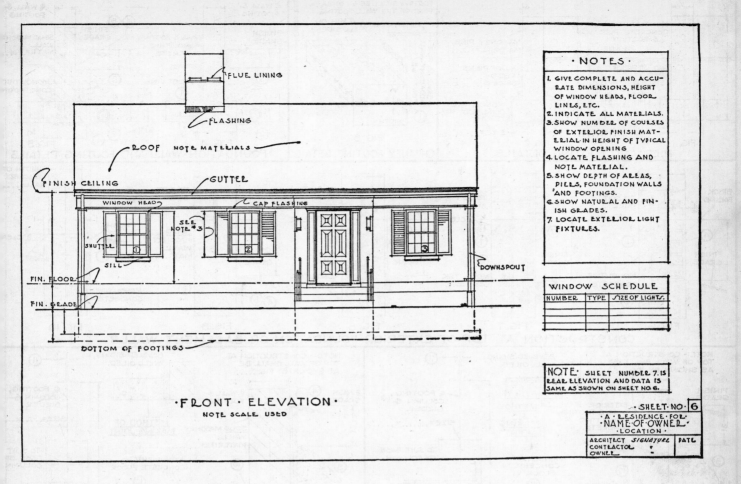

WINDOW SCHEDULE

NUMBER	TYPE	SIZE OF LIGHTS

NOTE· SHEET NUMBER 7. IS
REAR ELEVATION AND DATA IS
SAME AS SHOWN ON SHEET NO. 6.

·FRONT·ELEVATION·
NOTE SCALE USED

·SHEET·NO· 6
·A·RESIDENCE·FOR·
·NAME·OF·OWNER·
·LOCATION·

ARCHITECT SIGNATURE	DATE
CONTRACTOR :	
OWNER :	

21. Supplementary Contract Drawings — The 23 Plates shown on P. 42 to 64 were especially designed to accomplish these purposes:

(1) To indicate to the prospective home owner house construction details that conform to good practice.

(2) To illustrate various portions of the written matter given in the subsequent Sections of this Guide.

(3) *To provide the prospective home owner with available working drawings are inadequate and the supplementary working drawings in cases where the services of an architect are not available. (See Par. 13c.)*

An *example* of using the Plates contained in this Guide as supplementary working drawings would be to state in the specification that: "The pattern and type of construction for front walk shall conform to that shown by Plate 4, Figures 7 and 10, of book entitled How to Build a Better Home, current edition".

41

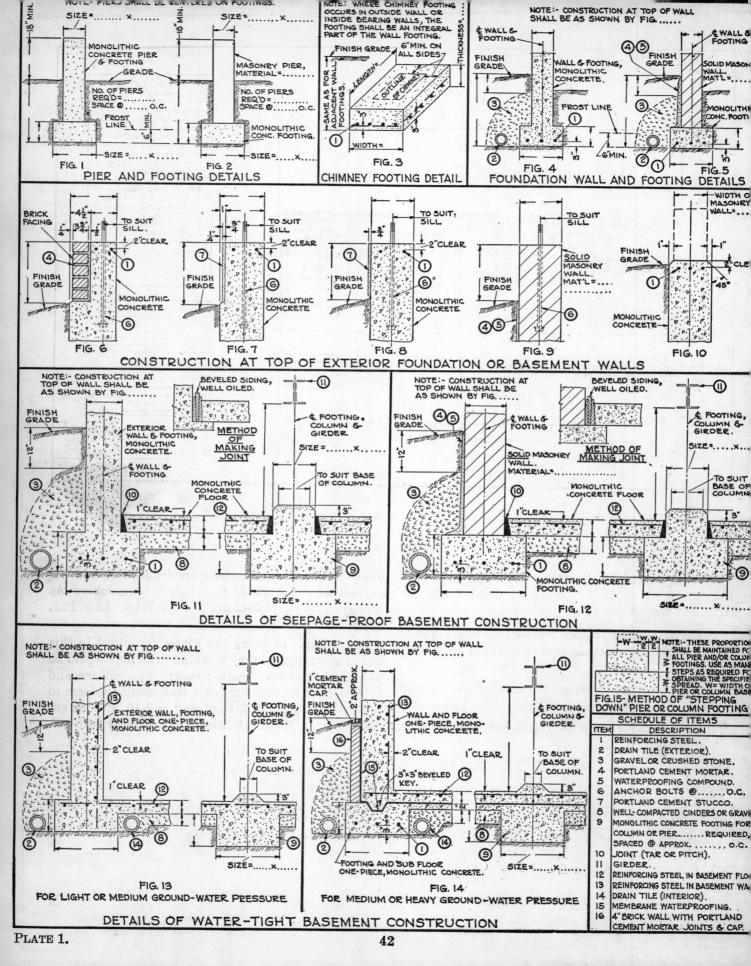

NOTE: PIERS SHALL BE CENTERED ON FOOTINGS.

SIZE = ... X ....

MONOLITHIC CONCRETE PIER & FOOTING

GRADE

NO. OF PIERS REQ'D = SPACE @ .... O.C.

FROST LINE

6" MIN.

SIZE = ... X ......

FIG. 1

SIZE = ... X ......

MASONRY PIER, MATERIAL = ...

NO. OF PIERS REQ'D = SPACE @ .... O.C.

MONOLITHIC CONC. FOOTING

SIZE = ... X ......

FIG. 2

PIER AND FOOTING DETAILS

NOTE: WHERE CHIMNEY FOOTING OCCURS IN OUTSIDE WALL OR INSIDE BEARING WALLS, THE FOOTING SHALL BE AN INTEGRAL PART OF THE WALL FOOTING.

FINISH GRADE

6" MIN. ON ALL SIDES

SAME AS FOR ADJACENT WALL FOOTINGS.

LENGTH =

OUTLINE OF CHIMNEY

THICKNESS

WIDTH =

FIG. 3

CHIMNEY FOOTING DETAIL

NOTE: CONSTRUCTION AT TOP OF WALL SHALL BE AS SHOWN BY FIG. ......

₡ WALL & FOOTING

FINISH GRADE

WALL & FOOTING, MONOLITHIC CONCRETE.

FROST LINE

6" MIN.

FIG. 4

₡ WALL & FOOTING

FINISH GRADE

SOLID MASONRY WALL. MAT'L = ...

MONOLITHIC CONC. FOOTI

FIG. 5

FOUNDATION WALL AND FOOTING DETAILS

BRICK FACING

4½"

3¾"
¼

TO SUIT SILL.

2" CLEAR

FINISH GRADE

MONOLITHIC CONCRETE

FIG. 6

1"
¾

TO SUIT SILL.

2" CLEAR

FINISH GRADE

MONOLITHIC CONCRETE

FIG. 7

¾

TO SUIT SILL.

2" CLEAR

FINISH GRADE

MONOLITHIC CONCRETE

FIG. 8

TO SUIT SILL.

FINISH GRADE

SOLID MASONRY WALL. MAT'L = ...

FIG. 9

WIDTH OF MASONRY WALL = ...

FINISH GRADE

1"   1"

2" CLE

45°

MONOLITHIC CONCRETE

FIG. 10

CONSTRUCTION AT TOP OF EXTERIOR FOUNDATION OR BASEMENT WALLS

NOTE: CONSTRUCTION AT TOP OF WALL SHALL BE AS SHOWN BY FIG. ......

FINISH GRADE

12"

EXTERIOR WALL & FOOTING, MONOLITHIC CONCRETE.

₡ WALL & FOOTING

1" CLEAR

BEVELED SIDING, WELL OILED.

METHOD OF MAKING JOINT

₡ FOOTING, COLUMN & GIRDER

SIZE = ... X ......

TO SUIT BASE OF COLUMN.

MONOLITHIC CONCRETE FLOOR

3"

FIG. 11

NOTE: CONSTRUCTION AT TOP OF WALL SHALL BE AS SHOWN BY FIG. ......

FINISH GRADE

12"

₡ WALL & FOOTING

SOLID MASONRY WALL. MATERIAL =

1" CLEAR

MONOLITHIC CONCRETE FOOTING.

BEVELED SIDING, WELL OILED.

METHOD OF MAKING JOINT

₡ FOOTING, COLUMN & GIRDER

SIZE = ... X ....

TO SUIT BASE OF COLUMN

MONOLITHIC CONCRETE FLOOR

3"

FIG. 12

SIZE = ... X ......

DETAILS OF SEEPAGE-PROOF BASEMENT CONSTRUCTION

NOTE: CONSTRUCTION AT TOP OF WALL SHALL BE AS SHOWN BY FIG. ......

FINISH GRADE

12"

₡ WALL & FOOTING

EXTERIOR WALL, FOOTING, AND FLOOR ONE-PIECE, MONOLITHIC CONCRETE.

2" CLEAR

1" CLEAR

₡ FOOTING, COLUMN & GIRDER.

TO SUIT BASE OF COLUMN.

3"

FIG. 13

FOR LIGHT OR MEDIUM GROUND-WATER PRESSURE

NOTE: CONSTRUCTION AT TOP OF WALL SHALL BE AS SHOWN BY FIG. ......

1" CEMENT MORTAR CAP.

2" APPROX.

FINISH GRADE

12"

WALL AND FLOOR ONE-PIECE, MONO-LITHIC CONCRETE.

2" CLEAR

3"×3" BEVELED KEY.

1" CLEAR

₡ FOOTING, COLUMN & GIRDER.

TO SUIT BASE OF COLUMN.

3"

FOOTING AND SUB FLOOR ONE-PIECE, MONOLITHIC CONCRETE.

FIG. 14

SIZE = ... X ......

FOR MEDIUM OR HEAVY GROUND-WATER PRESSURE

DETAILS OF WATER-TIGHT BASEMENT CONSTRUCTION

W   W W
2   2 2

W

W

NOTE: THESE PROPORTIONS SHALL BE MAINTAINED FOR ALL PIER AND/OR COLUMN FOOTINGS. USE AS MANY STEPS AS REQUIRED FOR OBTAINING THE SPECIFIED SPREAD. W = WIDTH OF PIER OR COLUMN BASE.

FIG. 15 - METHOD OF "STEPPING DOWN" PIER OR COLUMN FOOTING

SCHEDULE OF ITEMS

ITEM	DESCRIPTION
1	REINFORCING STEEL.
2	DRAIN TILE (EXTERIOR).
3	GRAVEL OR CRUSHED STONE.
4	PORTLAND CEMENT MORTAR.
5	WATERPROOFING COMPOUND.
6	ANCHOR BOLTS @ .... O.C.
7	PORTLAND CEMENT STUCCO.
8	WELL-COMPACTED CINDERS OR GRAVI
9	MONOLITHIC CONCRETE FOOTING FOR COLUMN OR PIER .... REQUIRED, SPACED @ APPROX. .... O.C.
10	JOINT (TAR OR PITCH).
11	GIRDER.
12	REINFORCING STEEL IN BASEMENT FLO
13	REINFORCING STEEL IN BASEMENT WA
14	DRAIN TILE (INTERIOR).
15	MEMBRANE WATERPROOFING.
16	4" BRICK WALL WITH PORTLAND CEMENT MORTAR JOINTS & CAP.

PLATE 1.

42

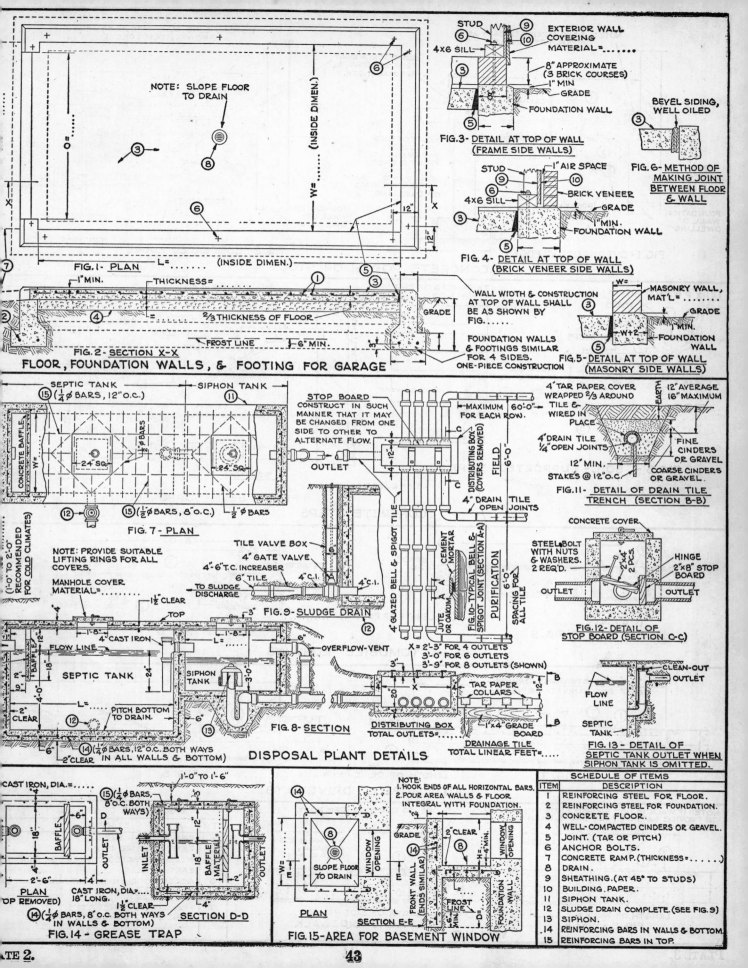

FIG.1 - PLAN

NOTE: SLOPE FLOOR TO DRAIN

(INSIDE DIMEN.)

L= .... (INSIDE DIMEN.)

FIG. 2- SECTION X-X
FLOOR, FOUNDATION WALLS, & FOOTING FOR GARAGE

FIG.3 - DETAIL AT TOP OF WALL
(FRAME SIDE WALLS)

STUD
4x6 SILL
EXTERIOR WALL COVERING MATERIAL=.......
8" APPROXIMATE (3 BRICK COURSES)
1" MIN
GRADE
FOUNDATION WALL

FIG.4 - DETAIL AT TOP OF WALL
(BRICK VENEER SIDE WALLS)

STUD
4x6 SILL
1" AIR SPACE
BRICK VENEER
GRADE
1"MIN.
FOUNDATION WALL

FIG.6- METHOD OF MAKING JOINT BETWEEN FLOOR & WALL

BEVEL SIDING, WELL OILED

WALL WIDTH & CONSTRUCTION AT TOP OF WALL SHALL BE AS SHOWN BY FIG. .....
FOUNDATION WALLS & FOOTINGS SIMILAR FOR 4 SIDES. ONE-PIECE CONSTRUCTION

FIG.5 - DETAIL AT TOP OF WALL
(MASONRY SIDE WALLS)

MASONRY WALL, MAT'L= ....
GRADE
1" MIN.
FOUNDATION WALL

DISPOSAL PLANT DETAILS

SEPTIC TANK   SIPHON TANK

15 (1/4 Ø BARS, 12" O.C.)   11

24" SQ.   24" SQ.

FIG. 7 - PLAN

15 (1/2 Ø BARS, 8" O.C.)   1/2 Ø BARS

NOTE: PROVIDE SUITABLE LIFTING RINGS FOR ALL COVERS.

(1'-0" TO 2'-0" RECOMMENDED FOR COLD CLIMATES)

MANHOLE COVER MATERIAL= ....

STOP BOARD CONSTRUCT IN SUCH MANNER THAT IT MAY BE CHANGED FROM ONE SIDE TO OTHER TO ALTERNATE FLOW.

OUTLET

MAXIMUM 60'-0" FOR EACH ROW.

DISTRIBUTING BOX (COVERS REMOVED)

4" DRAIN TILE OPEN JOINTS

FIG.11 - DETAIL OF DRAIN TILE TRENCH (SECTION B-B)

4" TAR PAPER COVER WRAPPED 2/3 AROUND TILE & WIRED IN PLACE
12" AVERAGE 16" MAXIMUM
EARTH
4" DRAIN TILE 1/4" OPEN JOINTS
12" MIN.
STAKES @ 12" O.C.
FINE CINDERS OR GRAVEL
COARSE CINDERS OR GRAVEL

TILE VALVE BOX
4" GATE VALVE
4'-6" T.C. INCREASER
6" TILE
4" C.I.
4" C.I.
TO SLUDGE DISCHARGE

FIG. 9 - SLUDGE DRAIN

FIG.10- TYPICAL BELL & SPIGOT JOINT (SECTION A-A)
JUTE OR OAKUM
CEMENT MORTAR

PURIFICATION

SPACING FOR ALL TILE
6'-0"

CONCRETE COVER
STEEL BOLT WITH NUTS & WASHERS. 2 REQ'D.
2"x4" 2 PCS.
HINGE
2"x8" STOP BOARD
OUTLET   OUTLET

FIG.12- DETAIL OF STOP BOARD (SECTION C-C)

SEPTIC TANK
FLOW LINE
BAFFLE
4" CAST IRON
TOP
1 1/2 CLEAR
24"
SIPHON TANK
3'-0"
OVERFLOW-VENT
PITCH BOTTOM TO DRAIN.

X= 2'-3" FOR 4 OUTLETS
3'-0" FOR 6 OUTLETS
3'-9" FOR 8 OUTLETS (SHOWN)

TAR PAPER COLLARS
1"x4" GRADE BOARD
DISTRIBUTING BOX TOTAL OUTLETS= ....
DRAINAGE TILE TOTAL LINEAR FEET= .....

FIG. 8 - SECTION

14 (1/4 Ø BARS, 12" O.C. BOTH WAYS IN ALL WALLS & BOTTOM)

CLEAN-OUT OUTLET
FLOW LINE
SEPTIC TANK

FIG. 13 - DETAIL OF SEPTIC TANK OUTLET WHEN SIPHON TANK IS OMITTED.

CAST IRON, DIA.= ....

BAFFLE

PLAN (TOP REMOVED)

CAST IRON, DIA.= 18" LONG.

14 (1/4 Ø BARS, 8" O.C. BOTH WAYS IN WALLS & BOTTOM)

FIG. 14 - GREASE TRAP

15 (1/4 Ø BARS, 8" O.C. BOTH WAYS)

INLET
OUTLET
BAFFLE
MATERIAL
1 1/2 CLEAR

SECTION D-D

NOTE:
1. HOOK ENDS OF ALL HORIZONTAL BARS.
2. POUR AREA WALLS & FLOOR INTEGRAL WITH FOUNDATION.

WINDOW OPENING
GRADE
SLOPE FLOOR TO DRAIN
PLAN

2" CLEAR
4" MIN.
WINDOW OPENING
FRONT WALL (ENDS SIMILAR)
FROST LINE
FOUNDATION WALL

SECTION E-E

FIG.15-AREA FOR BASEMENT WINDOW

SCHEDULE OF ITEMS	
ITEM	DESCRIPTION
1	REINFORCING STEEL FOR FLOOR.
2	REINFORCING STEEL FOR FOUNDATION.
3	CONCRETE FLOOR.
4	WELL-COMPACTED CINDERS OR GRAVEL.
5	JOINT. (TAR OR PITCH)
6	ANCHOR BOLTS.
7	CONCRETE RAMP. (THICKNESS= ......)
8	DRAIN.
9	SHEATHING. (AT 45° TO STUDS)
10	BUILDING PAPER.
11	SIPHON TANK.
12	SLUDGE DRAIN COMPLETE. (SEE FIG.9)
13	SIPHON.
14	REINFORCING BARS IN WALLS & BOTTOM.
15	REINFORCING BARS IN TOP.

PLATE 2.

43

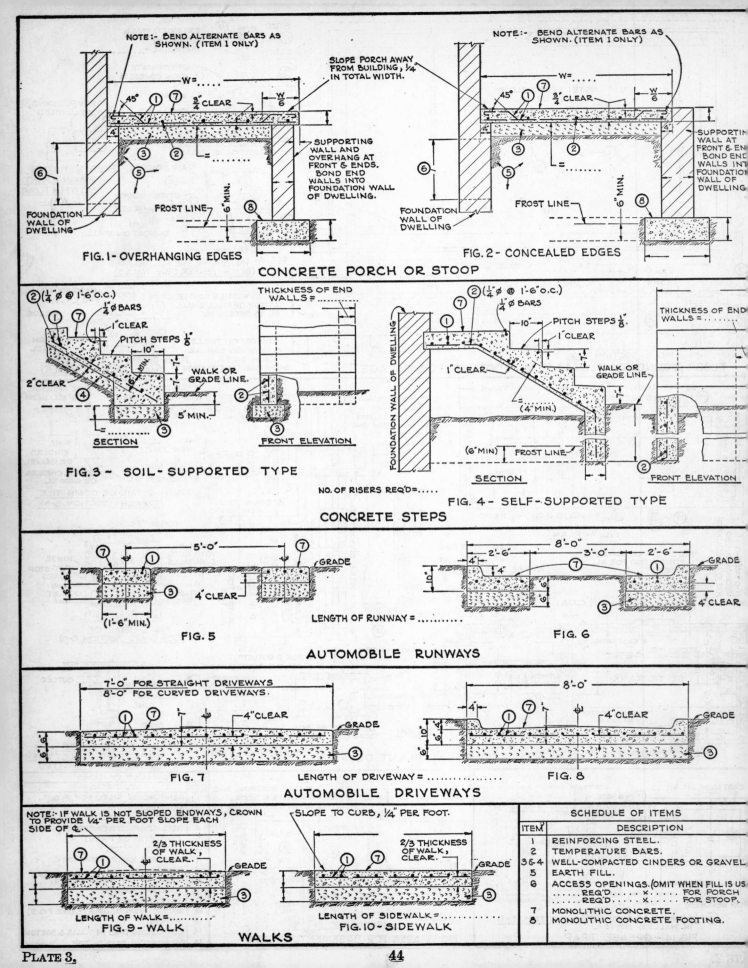

NOTE:- BEND ALTERNATE BARS AS SHOWN. (ITEM 1 ONLY)

SLOPE PORCH AWAY FROM BUILDING, ¼" IN TOTAL WIDTH.

W=......

45° ① ⑦ ¾" CLEAR

W/6

SUPPORTING WALL AND OVERHANG AT FRONT & ENDS. BOND END WALLS INTO FOUNDATION WALL OF DWELLING.

FOUNDATION WALL OF DWELLING

FROST LINE   6" MIN.   ⑧

FIG.1- OVERHANGING EDGES

NOTE:- BEND ALTERNATE BARS AS SHOWN. (ITEM 1 ONLY)

W=......

45° ① ⑦ ¾" CLEAR

W/6

SUPPORTING WALL AT FRONT & ENDS. BOND END WALLS INTO FOUNDATION WALL OF DWELLING.

FOUNDATION WALL OF DWELLING

FROST LINE   6" MIN.   ⑧

FIG.2- CONCEALED EDGES

CONCRETE PORCH OR STOOP

② (¼" ∅ @ 1'-6" O.C.)

¼" ∅ BARS

1" CLEAR

PITCH STEPS ⅛"

10"

7"

WALK OR GRADE LINE.

2" CLEAR

5" MIN.

THICKNESS OF END WALLS =......

SECTION   FRONT ELEVATION

FIG.3 - SOIL-SUPPORTED TYPE

② (¼" ∅ @ 1'-6" O.C.)

⑦ ① ¼" ∅ BARS

10" PITCH STEPS ⅛"

1" CLEAR

7"

1" CLEAR

WALK OR GRADE LINE.

(4" MIN.)

FOUNDATION WALL OF DWELLING

(6" MIN) FROST LINE

THICKNESS OF END WALLS =......

NO. OF RISERS REQ'D=......

SECTION   FRONT ELEVATION

FIG. 4- SELF-SUPPORTED TYPE

CONCRETE STEPS

⑦ ① ⑦ 5'-0" GRADE

4" CLEAR

(1'-6" MIN.) ③

FIG. 5

8'-0" GRADE

2'-6" 3'-0" 2'-6"

4" 4" ⑦ ① 10"

③ 4" CLEAR

LENGTH OF RUNWAY =..........

FIG. 6

AUTOMOBILE RUNWAYS

7'-0" FOR STRAIGHT DRIVEWAYS
8'-0" FOR CURVED DRIVEWAYS.

① ⑦ 4" CLEAR GRADE

③

FIG. 7   LENGTH OF DRIVEWAY =..............

8'-0"

4" ① ⑦ 4" CLEAR GRADE

10" ③

FIG. 8

AUTOMOBILE DRIVEWAYS

NOTE:- IF WALK IS NOT SLOPED ENDWAYS, CROWN TO PROVIDE ¼" PER FOOT SLOPE EACH SIDE OF ₵.

⅔ THICKNESS OF WALK, CLEAR.

⑦ ① GRADE

③

LENGTH OF WALK=..........

FIG. 9- WALK

SLOPE TO CURB, ¼" PER FOOT.

⅔ THICKNESS OF WALK, CLEAR.

① ⑦ GRADE

③

LENGTH OF SIDEWALK=..........

FIG. 10- SIDEWALK

WALKS

SCHEDULE OF ITEMS	
ITEM	DESCRIPTION
1	REINFORCING STEEL.
2	TEMPERATURE BARS.
3&4	WELL-COMPACTED CINDERS OR GRAVEL OR GRAVEL
	EARTH FILL.
5	ACCESS OPENINGS.(OMIT WHEN FILL IS US ......REQ'D..... X ... FOR PORCH ......REQ'D... X ... FOR STOOP.
7	MONOLITHIC CONCRETE.
8	MONOLITHIC CONCRETE FOOTING.

PLATE 3.   44

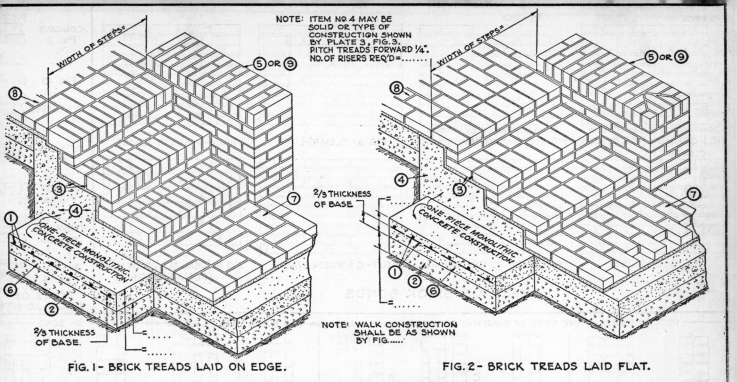

NOTE: ITEM Nº 4 MAY BE SOLID OR TYPE OF CONSTRUCTION SHOWN BY PLATE 3, FIG.3. PITCH TREADS FORWARD ¼". NO. OF RISERS REQ'D=........

ONE-PIECE MONOLITHIC CONCRETE CONSTRUCTION

2/3 THICKNESS OF BASE.

2/3 THICKNESS OF BASE

ONE-PIECE MONOLITHIC CONCRETE CONSTRUCTION

NOTE: WALK CONSTRUCTION SHALL BE AS SHOWN BY FIG......

FIG. 1- BRICK TREADS LAID ON EDGE.

FIG. 2- BRICK TREADS LAID FLAT.

TYPICAL DETAILS FOR BRICK STEPS

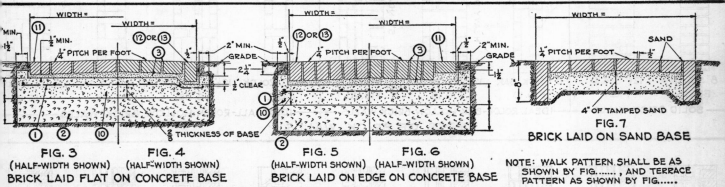

WIDTH =
½" MIN.
¼" PITCH PER FOOT
2" MIN. GRADE
2¼"
½" CLEAR
2/3 THICKNESS OF BASE

WIDTH =
¼" PITCH PER FOOT
2" MIN. GRADE
1½"

WIDTH =
¼" PITCH PER FOOT
SAND
8"
4" OF TAMPED SAND

FIG. 7
BRICK LAID ON SAND BASE

FIG. 3
(HALF-WIDTH SHOWN)

FIG. 4
(HALF-WIDTH SHOWN)

BRICK LAID FLAT ON CONCRETE BASE

FIG. 5
(HALF-WIDTH SHOWN)

FIG. 6
(HALF-WIDTH SHOWN)

BRICK LAID ON EDGE ON CONCRETE BASE

NOTE: WALK PATTERN SHALL BE AS SHOWN BY FIG......, AND TERRACE PATTERN AS SHOWN BY FIG......

TYPICAL DETAILS FOR WALKS AND TERRACES

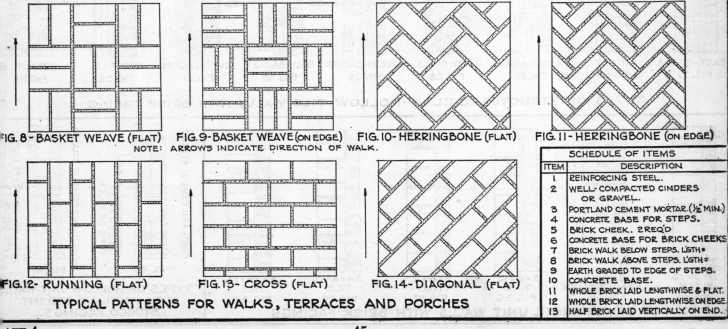

FIG. 8- BASKET WEAVE (FLAT)

FIG. 9- BASKET WEAVE (ON EDGE)

FIG. 10- HERRINGBONE (FLAT)

FIG. 11- HERRINGBONE (ON EDGE)

NOTE: ARROWS INDICATE DIRECTION OF WALK.

FIG.12- RUNNING (FLAT)

FIG.13- CROSS (FLAT)

FIG.14- DIAGONAL (FLAT)

SCHEDULE OF ITEMS	
ITEM	DESCRIPTION
1	REINFORCING STEEL.
2	WELL-COMPACTED CINDERS OR GRAVEL.
3	PORTLAND CEMENT MORTAR.(½" MIN.)
4	CONCRETE BASE FOR STEPS.
5	BRICK CHEEK. 2 REQ'D
6	CONCRETE BASE FOR BRICK CHEEKS.
7	BRICK WALK BELOW STEPS. L'GTH=
8	BRICK WALK ABOVE STEPS. L'GTH=
9	EARTH GRADED TO EDGE OF STEPS.
10	CONCRETE BASE.
11	WHOLE BRICK LAID LENGTHWISE & FLAT.
12	WHOLE BRICK LAID LENGTHWISE ON EDGE
13	HALF BRICK LAID VERTICALLY ON END.

TYPICAL PATTERNS FOR WALKS, TERRACES AND PORCHES

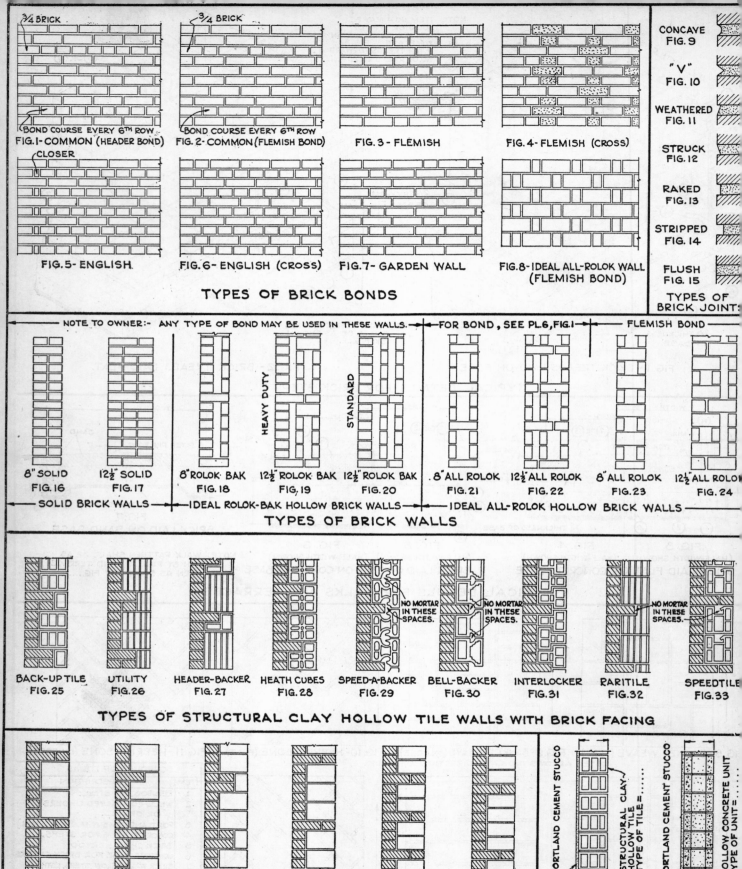

TYPES OF BRICK BONDS

¾ BRICK

BOND COURSE EVERY 6TH ROW
FIG.1- COMMON (HEADER BOND)

¾ BRICK

BOND COURSE EVERY 6TH ROW
FIG.2- COMMON (FLEMISH BOND)

FIG.3 - FLEMISH

FIG.4- FLEMISH (CROSS)

CLOSER
FIG.5- ENGLISH

FIG.6- ENGLISH (CROSS)

FIG.7- GARDEN WALL

FIG.8- IDEAL ALL-ROLOK WALL (FLEMISH BOND)

CONCAVE FIG. 9

"V" FIG. 10

WEATHERED FIG. 11

STRUCK FIG. 12

RAKED FIG. 13

STRIPPED FIG. 14

FLUSH FIG. 15

TYPES OF BRICK JOINTS

TYPES OF BRICK WALLS

NOTE TO OWNER:- ANY TYPE OF BOND MAY BE USED IN THESE WALLS. — FOR BOND, SEE PL.6, FIG.1 — FLEMISH BOND

8" SOLID FIG. 16

12½" SOLID FIG. 17

8" ROLOK BAK FIG. 18

HEAVY DUTY

12½" ROLOK BAK FIG. 19

STANDARD

12½" ROLOK BAK FIG. 20

8" ALL ROLOK FIG. 21

12½" ALL ROLOK FIG. 22

8" ALL ROLOK FIG. 23

12½" ALL ROLOK FIG. 24

SOLID BRICK WALLS — IDEAL ROLOK-BAK HOLLOW BRICK WALLS — IDEAL ALL-ROLOK HOLLOW BRICK WALLS

TYPES OF STRUCTURAL CLAY HOLLOW TILE WALLS WITH BRICK FACING

BACK-UP TILE FIG. 25

UTILITY FIG. 26

HEADER-BACKER FIG. 27

HEATH CUBES FIG. 28

SPEED-A-BACKER FIG. 29

NO MORTAR IN THESE SPACES.

BELL-BACKER FIG. 30

NO MORTAR IN THESE SPACES.

INTERLOCKER FIG. 31

RARITILE FIG. 32

NO MORTAR IN THESE SPACES.

SPEEDTILE FIG. 33

TYPES OF CONCRETE UNIT WALLS WITH BRICK FACINGS

8×8×16 BLOCK FIG. 34

8×8×16 HEADER BLOCK FIG. 35

5×8×12 TILE FIG. 36

5×8×12 TILE FIG. 37

3½×8×12 TILE FIG. 38

3½×8×12 TILE FIG. 39

PORTLAND CEMENT STUCCO

STRUCTURAL CLAY HOLLOW TILE TYPE OF TILE=......

FIG. 40

PORTLAND CEMENT STUCCO

HOLLOW CONCRETE UNIT TYPE OF UNIT=......

FIG. 41

TYPES OF HOLLOW UNIT WALLS WITH PORTLAND CEMENT STUCCO FACINGS.

PLATE 5. 46

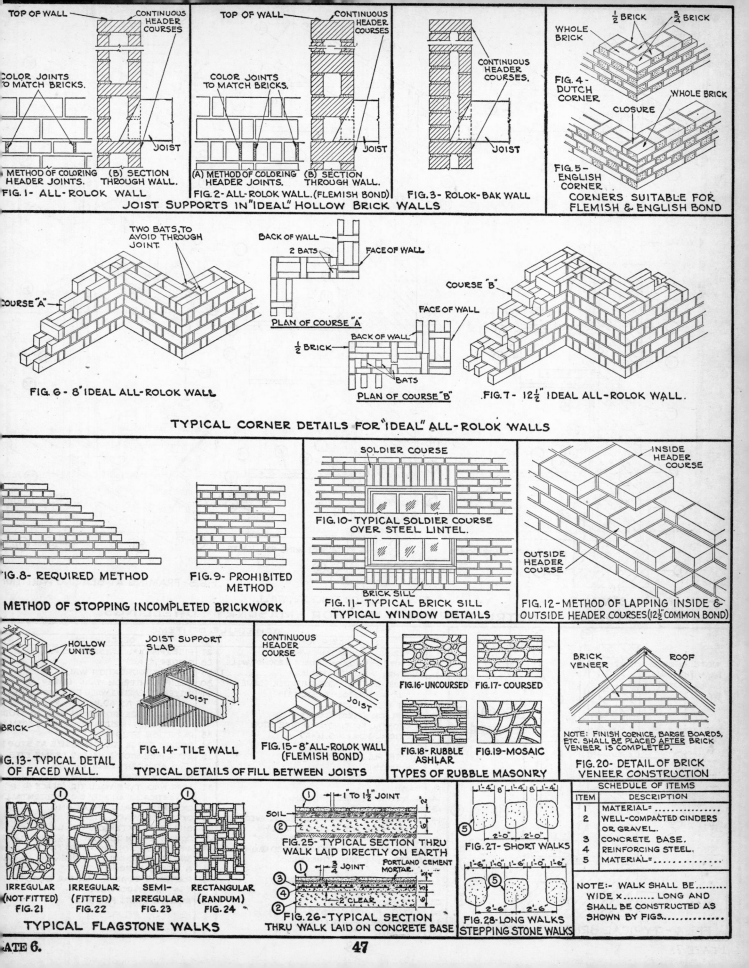

FIG. 1- ALL-ROLOK WALL

COLOR JOINTS TO MATCH BRICKS.

TOP OF WALL — CONTINUOUS HEADER COURSES

METHOD OF COLORING HEADER JOINTS.

(B) SECTION THROUGH WALL.

JOIST

FIG. 2- ALL-ROLOK WALL. (FLEMISH BOND)

TOP OF WALL — CONTINUOUS HEADER COURSES

COLOR JOINTS TO MATCH BRICKS.

(A) METHOD OF COLORING HEADER JOINTS.

(B) SECTION THROUGH WALL.

JOIST

FIG.3- ROLOK-BAK WALL

CONTINUOUS HEADER COURSES.

JOIST

FIG. 4 - DUTCH CORNER

½ BRICK   ¾ BRICK   WHOLE BRICK

WHOLE BRICK   CLOSURE

FIG. 5 - ENGLISH CORNER

CORNERS SUITABLE FOR FLEMISH & ENGLISH BOND

JOIST SUPPORTS IN "IDEAL" HOLLOW BRICK WALLS

TWO BATS, TO AVOID THROUGH JOINT.

COURSE "A"

FIG. 6 - 8" IDEAL ALL-ROLOK WALL

BACK OF WALL   2 BATS   FACE OF WALL

PLAN OF COURSE "A"

BACK OF WALL   FACE OF WALL

½ BRICK   BATS

PLAN OF COURSE "B"

COURSE "B"

FIG. 7 - 12½" IDEAL ALL-ROLOK WALL.

TYPICAL CORNER DETAILS FOR "IDEAL" ALL-ROLOK WALLS

FIG.8 - REQUIRED METHOD

FIG. 9 - PROHIBITED METHOD

METHOD OF STOPPING INCOMPLETED BRICKWORK

SOLDIER COURSE

FIG. 10- TYPICAL SOLDIER COURSE OVER STEEL LINTEL.

BRICK SILL

FIG. 11- TYPICAL BRICK SILL

TYPICAL WINDOW DETAILS

INSIDE HEADER COURSE

OUTSIDE HEADER COURSE

FIG. 12- METHOD OF LAPPING INSIDE & OUTSIDE HEADER COURSES (12½ COMMON BOND)

HOLLOW UNITS

BRICK

FIG. 13- TYPICAL DETAIL OF FACED WALL

JOIST SUPPORT SLAB

JOIST

FIG. 14- TILE WALL

CONTINUOUS HEADER COURSE

JOIST

FIG. 15- 8" ALL-ROLOK WALL (FLEMISH BOND)

TYPICAL DETAILS OF FILL BETWEEN JOISTS

FIG.16- UNCOURSED   **FIG.17- COURSED**

FIG.18- RUBBLE ASHLAR   **FIG.19- MOSAIC**

TYPES OF RUBBLE MASONRY

BRICK VENEER   ROOF

NOTE: FINISH CORNICE, BARGE BOARDS, ETC. SHALL BE PLACED AFTER BRICK VENEER IS COMPLETED.

FIG. 20- DETAIL OF BRICK VENEER CONSTRUCTION

IRREGULAR (NOT FITTED) FIG. 21

IRREGULAR (FITTED) FIG. 22

SEMI-IRREGULAR FIG. 23

RECTANGULAR (RANDUM) FIG. 24

TYPICAL FLAGSTONE WALKS

1" TO 1½" JOINT

SOIL

FIG.25- TYPICAL SECTION THRU WALK LAID DIRECTLY ON EARTH

¾ JOINT   PORTLAND CEMENT MORTAR

2" CLEAR

FIG.26-TYPICAL SECTION THRU WALK LAID ON CONCRETE BASE

FIG. 27- SHORT WALKS

FIG. 28- LONG WALKS

STEPPING STONE WALKS

SCHEDULE OF ITEMS	
ITEM	DESCRIPTION
1	MATERIAL= ....
2	WELL-COMPACTED CINDERS OR GRAVEL.
3	CONCRETE BASE.
4	REINFORCING STEEL.
5	MATERIAL= ....

NOTE:- WALK SHALL BE .... WIDE x .... LONG AND SHALL BE CONSTRUCTED AS SHOWN BY FIGS..............

PLATE 6.   47

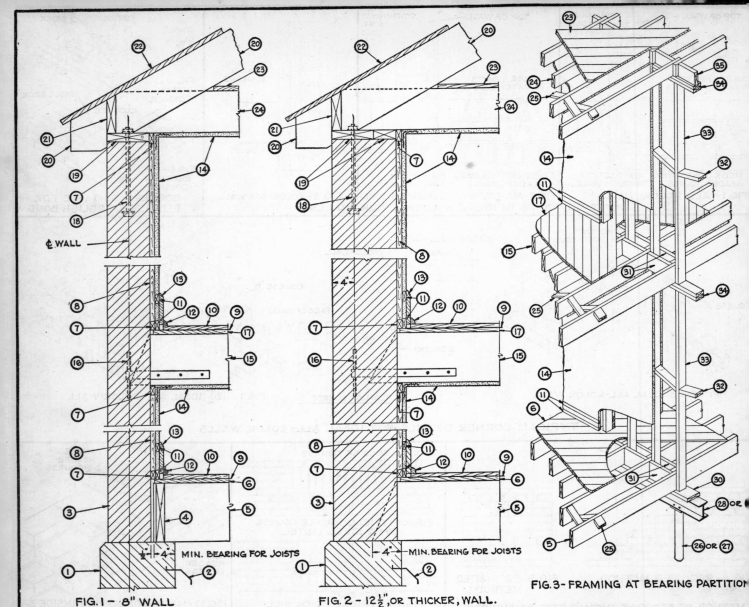

FIG. 1 – 8" WALL

¢ WALL

MIN. BEARING FOR JOISTS

FIG. 2 – 12½", OR THICKER, WALL.

MIN. BEARING FOR JOISTS

FIG. 3 – FRAMING AT BEARING PARTITION

TYPICAL CONSTRUCTION DETAILS FOR MASONRY DWELLINGS

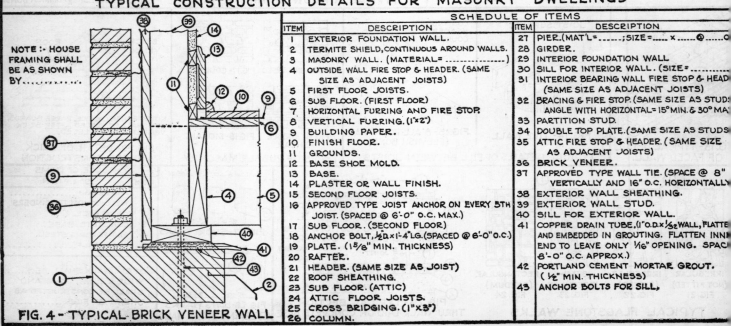

NOTE :- HOUSE
FRAMING SHALL
BE AS SHOWN
BY ....

FIG. 4 - TYPICAL BRICK VENEER WALL

SCHEDULE OF ITEMS

ITEM	DESCRIPTION	ITEM	DESCRIPTION
1	EXTERIOR FOUNDATION WALL.	27	PIER.(MAT'L=......; SIZE=.... x ...... @ ...... O
2	TERMITE SHIELD, CONTINUOUS AROUND WALLS.	28	GIRDER.
3	MASONRY WALL. (MATERIAL = ...)	29	INTERIOR FOUNDATION WALL
4	OUTSIDE WALL FIRE STOP & HEADER. (SAME SIZE AS ADJACENT JOISTS)	30	SILL FOR INTERIOR WALL. (SIZE=............
5	FIRST FLOOR JOISTS.	31	INTERIOR BEARING WALL FIRE STOP & HEAD (SAME SIZE AS ADJACENT JOISTS)
6	SUB FLOOR. (FIRST FLOOR)	32	BRACING & FIRE STOP. (SAME SIZE AS STUDS ANGLE WITH HORIZONTAL= 15° MIN. & 30° MA)
7	HORIZONTAL FURRING AND FIRE STOP.	33	PARTITION STUD.
8	VERTICAL FURRING. (1"x2")	34	DOUBLE TOP PLATE.(SAME SIZE AS STUDS
9	BUILDING PAPER.	35	ATTIC FIRE STOP & HEADER. (SAME SIZE AS ADJACENT JOISTS)
10	FINISH FLOOR.	36	BRICK VENEER.
11	GROUNDS.	37	APPROVED TYPE WALL TIE. (SPACE @ 8" VERTICALLY AND 16" O.C. HORIZONTALLY
12	BASE SHOE MOLD.	38	EXTERIOR WALL SHEATHING.
13	BASE.	39	EXTERIOR WALL STUD.
14	PLASTER OR WALL FINISH.	40	SILL FOR EXTERIOR WALL.
15	SECOND FLOOR JOISTS.	41	COPPER DRAIN TUBE,(1"O.D.x½₂WALL, FLATTE AND EMBEDDED IN GROUTING. FLATTEN INN END TO LEAVE ONLY 1/16" OPENING. SPAC 8'-0" O.C. APPROX.)
16	APPROVED TYPE JOIST ANCHOR ON EVERY 5TH JOIST. (SPACED @ 6'-0" O.C. MAX.)		
17	SUB FLOOR. (SECOND FLOOR)	42	PORTLAND CEMENT MORTAR GROUT. (½" MIN. THICKNESS)
18	ANCHOR BOLT, ½D x 1'-4"LG. (SPACED @ 6'-0"O.C.)	43	ANCHOR BOLTS FOR SILL,
19	PLATE. (1⅝" MIN. THICKNESS)		
20	RAFTER.		
21	HEADER. (SAME SIZE AS JOIST)		
22	ROOF SHEATHING.		
23	SUB FLOOR. (ATTIC)		
24	ATTIC FLOOR JOISTS.		
25	CROSS BRIDGING. (1"x3")		
26	COLUMN.		

PLATE 7.   48

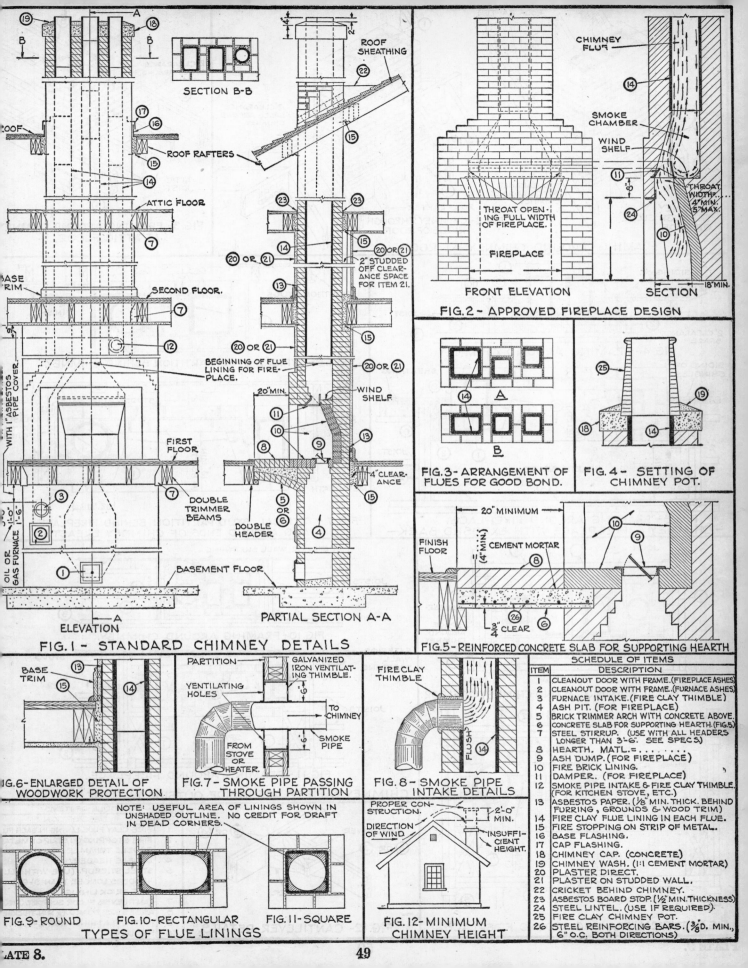

SECTION B-B

FIG.1 - STANDARD CHIMNEY DETAILS

ROOF SHEATHING
ROOF RAFTERS
ATTIC FLOOR
SECOND FLOOR.
BEGINNING OF FLUE LINING FOR FIREPLACE.
WIND SHELF
20" MIN.
FIRST FLOOR
DOUBLE TRIMMER BEAMS
DOUBLE HEADER
BASEMENT FLOOR
2" STUDDED OFF CLEARANCE SPACE FOR ITEM 21.
4" CLEARANCE
PARTIAL SECTION A-A

ROOF
BASE TRIM
OIL OR GAS FURNACE 1'-6"
WITH 1" ASBESTOS PIPE COVER.
ELEVATION

FIG.2 - APPROVED FIREPLACE DESIGN

CHIMNEY FLUE
SMOKE CHAMBER
WIND SHELF
THROAT WIDTH 4" MIN. 5" MAX.
THROAT OPENING FULL WIDTH OF FIREPLACE.
FIREPLACE
FRONT ELEVATION
SECTION
18" MIN.

FIG.3 - ARRANGEMENT OF FLUES FOR GOOD BOND.

A
B

FIG.4 - SETTING OF CHIMNEY POT.

FIG.5 - REINFORCED CONCRETE SLAB FOR SUPPORTING HEARTH

20" MINIMUM
FINISH FLOOR
CEMENT MORTAR
(4" MIN.)
3" CLEAR

FIG.6 - ENLARGED DETAIL OF WOODWORK PROTECTION.

BASE TRIM

FIG.7 - SMOKE PIPE PASSING THROUGH PARTITION

PARTITION
GALVANIZED IRON VENTILATING THIMBLE.
VENTILATING HOLES
TO CHIMNEY
FROM STOVE OR HEATER.
SMOKE PIPE

FIG.8 - SMOKE PIPE INTAKE DETAILS

FIRE CLAY THIMBLE
FLUSH

FIG.9 - ROUND   **FIG.10 - RECTANGULAR**   **FIG.11 - SQUARE**

TYPES OF FLUE LININGS

NOTE: USEFUL AREA OF LININGS SHOWN IN UNSHADED OUTLINE. NO CREDIT FOR DRAFT IN DEAD CORNERS.

FIG.12 - MINIMUM CHIMNEY HEIGHT

PROPER CONSTRUCTION.
DIRECTION OF WIND
2'-0" MIN.
INSUFFICIENT HEIGHT.

SCHEDULE OF ITEMS

ITEM	DESCRIPTION
1	CLEANOUT DOOR WITH FRAME. (FIREPLACE ASHES)
2	CLEANOUT DOOR WITH FRAME. (FURNACE ASHES)
3	FURNACE INTAKE. (FIRE CLAY THIMBLE)
4	ASH PIT. (FOR FIREPLACE)
5	BRICK TRIMMER ARCH WITH CONCRETE ABOVE.
6	CONCRETE SLAB FOR SUPPORTING HEARTH. (FIG.5)
7	STEEL STIRRUP. (USE WITH ALL HEADERS LONGER THAN 3'-6". SEE SPECS.)
8	HEARTH. MATL.= . . . .
9	ASH DUMP. (FOR FIREPLACE)
10	FIRE BRICK LINING.
11	DAMPER. (FOR FIREPLACE)
12	SMOKE PIPE INTAKE & FIRE CLAY THIMBLE. (FOR KITCHEN STOVE, ETC.)
13	ASBESTOS PAPER. (1/8 MIN. THICK. BEHIND FURRING, GROUNDS & WOOD TRIM)
14	FIRE CLAY FLUE LINING IN EACH FLUE.
15	FIRE STOPPING ON STRIP OF METAL.
16	BASE FLASHING.
17	CAP FLASHING.
18	CHIMNEY CAP. (CONCRETE)
19	CHIMNEY WASH. (1:1 CEMENT MORTAR)
20	PLASTER DIRECT.
21	PLASTER ON STUDDED WALL.
22	CRICKET BEHIND CHIMNEY.
23	ASBESTOS BOARD STOP. (1/2 MIN. THICKNESS)
24	STEEL LINTEL. (USE IF REQUIRED)
25	FIRE CLAY CHIMNEY POT.
26	STEEL REINFORCING BARS. (3/8 D. MIN., 6" O.C. BOTH DIRECTIONS)

PLATE 8.   49

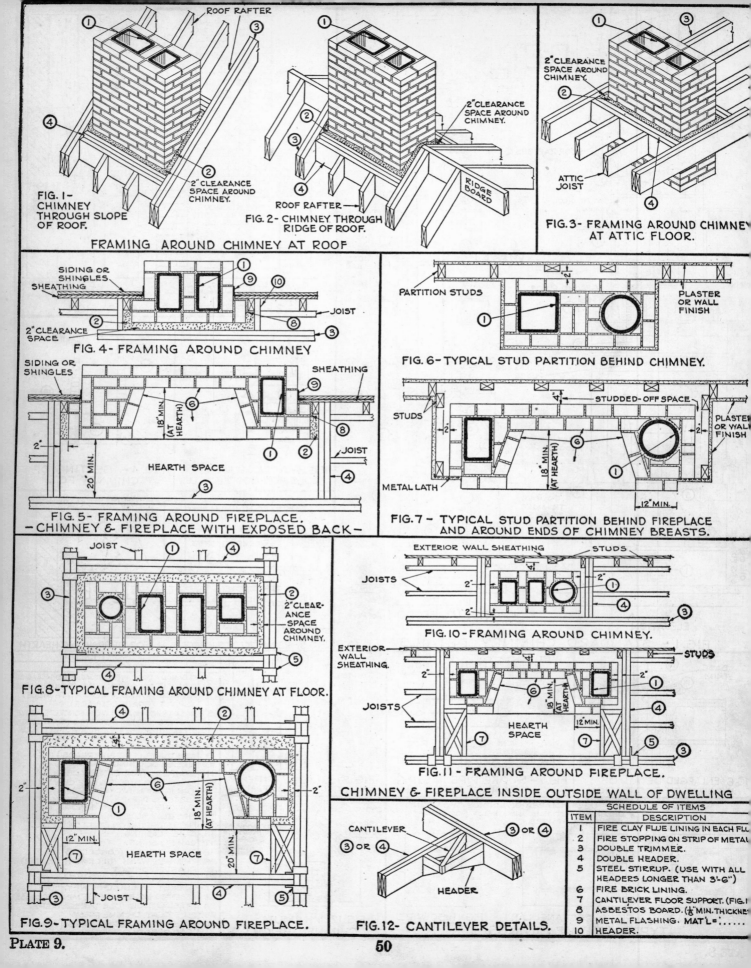

FIG. 1—CHIMNEY THROUGH SLOPE OF ROOF.

ROOF RAFTER

2" CLEARANCE SPACE AROUND CHIMNEY.

FIG. 2— CHIMNEY THROUGH RIDGE OF ROOF.

ROOF RAFTER

RIDGE BOARD

2" CLEARANCE SPACE AROUND CHIMNEY.

FRAMING AROUND CHIMNEY AT ROOF

2" CLEARANCE SPACE AROUND CHIMNEY.

ATTIC JOIST

FIG. 3- FRAMING AROUND CHIMNEY AT ATTIC FLOOR.

SIDING OR SHINGLES
SHEATHING

JOIST

2" CLEARANCE SPACE

FIG. 4- FRAMING AROUND CHIMNEY

SIDING OR SHINGLES

SHEATHING

18" MIN. (AT HEARTH)

20" MIN.

HEARTH SPACE

2"

JOIST

FIG. 5- FRAMING AROUND FIREPLACE.
- CHIMNEY & FIREPLACE WITH EXPOSED BACK -

PARTITION STUDS

PLASTER OR WALL FINISH

FIG. 6- TYPICAL STUD PARTITION BEHIND CHIMNEY.

STUDS

STUDDED-OFF SPACE

METAL LATH

18" MIN. (AT HEARTH)

12" MIN.

PLASTER OR WALL FINISH

FIG. 7 - TYPICAL STUD PARTITION BEHIND FIREPLACE AND AROUND ENDS OF CHIMNEY BREASTS.

JOIST

2" CLEAR-ANCE SPACE AROUND CHIMNEY.

FIG. 8-TYPICAL FRAMING AROUND CHIMNEY AT FLOOR.

2"

18" MIN. (AT HEARTH)

12" MIN.

20" MIN.

HEARTH SPACE

JOIST

FIG. 9- TYPICAL FRAMING AROUND FIREPLACE.

EXTERIOR WALL SHEATHING

STUDS

JOISTS

2"

2"

FIG. 10-FRAMING AROUND CHIMNEY.

EXTERIOR WALL SHEATHING.

STUDS

JOISTS

2"

2"

18" MIN. (AT HEARTH)

12" MIN.

HEARTH SPACE

FIG. 11 - FRAMING AROUND FIREPLACE.

CHIMNEY & FIREPLACE INSIDE OUTSIDE WALL OF DWELLING

CANTILEVER

3 or 4

3 or 4

HEADER

FIG. 12- CANTILEVER DETAILS.

ITEM	DESCRIPTION
SCHEDULE OF ITEMS	
1	FIRE CLAY FLUE LINING IN EACH FLUE
2	FIRE STOPPING ON STRIP OF METAL
3	DOUBLE TRIMMER.
4	DOUBLE HEADER.
5	STEEL STIRRUP. (USE WITH ALL HEADERS LONGER THAN 3'-6")
6	FIRE BRICK LINING.
7	CANTILEVER FLOOR SUPPORT. (FIG.12
8	ASBESTOS BOARD. (⅛" MIN. THICKNESS)
9	METAL FLASHING. MAT'L= ......
10	HEADER

PLATE 9.   50

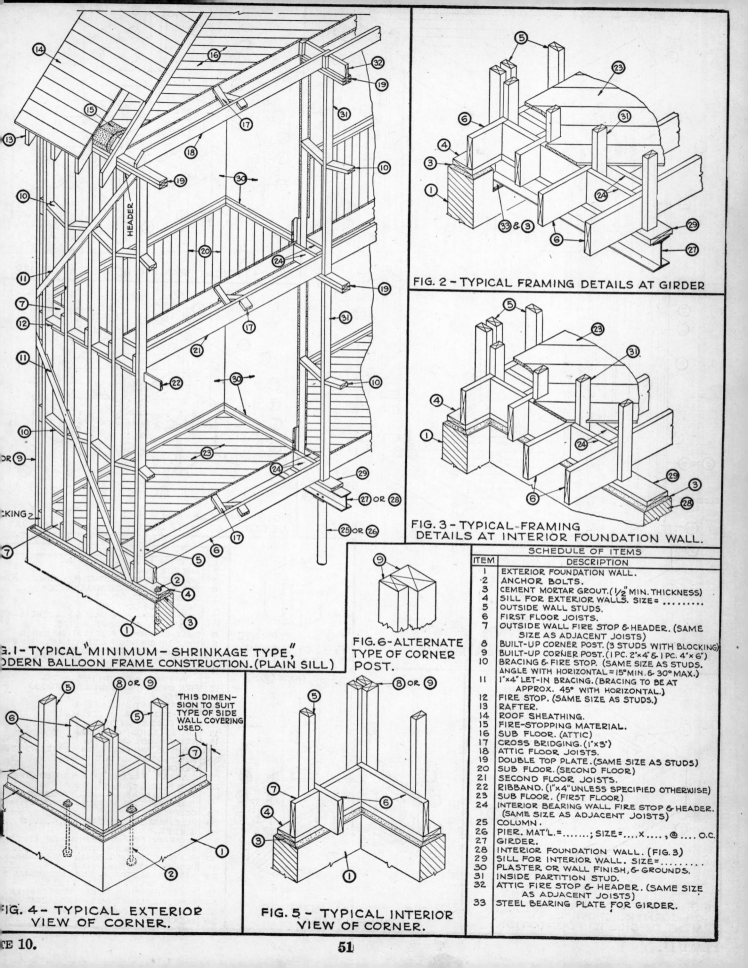

FIG. 2 - TYPICAL FRAMING DETAILS AT GIRDER

FIG. 3 - TYPICAL FRAMING
DETAILS AT INTERIOR FOUNDATION WALL.

HEADER

FIG. 1 - TYPICAL "MINIMUM – SHRINKAGE TYPE",
MODERN BALLOON FRAME CONSTRUCTION. (PLAIN SILL)

FIG. 6 - ALTERNATE
TYPE OF CORNER
POST.

THIS DIMEN-
SION TO SUIT
TYPE OF SIDE
WALL COVERING
USED.

FIG. 4 - TYPICAL EXTERIOR
VIEW OF CORNER.

FIG. 5 - TYPICAL INTERIOR
VIEW OF CORNER.

SCHEDULE OF ITEMS	
ITEM	DESCRIPTION
1	EXTERIOR FOUNDATION WALL.
2	ANCHOR BOLTS.
3	CEMENT MORTAR GROUT. (1/2" MIN. THICKNESS)
4	SILL FOR EXTERIOR WALLS. SIZE = ...
5	OUTSIDE WALL STUDS.
6	FIRST FLOOR JOISTS.
7	OUTSIDE WALL FIRE STOP & HEADER. (SAME SIZE AS ADJACENT JOISTS)
8	BUILT-UP CORNER POST. (3 STUDS WITH BLOCKING)
9	BUILT-UP CORNER POST. (1 PC. 2"×4" & 1 PC. 4"×6")
10	BRACING & FIRE STOP. (SAME SIZE AS STUDS. ANGLE WITH HORIZONTAL = 15° MIN. & 30° MAX.)
11	1"×4" LET-IN BRACING. (BRACING TO BE AT APPROX. 45° WITH HORIZONTAL.)
12	FIRE STOP. (SAME SIZE AS STUDS.)
13	RAFTER.
14	ROOF SHEATHING.
15	FIRE-STOPPING MATERIAL.
16	SUB FLOOR. (ATTIC)
17	CROSS BRIDGING. (1"×3")
18	ATTIC FLOOR JOISTS.
19	DOUBLE TOP PLATE. (SAME SIZE AS STUDS.)
20	SUB FLOOR. (SECOND FLOOR)
21	SECOND FLOOR JOISTS.
22	RIBBAND. (1"×4" UNLESS SPECIFIED OTHERWISE)
23	SUB FLOOR. (FIRST FLOOR)
24	INTERIOR BEARING WALL FIRE STOP & HEADER. (SAME SIZE AS ADJACENT JOISTS)
25	COLUMN.
26	PIER. MAT'L.= .... ; SIZE = ... × .... , @ .... O.C.
27	GIRDER.
28	INTERIOR FOUNDATION WALL. (FIG. 3)
29	SILL FOR INTERIOR WALL. SIZE = ...
30	PLASTER OR WALL FINISH, & GROUNDS.
31	INSIDE PARTITION STUD.
32	ATTIC FIRE STOP & HEADER. (SAME SIZE AS ADJACENT JOISTS)
33	STEEL BEARING PLATE FOR GIRDER.

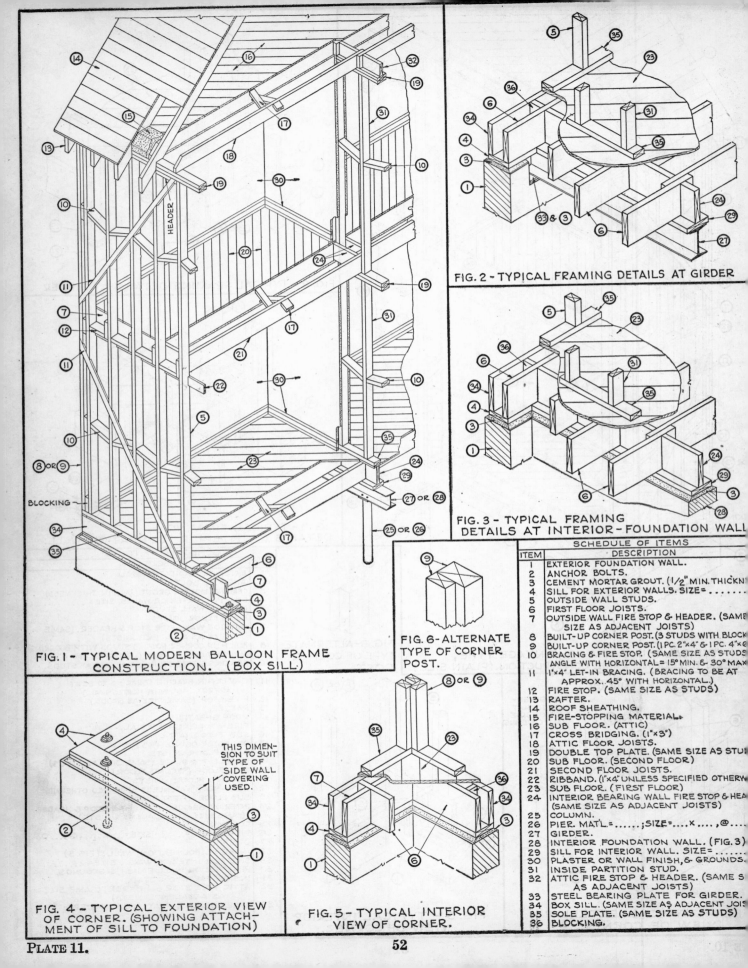

FIG. 1 - TYPICAL MODERN BALLOON FRAME CONSTRUCTION. (BOX SILL.)

HEADER

BLOCKING

FIG. 2 - TYPICAL FRAMING DETAILS AT GIRDER

FIG. 3 - TYPICAL FRAMING DETAILS AT INTERIOR-FOUNDATION WALL

FIG. 4 - TYPICAL EXTERIOR VIEW OF CORNER. (SHOWING ATTACHMENT OF SILL TO FOUNDATION)

THIS DIMENSION TO SUIT TYPE OF SIDE WALL COVERING USED.

FIG. 5 - TYPICAL INTERIOR VIEW OF CORNER.

FIG. 6 - ALTERNATE TYPE OF CORNER POST.

SCHEDULE OF ITEMS	
ITEM	DESCRIPTION
1	EXTERIOR FOUNDATION WALL.
2	ANCHOR BOLTS.
3	CEMENT MORTAR GROUT. (1/2" MIN. THICKN
4	SILL FOR EXTERIOR WALLS. SIZE= ......
5	OUTSIDE WALL STUDS.
6	FIRST FLOOR JOISTS.
7	OUTSIDE WALL FIRE STOP & HEADER. (SAME SIZE AS ADJACENT JOISTS)
8	BUILT-UP CORNER POST. (3 STUDS WITH BLOCK
9	BUILT-UP CORNER POST. (1 PC. 2"x4" & 1 PC. 4"x6
10	BRACING & FIRE STOP. (SAME SIZE AS STUDS ANGLE WITH HORIZONTAL= 15° MIN. & 30° MAX
11	1"x4" LET-IN BRACING. (BRACING TO BE AT APPROX. 45° WITH HORIZONTAL.)
12	FIRE STOP. (SAME SIZE AS STUDS)
13	RAFTER.
14	ROOF SHEATHING.
15	FIRE-STOPPING MATERIAL
16	SUB FLOOR. (ATTIC)
17	CROSS BRIDGING. (1"x3")
18	ATTIC FLOOR JOISTS.
19	DOUBLE TOP PLATE. (SAME SIZE AS STU
20	SUB FLOOR. (SECOND FLOOR)
21	SECOND FLOOR JOISTS.
22	RIBBAND. (1"x4" UNLESS SPECIFIED OTHERW
23	SUB FLOOR. (FIRST FLOOR)
24	INTERIOR BEARING WALL FIRE STOP & HEA (SAME SIZE AS ADJACENT JOISTS)
25	COLUMN.
26	PIER. MAT'L= ...... ;SIZE=.... x .... ,@....
27	GIRDER.
28	INTERIOR FOUNDATION WALL. (FIG. 3)
29	SILL FOR INTERIOR WALL. SIZE= ......
30	PLASTER OR WALL FINISH, & GROUNDS.
31	INSIDE PARTITION STUD.
32	ATTIC FIRE STOP & HEADER. (SAME S AS ADJACENT JOISTS)
33	STEEL BEARING PLATE FOR GIRDER.
34	BOX SILL. (SAME SIZE AS ADJACENT JOIS
35	SOLE PLATE. (SAME SIZE AS STUDS)
36	BLOCKING.

PLATE 11.   52

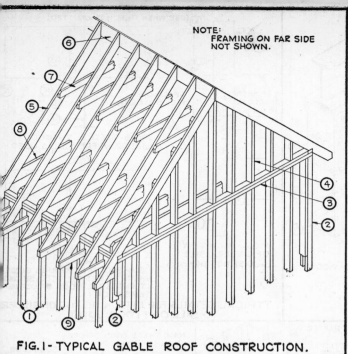

NOTE:
FRAMING ON FAR SIDE
NOT SHOWN.

FIG. 1 - TYPICAL GABLE ROOF CONSTRUCTION.

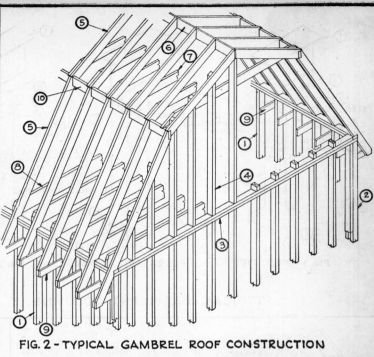

FIG. 2 - TYPICAL GAMBREL ROOF CONSTRUCTION

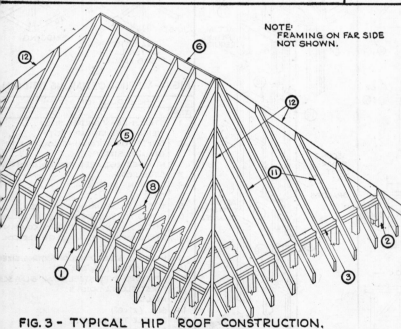

NOTE:
FRAMING ON FAR SIDE
NOT SHOWN.

FIG. 3 - TYPICAL HIP ROOF CONSTRUCTION.

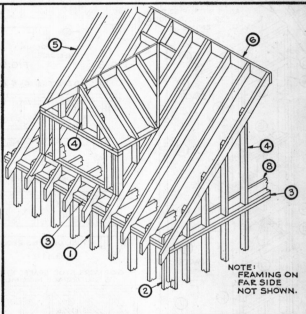

NOTE:
FRAMING ON
FAR SIDE
NOT SHOWN.

FIG. 4 - TYPICAL ROOF AND DORMER CONSTRUCTION.

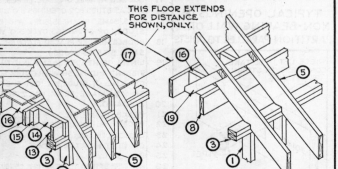

THIS FLOOR EXTENDS
FOR DISTANCE
SHOWN, ONLY.

FIG. 5 - PREFERRED METHOD   FIG. 6 - ALTERNATE METHOD

METHODS OF BRACING ROOF WHERE RAFTERS
ARE AT RIGHT ANGLES TO JOISTS.

ROOF SHEATHING

METAL
FLASHING

CURB
HEADERS

FIG. 7 - FRAMING AT SCUTTLE.

SCHEDULE OF ITEMS	
ITEM	DESCRIPTION
1	OUTSIDE WALL STUDS.
2	CORNER POST.
3	DOUBLE TOP PLATE.
4	END WALL STUDS. (NOTCH FOR RAFTER)
5	RAFTER.
6	RIDGE BOARD.
7	COLLAR BEAM.
8	ATTIC FLOOR JOIST.
9	LOOKOUT. (TO SUIT CORNICE CONSTRUCTION)
10	PURLIN.
11	HIP JACK RAFTER.
12	HIP RAFTER.
13	BLOCKING & NAILING STRIP.
14	BLOCKING & TIE MEMBER. (SAME SIZE AS JOIST & SPACED SAME AS RAFTERS)
15	NAILING CLEAT. (2"x4")
16	TIE MEMBER. (SAME SIZE AS JOIST; ONE ROW; SPACED SAME AS RAFTERS)
17	SUB FLOOR AT 90° TO JOISTS.
18	SUB FLOOR AT 45° TO JOISTS.
19	TIE STRIP. (NOT LESS THAN 2"x4")

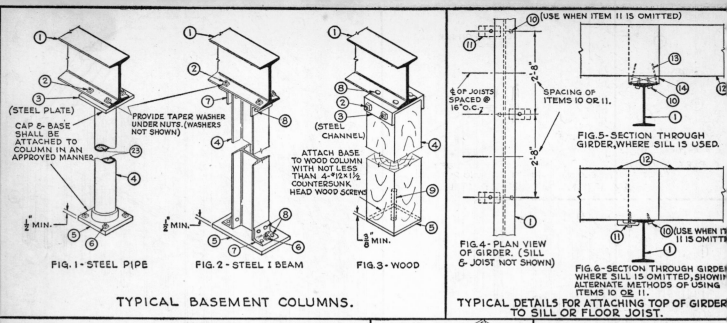

TYPICAL BASEMENT COLUMNS.

FIG.1-STEEL PIPE FIG.2-STEEL I BEAM FIG.3-WOOD

(STEEL PLATE)

CAP & BASE SHALL BE ATTACHED TO COLUMN IN AN APPROVED MANNER

PROVIDE TAPER WASHER UNDER NUTS. (WASHERS NOT SHOWN)

ATTACH BASE TO WOOD COLUMN WITH NOT LESS THAN 4-#12x1½ COUNTERSUNK HEAD WOOD SCREWS

(STEEL CHANNEL)

½" MIN.

⅜" MIN.

TYPICAL DETAILS FOR ATTACHING TOP OF GIRDER TO SILL OR FLOOR JOIST.

(USE WHEN ITEM 11 IS OMITTED)

℄ OF JOISTS SPACED @ 16" O.C.

SPACING OF ITEMS 10 OR 11.

FIG.4- PLAN VIEW OF GIRDER. (SILL & JOIST NOT SHOWN)

FIG.5-SECTION THROUGH GIRDER, WHERE SILL IS USED.

FIG.6-SECTION THROUGH GIRDER WHERE SILL IS OMITTED, SHOWING ALTERNATE METHODS OF USING ITEMS 10 OR 11.

(USE WHEN IT IS OMITTED)

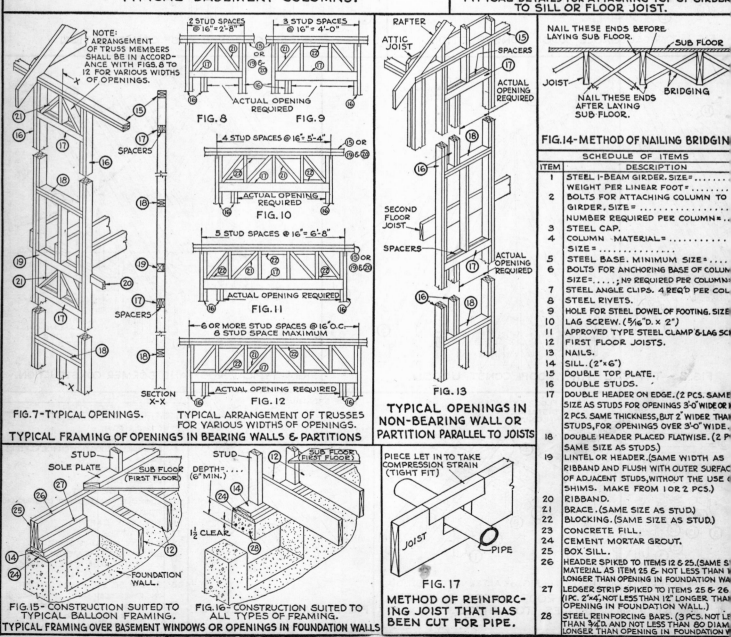

FIG.7-TYPICAL OPENINGS.

NOTE: ARRANGEMENT OF TRUSS MEMBERS SHALL BE IN ACCORDANCE WITH FIGS. 8 TO 12 FOR VARIOUS WIDTHS OF OPENINGS.

SPACERS

SECTION X-X

TYPICAL FRAMING OF OPENINGS IN BEARING WALLS & PARTITIONS

2 STUD SPACES @ 16"=2'-8"   3 STUD SPACES @ 16" = 4'-0"

FIG.8   FIG.9

ACTUAL OPENING REQUIRED

4 STUD SPACES @ 16"=5'-4"

FIG.10

ACTUAL OPENING REQUIRED

5 STUD SPACES @ 16"=6'-8"

FIG.11

ACTUAL OPENING REQUIRED

6 OR MORE STUD SPACES @ 16"O.C. 8 STUD SPACE MAXIMUM

FIG.12

ACTUAL OPENING REQUIRED

TYPICAL ARRANGEMENT OF TRUSSES FOR VARIOUS WIDTHS OF OPENINGS.

RAFTER

ATTIC JOIST

SPACERS

ACTUAL OPENING REQUIRED

SECOND FLOOR JOIST

SPACERS

ACTUAL OPENING REQUIRED

FIG.13

TYPICAL OPENINGS IN NON-BEARING WALL OR PARTITION PARALLEL TO JOISTS

NAIL THESE ENDS BEFORE LAYING SUB FLOOR.

SUB FLOOR

JOIST   BRIDGING

NAIL THESE ENDS AFTER LAYING SUB FLOOR.

FIG.14-METHOD OF NAILING BRIDGING

SCHEDULE OF ITEMS

ITEM	DESCRIPTION
1	STEEL I-BEAM GIRDER. SIZE= .... WEIGHT PER LINEAR FOOT= ....
2	BOLTS FOR ATTACHING COLUMN TO GIRDER, SIZE = ... NUMBER REQUIRED PER COLUMN= ..
3	STEEL CAP.
4	COLUMN MATERIAL= .... SIZE = ...
5	STEEL BASE. MINIMUM SIZE= ....
6	BOLTS FOR ANCHORING BASE OF COLUMN SIZE=.....; N° REQUIRED PER COLUMN=
7	STEEL ANGLE CLIPS. 4 REQ'D PER COL
8	STEEL RIVETS.
9	HOLE FOR STEEL DOWEL OF FOOTING. SIZE
10	LAG SCREW. (⁵⁄₁₆"D. x 2")
11	APPROVED TYPE STEEL CLAMP & LAG SC
12	FIRST FLOOR JOISTS.
13	NAILS.
14	SILL. (2"x 6")
15	DOUBLE TOP PLATE.
16	DOUBLE STUDS.
17	DOUBLE HEADER ON EDGE. (2 PCS. SAME SIZE AS STUDS FOR OPENINGS 3'-0" WIDE OR 2 PCS. SAME THICKNESS, BUT 2" WIDER THAN STUDS, FOR OPENINGS OVER 3'-0" WIDE.
18	DOUBLE HEADER PLACED FLATWISE. (2 P SAME SIZE AS STUDS.)
19	LINTEL OR HEADER. (SAME WIDTH AS RIBBAND AND FLUSH WITH OUTER SURFACE OF ADJACENT STUDS, WITHOUT THE USE SHIMS. MAKE FROM 1 OR 2 PCS.)
20	RIBBAND.
21	BRACE. (SAME SIZE AS STUD.)
22	BLOCKING. (SAME SIZE AS STUD.)
23	CONCRETE FILL.
24	CEMENT MORTAR GROUT.
25	BOX SILL.
26	HEADER SPIKED TO ITEMS 12 & 25. (SAME MATERIAL AS ITEM 25 & NOT LESS THAN LONGER THAN OPENING IN FOUNDATION WA
27	LEDGER STRIP SPIKED TO ITEMS 25 & 26 (1 PC. 2"x4", NOT LESS THAN 12" LONGER THAN OPENING IN FOUNDATION WALL.)
28	STEEL REINFORCING BARS. (3 PCS. NOT LE THAN ¾"D. AND NOT LESS THAN 80 DIAM LONGER THAN OPENING IN FOUNDATION W

STUD   SOLE PLATE   SUB FLOOR (FIRST FLOOR)

FOUNDATION WALL.

FIG.15-CONSTRUCTION SUITED TO TYPICAL BALLOON FRAMING.

STUD   SUB FLOOR (FIRST FLOOR)

DEPTH=.... (6" MIN.)

1½ CLEAR

FIG.16-CONSTRUCTION SUITED TO ALL TYPES OF FRAMING.

TYPICAL FRAMING OVER BASEMENT WINDOWS OR OPENINGS IN FOUNDATION WALLS

PIECE LET IN TO TAKE COMPRESSION STRAIN (TIGHT FIT)

JOIST   PIPE

FIG. 17

METHOD OF REINFORCING JOIST THAT HAS BEEN CUT FOR PIPE.

PLATE 13.   54

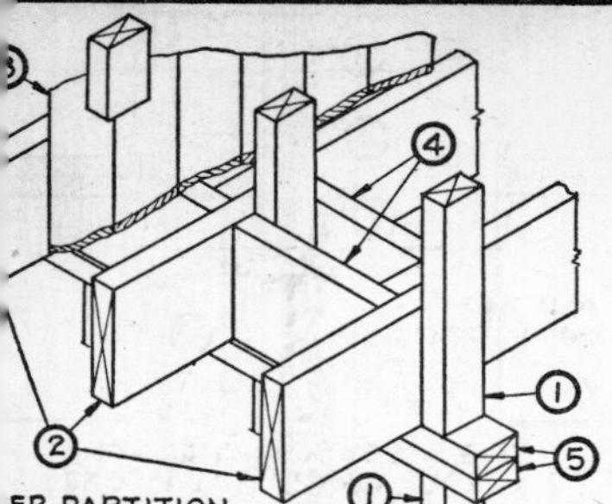

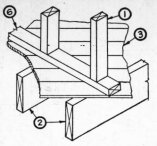

FIG.1- PARTITION OVER
PARTITION BELOW.

FIG.2-LOWER END OF NON-BEARING
PARTITION.(NO PARTITION BELOW)

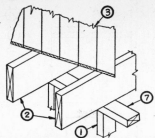

FIG.3-UPPER END OF NON-BEARING
PARTITION.(NO PARTITION ABOVE)

PARTITIONS AT RIGHT ANGLES TO JOISTS

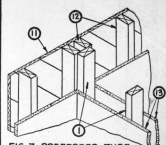

FIG.7-PREFERRED TYPE
(USE WHEREVER
PRACTICABLE)

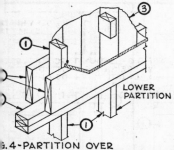

LOWER
PARTITION

FIG.4-PARTITION OVER
PARTITION BELOW

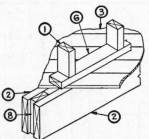

FIG.5-LOWER END OF NON-BEARING
PARTITION.(NO PARTITION BELOW)

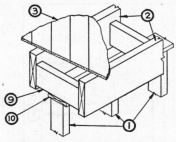

FIG.6-UPPER END OF NON-BEARING
PARTITION.(NO PARTITION ABOVE)

PARTITIONS PARALLEL TO JOISTS

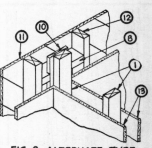

FIG. 8-ALTERNATE TYPE

INTERSECTING PARTITIONS

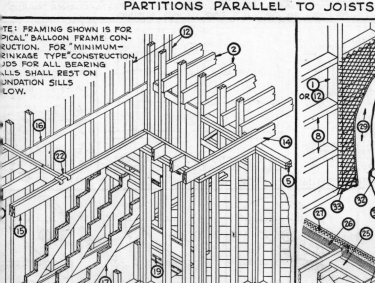

NOTE: FRAMING SHOWN IS FOR TYPICAL" BALLOON FRAME CONSTRUCTION. FOR "MINIMUM-SHRINKAGE TYPE" CONSTRUCTION, STUDS FOR ALL BEARING WALLS SHALL REST ON FOUNDATION SILLS BELOW.

FIG.9-TYPICAL FRAMING AROUND STAIRWAY

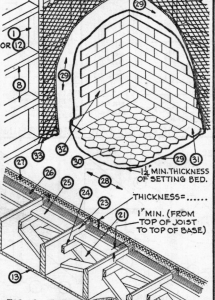

1½" MIN. THICKNESS
OF SETTING BED.

THICKNESS=......

1" MIN. (FROM
TOP OF JOIST
TO TOP OF BASE)

FIG.10-TYPICAL BATHROOM
CONSTRUCTION DETAILS.

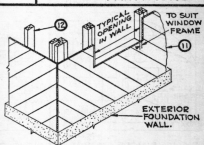

TYPICAL
OPENING
IN WALL

TO SUIT
WINDOW
FRAME

EXTERIOR
FOUNDATION
WALL.

FIG.11-TYPICAL APPLICATION OF
OUTSIDE WALL SHEATHING.

SCHEDULE OF ITEMS

ITEM	DESCRIPTION
1	PARTITION STUDS.
2	JOIST.
3	SUB FLOOR.(LAID AT 45° ANGLE WITH JOISTS)
4	FIRE STOP & HEADER.(SAME SIZE AS JOISTS)
5	DOUBLE TOP PLATE.
6	SOLE PLATE.
7	SINGLE TOP PLATE.
8	BLOCKING. (2"x 4"-16"O.C.)
9	HEADER. (2"x 6"-16"O.C.)
10	LATHING BOARD. (1"x 6")
11	EXTERIOR WALL SHEATHING.
12	EXTERIOR WALL STUD.
13	INTERIOR WALL PLASTER, PANELING,ETC.
14	DOUBLE HEADER.
15	DOUBLE TRIMMER.
16	RIBBAND.
17	STAIR STRINGER (CARRIAGE).
18	KICK PLATE.
19	GIRDER.
20	BASEMENT COLUMN.
21	CROSS BRIDGING.
22	STEEL STIRRUP.
23	BEVELED JOISTS.
24	CLEATS.
25	SUB FLOOR.(LAID AT 90°ANGLE TO JOISTS)
26	BUILDING PAPER.
27	METAL SHRINKAGE MESH.
28	CONCRETE BASE.(2½"MIN. THICKNESS).
29	PORTLAND CEMENT MORTAR.
30	FLOOR TILE.
31	COVE.
32	WALL TILE.
33	METAL LATH.
34	INCOMBUSTIBLE MATERIAL

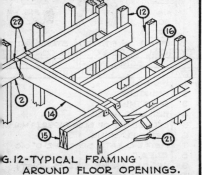

FIG.12-TYPICAL FRAMING
AROUND FLOOR OPENINGS.

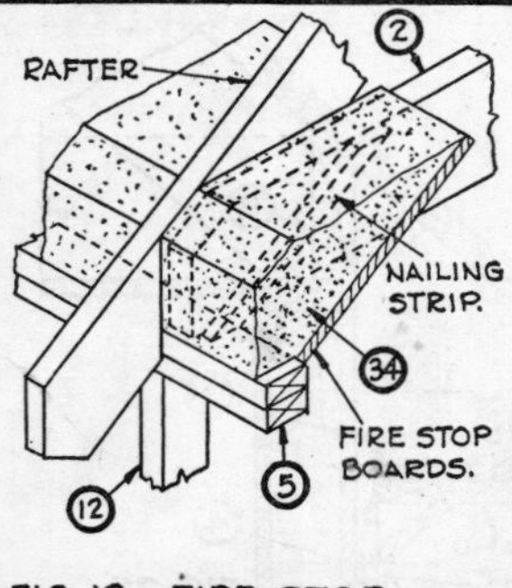

RAFTER

NAILING
STRIP.

FIRE STOP
BOARDS.

FIG.13- FIRE STOP
AT CORNICE

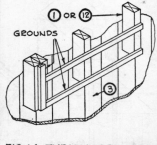

GROUNDS

FIG.14-TYPICAL GROUNDS
FOR PLASTERING.

PLATE 14. 55

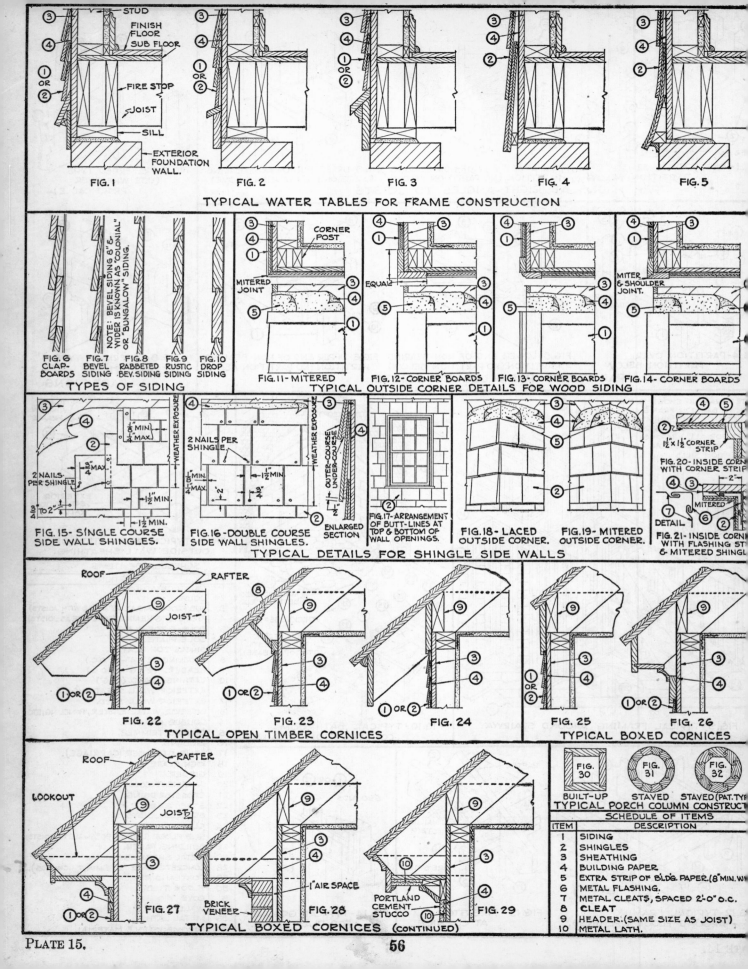

TYPICAL WATER TABLES FOR FRAME CONSTRUCTION

FIG. 1 — STUD, FINISH FLOOR, SUB FLOOR, FIRE STOP, JOIST, SILL, EXTERIOR FOUNDATION WALL.

FIG. 2

FIG. 3

FIG. 4

FIG. 5

TYPES OF SIDING

FIG. 6 CLAP-BOARDS
FIG. 7 BEVEL SIDING
FIG. 8 RABBETED BEV. SIDING
FIG. 9 RUSTIC SIDING
FIG. 10 DROP SIDING

NOTE: BEVEL SIDING 8" & WIDER IS KNOWN AS "COLONIAL" OR "BUNGALOW" SIDING.

TYPICAL OUTSIDE CORNER DETAILS FOR WOOD SIDING

FIG. 11 — MITERED — CORNER POST, MITERED JOINT, EQUAL

FIG. 12 — CORNER BOARDS

FIG. 13 — CORNER BOARDS

FIG. 14 — CORNER BOARDS — MITER & SHOULDER JOINT.

TYPICAL DETAILS FOR SHINGLE SIDE WALLS

FIG. 15 — SINGLE COURSE SIDE WALL SHINGLES. — 2 NAILS PER SHINGLE, 3/4" TO 2 1/4", 1 1/2" MIN., 3/4" MAX., 1/8" MIN. 1/4" MAX., WEATHER EXPOSURE

FIG. 16 — DOUBLE COURSE SIDE WALL SHINGLES. — 2 NAILS PER SHINGLE, 1/8" MIN. 1/4" MAX., 1 1/2" MIN., 3/4" MAX., WEATHER EXPOSURE, OUTER-COURSE, UNDER-COURSE, ENLARGED SECTION

FIG. 17 — ARRANGEMENT OF BUTT-LINES AT TOP & BOTTOM OF WALL OPENINGS.

FIG. 18 — LACED OUTSIDE CORNER.

FIG. 19 — MITERED OUTSIDE CORNER.

FIG. 20 — INSIDE CORNER WITH CORNER STRIP — 1 1/2" x 1 1/2" CORNER STRIP

FIG. 21 — INSIDE CORNER WITH FLASHING STRIP & MITERED SHINGLES — MITERED, DETAIL

TYPICAL OPEN TIMBER CORNICES

FIG. 22 — ROOF, RAFTER, JOIST

FIG. 23

FIG. 24

TYPICAL BOXED CORNICES

FIG. 25

FIG. 26

TYPICAL BOXED CORNICES (CONTINUED)

FIG. 27 — ROOF, RAFTER, LOOKOUT, JOIST

FIG. 28 — BRICK VENEER, 1" AIR SPACE

FIG. 29 — PORTLAND CEMENT STUCCO

TYPICAL PORCH COLUMN CONSTRUCTION

FIG. 30 BUILT-UP

FIG. 31 STAVED

FIG. 32 STAVED (PAT. TYPE)

SCHEDULE OF ITEMS

ITEM	DESCRIPTION
1	SIDING
2	SHINGLES
3	SHEATHING
4	BUILDING PAPER
5	EXTRA STRIP OF BLDG. PAPER.(8"MIN. W)
6	METAL FLASHING.
7	METAL CLEATS, SPACED 2'-0" O.C.
8	CLEAT
9	HEADER.(SAME SIZE AS JOIST)
10	METAL LATH.

PLATE 15.   56

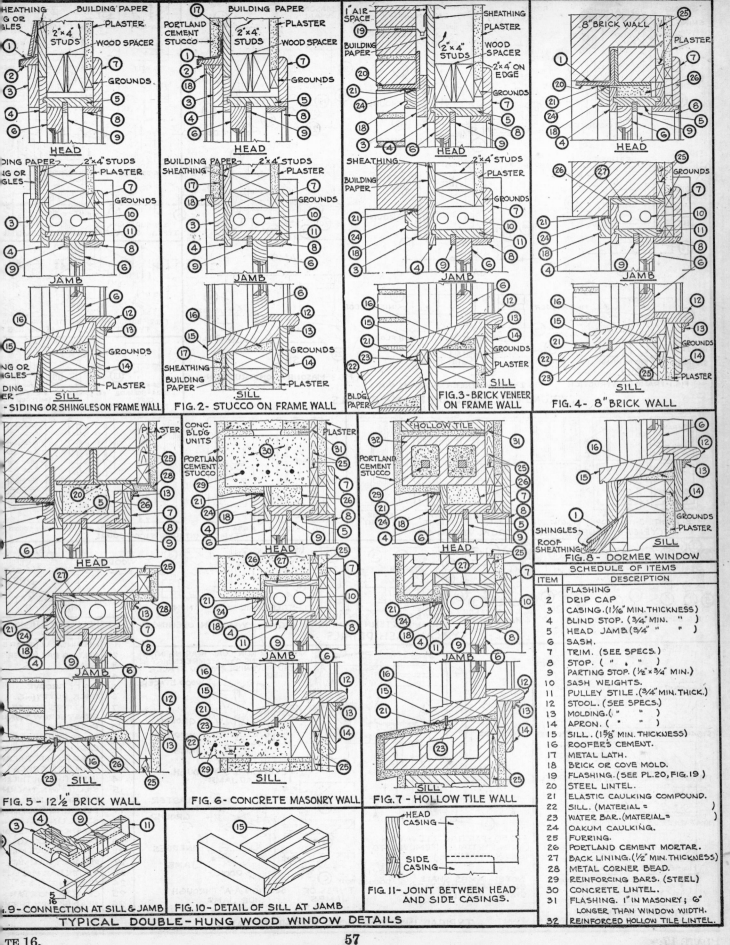

TYPICAL DOUBLE-HUNG WOOD WINDOW DETAILS

FIG. 1 - SIDING OR SHINGLES ON FRAME WALL

FIG. 2 - STUCCO ON FRAME WALL

FIG. 3 - BRICK VENEER ON FRAME WALL

FIG. 4 - 8" BRICK WALL

FIG. 5 - 12½ BRICK WALL

FIG. 6 - CONCRETE MASONRY WALL

FIG. 7 - HOLLOW TILE WALL

FIG. 8 - DORMER WINDOW

FIG. 9 - CONNECTION AT SILL & JAMB

FIG. 10 - DETAIL OF SILL AT JAMB

FIG. 11 - JOINT BETWEEN HEAD AND SIDE CASINGS.

SCHEDULE OF ITEMS

ITEM	DESCRIPTION
1	FLASHING
2	DRIP CAP
3	CASING. (1 1/16" MIN. THICKNESS)
4	BLIND STOP. (3/4" MIN. ")
5	HEAD JAMB (3/4" " ")
6	SASH.
7	TRIM. (SEE SPECS.)
8	STOP. (" , ")
9	PARTING STOP. (1/2 × 3/4" MIN.)
10	SASH WEIGHTS.
11	PULLEY STILE. (3/4" MIN. THICK.)
12	STOOL. (SEE SPECS.)
13	MOLDING. (" ")
14	APRON. (" ")
15	SILL. (1 5/8" MIN. THICKNESS)
16	ROOFER'S CEMENT.
17	METAL LATH.
18	BRICK OR COVE MOLD.
19	FLASHING. (SEE PL.20, FIG.19)
20	STEEL LINTEL.
21	ELASTIC CAULKING COMPOUND.
22	SILL. (MATERIAL =)
23	WATER BAR. (MATERIAL =)
24	OAKUM CAULKING.
25	FURRING.
26	PORTLAND CEMENT MORTAR.
27	BACK LINING. (1/2" MIN. THICKNESS)
28	METAL CORNER BEAD.
29	REINFORCING BARS. (STEEL)
30	CONCRETE LINTEL.
31	FLASHING. 1" IN MASONRY; 6" LONGER THAN WINDOW WIDTH.
32	REINFORCED HOLLOW TILE LINTEL.

PLATE 16.   57

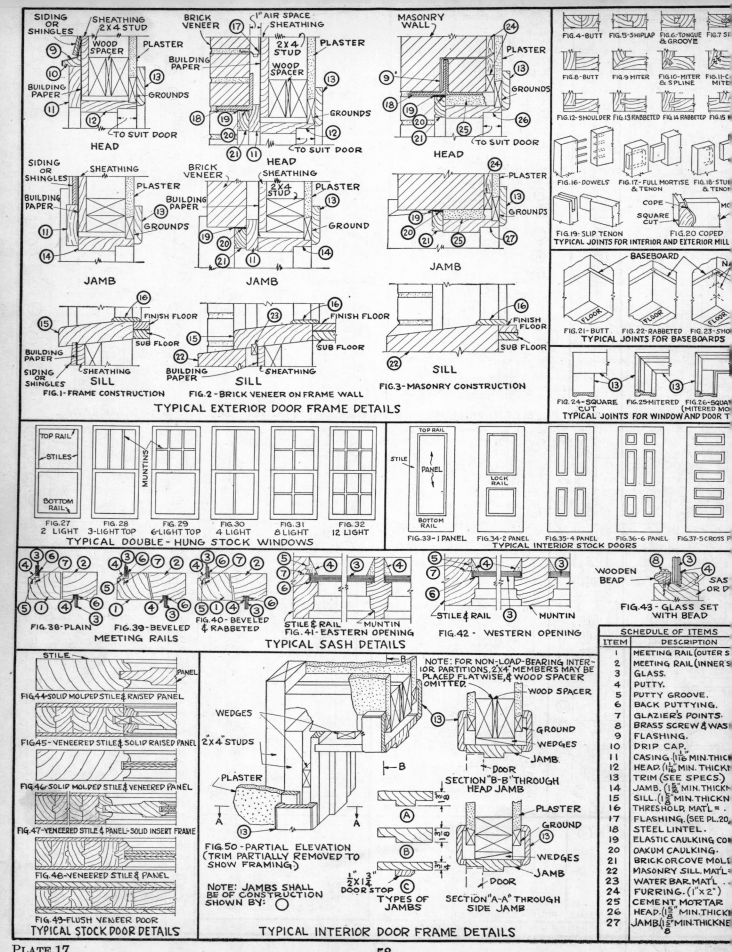

TYPICAL EXTERIOR DOOR FRAME DETAILS

FIG.1- FRAME CONSTRUCTION

FIG.2 - BRICK VENEER ON FRAME WALL

FIG.3-MASONRY CONSTRUCTION

TYPICAL JOINTS FOR INTERIOR AND EXTERIOR MILL

TYPICAL JOINTS FOR BASEBOARDS

TYPICAL JOINTS FOR WINDOW AND DOOR T

TYPICAL DOUBLE - HUNG STOCK WINDOWS

TYPICAL INTERIOR STOCK DOORS

MEETING RAILS

TYPICAL SASH DETAILS

TYPICAL STOCK DOOR DETAILS

TYPICAL INTERIOR DOOR FRAME DETAILS

SCHEDULE OF ITEMS

ITEM	DESCRIPTION
1	MEETING RAIL (OUTER S
2	MEETING RAIL (INNER'S
3	GLASS.
4	PUTTY.
5	PUTTY GROOVE.
6	BACK PUTTYING
7	GLAZIER'S POINTS.
8	BRASS SCREW & WAS
9	FLASHING.
10	DRIP CAP.
11	CASING.(1 1/8" MIN.THICK
12	HEAD. (1 1/8" MIN. THICKN
13	TRIM (SEE SPECS.)
14	JAMB. (1 5/8" MIN.THICKN
15	SILL.(1 5/8" MIN.THICKN
16	THRESHOLD. MAT'L = .
17	FLASHING. (SEE PL.20
18	STEEL LINTEL.
19	ELASTIC CAULKING CO
20	OAKUM CAULKING.
21	BRICK OR COVE MOLD
22	MASONRY SILL.MAT'L =
23	WATER BAR.MAT'L =
24	FURRING. (1"x 2")
25	CEMENT MORTAR
26	HEAD.(1 5/8" MIN.THICK
27	JAMB.(1 5/8"MIN.THICKNE

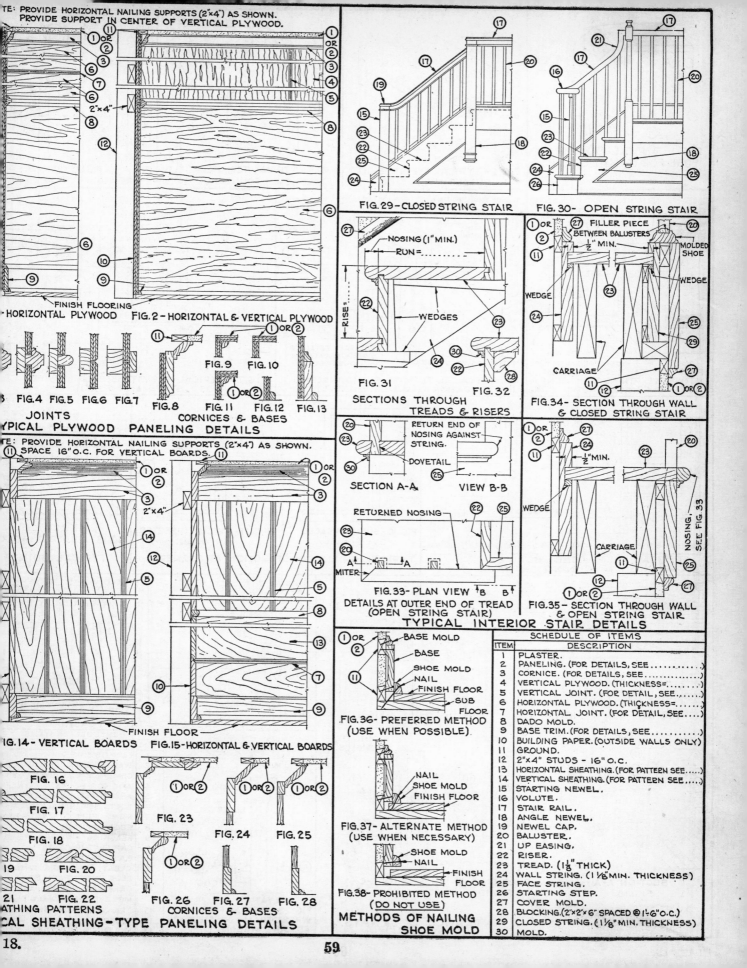

NOTE: PROVIDE HORIZONTAL NAILING SUPPORTS (2"×4") AS SHOWN. PROVIDE SUPPORT IN CENTER OF VERTICAL PLYWOOD.

2"×4"

FINISH FLOORING

HORIZONTAL PLYWOOD   FIG. 2 – HORIZONTAL & VERTICAL PLYWOOD

FIG. 9   FIG. 10

FIG. 4 FIG. 5 FIG. 6 FIG. 7   FIG. 8   FIG. 11   FIG. 12   FIG. 13

JOINTS   CORNICES & BASES

TYPICAL PLYWOOD PANELING DETAILS

NOTE: PROVIDE HORIZONTAL NAILING SUPPORTS (2"×4") AS SHOWN. SPACE 16" O.C. FOR VERTICAL BOARDS.

2"×4"

FINISH FLOOR

FIG. 14 – VERTICAL BOARDS   FIG. 15 – HORIZONTAL & VERTICAL BOARDS

FIG. 16
FIG. 17
FIG. 18
FIG. 19   FIG. 20
FIG. 21   FIG. 22
SHEATHING PATTERNS

FIG. 23
FIG. 24   FIG. 25
FIG. 26   FIG. 27   FIG. 28
CORNICES & BASES

TYPICAL SHEATHING-TYPE PANELING DETAILS

FIG. 29 – CLOSED STRING STAIR   FIG. 30 – OPEN STRING STAIR

NOSING (1" MIN.)
RUN =
RISE =
WEDGES

FIG. 31   FIG. 32

SECTIONS THROUGH TREADS & RISERS

FILLER PIECE BETWEEN BALUSTERS
½" MIN.
MOLDED SHOE
WEDGE
WEDGE
CARRIAGE

FIG. 34 – SECTION THROUGH WALL & CLOSED STRING STAIR

RETURN END OF NOSING AGAINST STRING.
DOVETAIL

SECTION A-A   VIEW B-B

RETURNED NOSING
A
MITER

FIG. 33 – PLAN VIEW

DETAILS AT OUTER END OF TREAD (OPEN STRING STAIR)

½" MIN.
WEDGE
CARRIAGE
NOSING, SEE FIG. 33

FIG. 35 – SECTION THROUGH WALL & OPEN STRING STAIR

TYPICAL INTERIOR STAIR DETAILS

BASE MOLD
BASE
SHOE MOLD
NAIL
FINISH FLOOR
SUB FLOOR

FIG. 36 – PREFERRED METHOD (USE WHEN POSSIBLE).

NAIL
SHOE MOLD
FINISH FLOOR

FIG. 37 – ALTERNATE METHOD (USE WHEN NECESSARY)

SHOE MOLD
NAIL
FINISH FLOOR

FIG. 38 – PROHIBITED METHOD (DO NOT USE)

METHODS OF NAILING SHOE MOLD

SCHEDULE OF ITEMS

ITEM	DESCRIPTION
1	PLASTER.
2	PANELING. (FOR DETAILS, SEE ....)
3	CORNICE. (FOR DETAILS, SEE ....)
4	VERTICAL PLYWOOD. (THICKNESS = ...)
5	VERTICAL JOINT. (FOR DETAIL, SEE ....)
6	HORIZONTAL PLYWOOD. (THICKNESS = ...)
7	HORIZONTAL JOINT. (FOR DETAIL, SEE ....)
8	DADO MOLD.
9	BASE TRIM. (FOR DETAILS, SEE ....)
10	BUILDING PAPER. (OUTSIDE WALLS ONLY)
11	GROUND.
12	2"×4" STUDS - 16" O.C.
13	HORIZONTAL SHEATHING. (FOR PATTERN SEE.....)
14	VERTICAL SHEATHING. (FOR PATTERN SEE.....)
15	STARTING NEWEL.
16	VOLUTE.
17	STAIR RAIL.
18	ANGLE NEWEL.
19	NEWEL CAP.
20	BALUSTER.
21	UP EASING.
22	RISER.
23	TREAD. (1⅛" THICK)
24	WALL STRING. (1⅛" MIN. THICKNESS)
25	FACE STRING.
26	STARTING STEP.
27	COVER MOLD.
28	BLOCKING. (2"×2"×6" SPACED @ 1'-6" O.C.)
29	CLOSED STRING. (1⅛" MIN. THICKNESS)
30	MOLD.

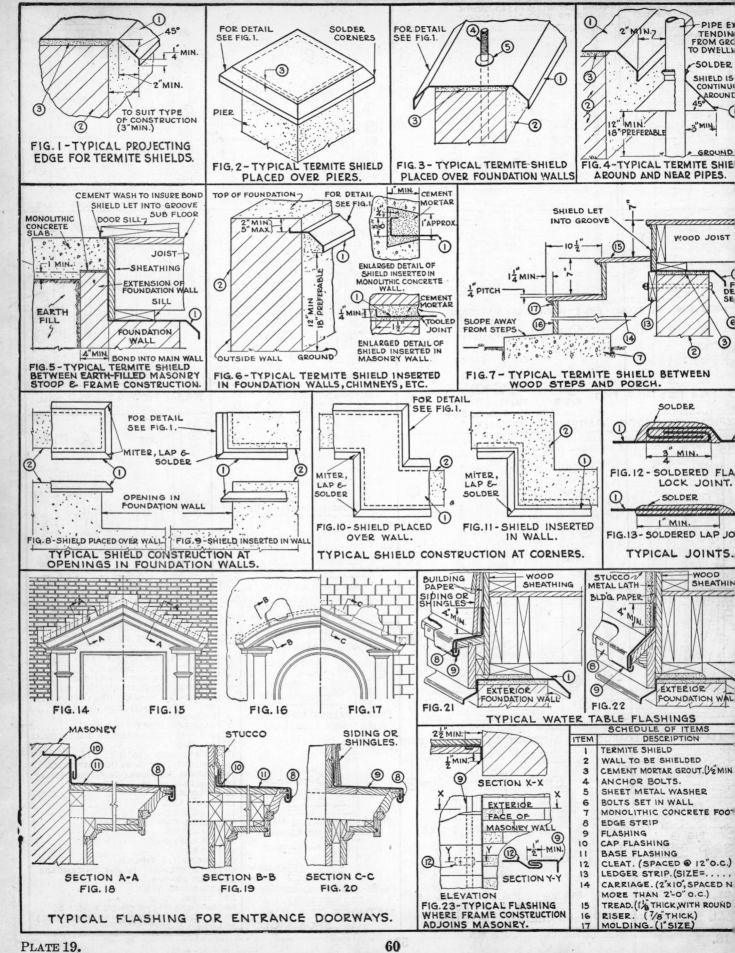

FIG. I—TYPICAL PROJECTING EDGE FOR TERMITE SHIELDS.

FIG. 2—TYPICAL TERMITE SHIELD PLACED OVER PIERS.

FIG. 3—TYPICAL TERMITE-SHIELD PLACED OVER FOUNDATION WALLS

FIG. 4—TYPICAL TERMITE SHIELD AROUND AND NEAR PIPES.

FIG. 5—TYPICAL TERMITE SHIELD BETWEEN EARTH-FILLED MASONRY STOOP & FRAME CONSTRUCTION.

FIG. 6—TYPICAL TERMITE SHIELD INSERTED IN FOUNDATION WALLS, CHIMNEYS, ETC.

FIG. 7—TYPICAL TERMITE SHIELD BETWEEN WOOD STEPS AND PORCH.

FIG. 8—SHIELD PLACED OVER WALL. FIG. 9—SHIELD INSERTED IN WALL

TYPICAL SHIELD CONSTRUCTION AT OPENINGS IN FOUNDATION WALLS.

FIG. 10—SHIELD PLACED OVER WALL. FIG. 11—SHIELD INSERTED IN WALL.

TYPICAL SHIELD CONSTRUCTION AT CORNERS.

FIG. 12—SOLDERED FLA LOCK JOINT.

FIG. 13—SOLDERED LAP JO

TYPICAL JOINTS.

FIG. 14 FIG. 15 FIG. 16 FIG. 17

SECTION A-A FIG. 18

SECTION B-B FIG. 19

SECTION C-C FIG. 20

TYPICAL FLASHING FOR ENTRANCE DOORWAYS.

TYPICAL WATER TABLE FLASHINGS

SECTION X-X

ELEVATION
FIG. 23—TYPICAL FLASHING WHERE FRAME CONSTRUCTION ADJOINS MASONRY.

ITEM	SCHEDULE OF ITEMS DESCRIPTION
1	TERMITE SHIELD
2	WALL TO BE SHIELDED
3	CEMENT MORTAR GROUT. (1½ MIN
4	ANCHOR BOLTS.
5	SHEET METAL WASHER
6	BOLTS SET IN WALL
7	MONOLITHIC CONCRETE FOO
8	EDGE STRIP
9	FLASHING
10	CAP FLASHING
11	BASE FLASHING
12	CLEAT. (SPACED @ 12" O.C.)
13	LEDGER STRIP. (SIZE=.....
14	CARRIAGE. (2"x10", SPACED N MORE THAN 2'-0" O.C.)
15	TREAD. (1⅛ THICK, WITH ROUND
16	RISER. (7/8" THICK)
17	MOLDING. (1" SIZE)

PLATE 19.   60

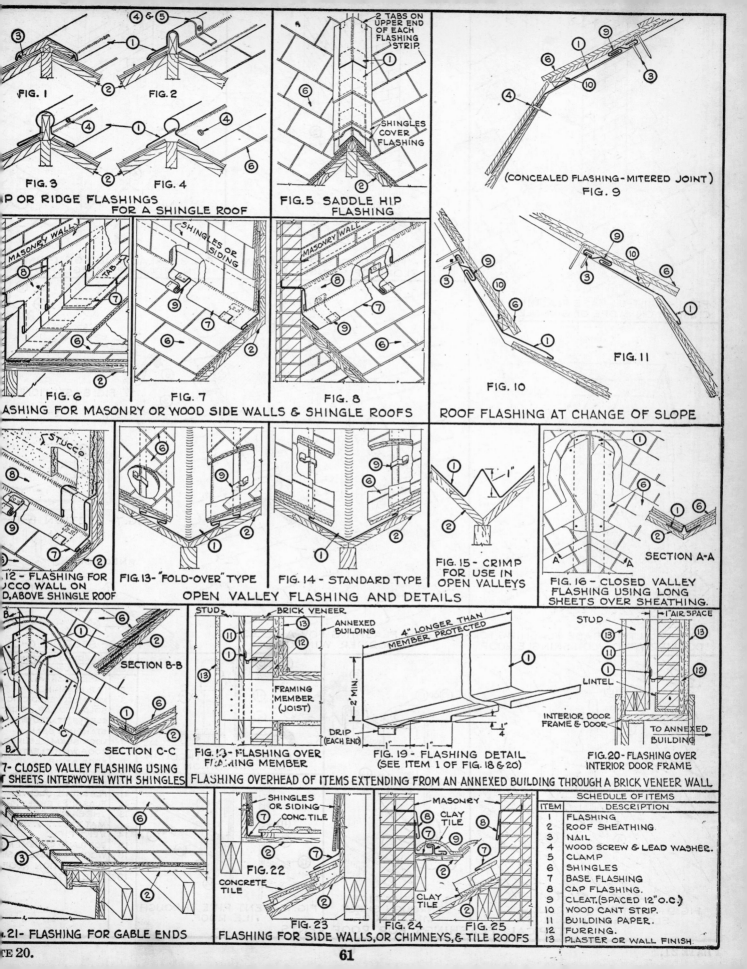

FIG. 1

FIG. 2

FIG. 3

FIG. 4

P OR RIDGE FLASHINGS
FOR A SHINGLE ROOF

2 TABS ON
UPPER END
OF EACH
FLASHING
STRIP

SHINGLES
COVER
FLASHING

FIG.5 SADDLE HIP
FLASHING

(CONCEALED FLASHING - MITERED JOINT)
FIG. 9

FIG. 10

FIG. 11

MASONRY WALL

TAB

SHINGLES
OR
SIDING

MASONRY WALL

FIG. 6

FIG. 7

FIG. 8

ASHING FOR MASONRY OR WOOD SIDE WALLS & SHINGLE ROOFS

ROOF FLASHING AT CHANGE OF SLOPE

STUCCO

12 - FLASHING FOR
UCCO WALL ON
D, ABOVE SHINGLE ROOF

FIG. 13-"FOLD-OVER" TYPE

FIG. 14 - STANDARD TYPE

FIG. 15 - CRIMP
FOR USE IN
OPEN VALLEYS

SECTION A-A

FIG. 16 - CLOSED VALLEY
FLASHING USING LONG
SHEETS OVER SHEATHING.

OPEN VALLEY FLASHING AND DETAILS

SECTION B-B

SECTION C-C

7- CLOSED VALLEY FLASHING USING
SHEETS INTERWOVEN WITH SHINGLES

STUD

BRICK VENEER

ANNEXED
BUILDING

4" LONGER THAN
MEMBER PROTECTED

2' MIN.

DRIP
(EACH END)

FRAMING
MEMBER
(JOIST)

FIG. 18- FLASHING OVER
FRAMING MEMBER

FIG. 19 - FLASHING DETAIL
(SEE ITEM 1 OF FIG. 18 & 20)

STUD

1" AIR SPACE

LINTEL

INTERIOR DOOR
FRAME & DOOR

TO ANNEXED
BUILDING

FIG. 20- FLASHING OVER
INTERIOR DOOR FRAME

FLASHING OVERHEAD OF ITEMS EXTENDING FROM AN ANNEXED BUILDING THROUGH A BRICK VENEER WALL

21- FLASHING FOR GABLE ENDS

SHINGLES
OR SIDING

CONC. TILE

FIG. 22

CONCRETE
TILE

FIG. 23

MASONRY

CLAY
TILE

CLAY
TILE

FIG. 24

FIG. 25

FLASHING FOR SIDE WALLS, OR CHIMNEYS, & TILE ROOFS

SCHEDULE OF ITEMS	
ITEM	DESCRIPTION
1	FLASHING
2	ROOF SHEATHING.
3	NAIL
4	WOOD SCREW & LEAD WASHER.
5	CLAMP
6	SHINGLES
7	BASE FLASHING
8	CAP FLASHING.
9	CLEAT.(SPACED 12"O.C.)
10	WOOD CANT STRIP.
11	BUILDING PAPER.
12	FURRING.
13	PLASTER OR WALL FINISH.

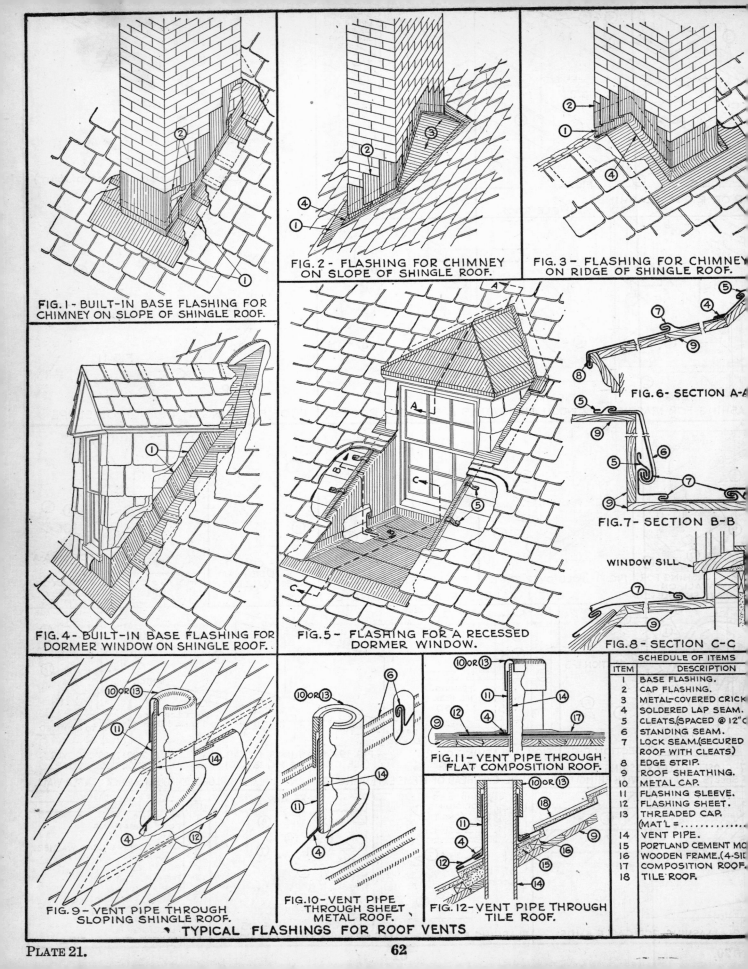

FIG.1- BUILT-IN BASE FLASHING FOR CHIMNEY ON SLOPE OF SHINGLE ROOF.

FIG.2 - FLASHING FOR CHIMNEY ON SLOPE OF SHINGLE ROOF.

FIG.3 - FLASHING FOR CHIMNEY ON RIDGE OF SHINGLE ROOF.

FIG.4 - BUILT-IN BASE FLASHING FOR DORMER WINDOW ON SHINGLE ROOF.

FIG.5 - FLASHING FOR A RECESSED DORMER WINDOW.

FIG.6- SECTION A-A

FIG.7- SECTION B-B

WINDOW SILL

FIG.8 - SECTION C-C

FIG.9 - VENT PIPE THROUGH SLOPING SHINGLE ROOF.

FIG.10- VENT PIPE THROUGH SHEET METAL ROOF.

FIG.11- VENT PIPE THROUGH FLAT COMPOSITION ROOF.

FIG. 12- VENT PIPE THROUGH TILE ROOF.

SCHEDULE OF ITEMS

ITEM	DESCRIPTION
1	BASE FLASHING.
2	CAP FLASHING.
3	METAL-COVERED CRICK
4	SOLDERED LAP SEAM.
5	CLEATS.(SPACED @ 12"C
6	STANDING SEAM.
7	LOCK SEAM.(SECURED ROOF WITH CLEATS)
8	EDGE STRIP.
9	ROOF SHEATHING.
10	METAL CAP.
11	FLASHING SLEEVE.
12	FLASHING SHEET.
13	THREADED CAP. (MAT'L =.............
14	VENT PIPE.
15	PORTLAND CEMENT MO
16	WOODEN FRAME.(4-SID
17	COMPOSITION ROOF
18	TILE ROOF.

TYPICAL FLASHINGS FOR ROOF VENTS

PLATE 21.   62

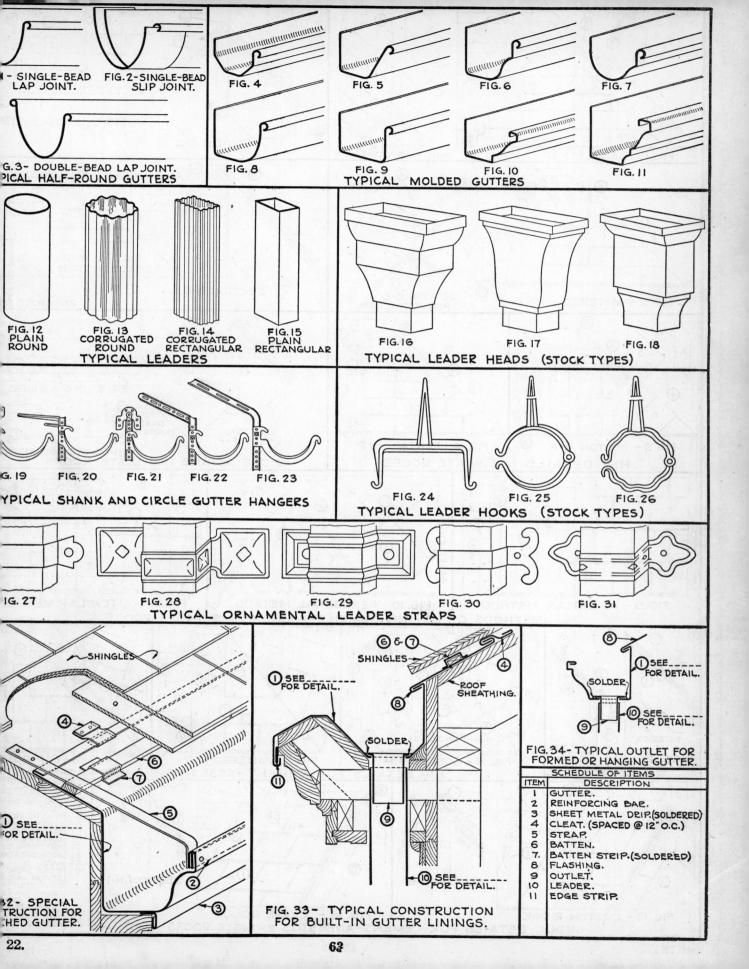

SINGLE-BEAD LAP JOINT.

FIG.2-SINGLE-BEAD SLIP JOINT.

G.3- DOUBLE-BEAD LAP JOINT.

PICAL HALF-ROUND GUTTERS

FIG. 4

FIG. 5

FIG. 6

FIG. 7

FIG. 8

FIG. 9

FIG. 10

FIG. 11

TYPICAL MOLDED GUTTERS

FIG. 12 PLAIN ROUND

FIG. 13 CORRUGATED ROUND

FIG. 14 CORRUGATED RECTANGULAR

FIG. 15 PLAIN RECTANGULAR

TYPICAL LEADERS

FIG. 16

FIG. 17

FIG. 18

TYPICAL LEADER HEADS (STOCK TYPES)

FIG. 19   FIG. 20   FIG. 21   FIG. 22   FIG. 23

YPICAL SHANK AND CIRCLE GUTTER HANGERS

FIG. 24   FIG. 25   FIG. 26

TYPICAL LEADER HOOKS (STOCK TYPES)

FIG. 27   FIG. 28   FIG. 29   FIG. 30   FIG. 31

TYPICAL ORNAMENTAL LEADER STRAPS

SHINGLES

④

⑥

⑦

⑤

① SEE ____ FOR DETAIL.

②

③

32- SPECIAL
TRUCTION FOR
CHED GUTTER.

⑥ & ⑦

SHINGLES

④

⑧

ROOF SHEATHING.

① SEE ____ FOR DETAIL.

SOLDER

⑪

⑨

⑩ SEE ____ FOR DETAIL.

FIG. 33- TYPICAL CONSTRUCTION FOR BUILT-IN GUTTER LININGS.

⑧

① SEE ____ FOR DETAIL.

SOLDER

⑨

⑩ SEE ____ FOR DETAIL.

FIG. 34- TYPICAL OUTLET FOR FORMED OR HANGING GUTTER.

SCHEDULE OF ITEMS	
ITEM	DESCRIPTION
1	GUTTER.
2	REINFORCING BAR.
3	SHEET METAL DRIP.(SOLDERED)
4	CLEAT.(SPACED @ 12" O.C.)
5	STRAP.
6	BATTEN.
7	BATTEN STRIP.(SOLDERED)
8	FLASHING.
9	OUTLET.
10	LEADER.
11	EDGE STRIP.

A
A

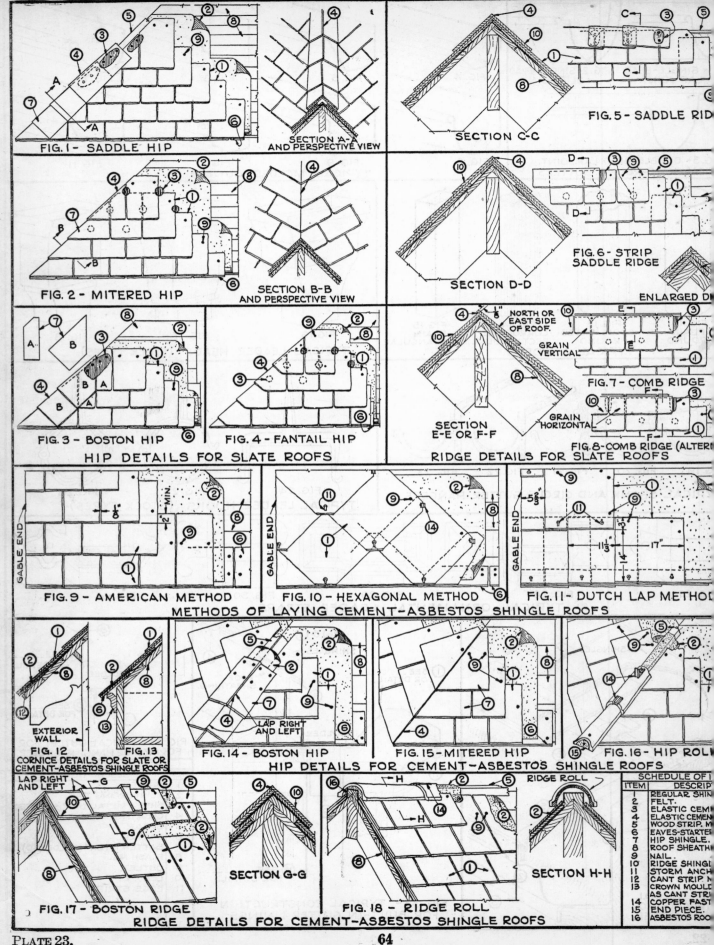

FIG. 1 - SADDLE HIP

SECTION A-A AND PERSPECTIVE VIEW

C
C

SECTION C-C

FIG. 5 - SADDLE RID

B
B

FIG. 2 - MITERED HIP

SECTION B-B AND PERSPECTIVE VIEW

D
D

SECTION D-D

FIG. 6 - STRIP SADDLE RIDGE

ENLARGED D

A
B
B
A
B
A
B

FIG. 3 - BOSTON HIP

FIG. 4 - FANTAIL HIP

HIP DETAILS FOR SLATE ROOFS

1/8"
NORTH OR EAST SIDE OF ROOF.
GRAIN VERTICAL
E
E
GRAIN HORIZONTAL
F
F

SECTION E-E OR F-F

FIG. 7 - COMB RIDGE

FIG. 8 - COMB RIDGE (ALTER

RIDGE DETAILS FOR SLATE ROOFS

GABLE END
1/8"
2" MIN.

FIG. 9 - AMERICAN METHOD

GABLE END

FIG. 10 - HEXAGONAL METHOD

GABLE END
5 2/3"
3"
11 1/3"
17"
14"

FIG. 11 - DUTCH LAP METHOD

METHODS OF LAYING CEMENT-ASBESTOS SHINGLE ROOFS

EXTERIOR WALL

FIG. 12 FIG. 13

CORNICE DETAILS FOR SLATE OR CEMENT-ASBESTOS SHINGLE ROOFS

LAP RIGHT AND LEFT

FIG. 14 - BOSTON HIP

FIG. 15 - MITERED HIP

FIG. 16 - HIP ROLL

HIP DETAILS FOR CEMENT-ASBESTOS SHINGLE ROOFS

LAP RIGHT AND LEFT
G
G

FIG. 17 - BOSTON RIDGE

SECTION G-G

H
H
RIDGE ROLL

FIG. 18 - RIDGE ROLL

SECTION H-H

RIDGE DETAILS FOR CEMENT-ASBESTOS SHINGLE ROOFS

SCHEDULE OF I

ITEM	DESCRIPT
1	REGULAR SHIN
2	FELT.
3	ELASTIC CEMI
4	ELASTIC CEMEN
5	WOOD STRIP. M
6	EAVES-STARTER
7	HIP SHINGLE.
8	ROOF SHEATHI
9	NAIL.
10	RIDGE SHINGL
11	STORM ANCH
12	CANT STRIP. M
13	CROWN MOULD AS CANT STRI
14	COPPER FAST
15	END PIECE.
16	ASBESTOS ROO

OBTAINING GOOD CONSTRUCTION

CONSTRUCTION DEFECTS AND THEIR CAUSES

1. Defects of an Improperly Constructed House—Such a house is sure to have some, if not all, of the following defects *plus* others too numerous to list: (1) Cracked plaster on walls and ceilings throughout the house. (2) Leaks of every kind, resulting in stained walls, and rotting of concealed timbers. (3) Termite infestation, resulting in the destruction of foundation timbers and other important portions of the house. (4) Cracked and leaky basements. (5) Bulging and unsightly walls. (6) Shrunken trim around doors, windows, etc., presenting an unsightly appearance. (7) Sagging and creaking floors. (8) Rickety, squeaking stairs. (9) Windows that rattle, and doors that stick. (10) Paintwork that has peeled and blistered. (11) Chimneys that fail to draw properly, and that present and ever-present fire hazard. (12) Mechanical equipment, such as heating, plumbing, etc., that is a constant source of trouble. (13) Electrical wiring that is insufficient for present day needs, and which also presents an ever-present fire hazard.

2. Direct Causes of These Defects — Such causes may be summed up in six words: *Poor designs; poor materials; poor workmanship*. A more detailed outline of a few of these direct causes is as follows: (1) Insufficient footings. (2) Poorly constructed foundations. (3) Lack of drainage facilities. (4) Poor mortar joints. (5) Lack of termite shields. (6) Inadequate sizes and wide spacing of framing timbers, especially joists and rafters. (7) Improper nailing throughout. (8) Failure to provide full bearing areas. (9) Lack of proper bridging and bracing. (10) Omission of fire stops. (11) Lack of, or improper, flashings on roof and around openings. (12) Frail construction over openings. (13) Careless nailing of floors. (14) Unseasoned lumber. (15) Inaccurate cutting, and improper fittings. (16) Faulty construction of chimney and portions of house adjacent to chimney. (17) Improperly designed or constructed roofs. (18) Poorly designed or constructed gutters. (19) Wrong kind of nails for roofing. (20) Use of building paper of inferior quality. (21) Poor design and installation of miscellaneous mechanical equipment, such as heating, plumbing, etc. (22) Inadequate electrical wiring.

AVOIDING CONSTRUCTION DEFECTS

3. Familiarize Yourself With Good Construction Practice—Study over the subsequent Sections of this Guide, and examine the good and bad construction features of existing houses and of houses being constructed. This will not only enable you to discriminate between good and bad construction, but will also enable you to *specify* and obtain construction of a type that will reduce physical depreciation and resultant upkeep costs to a minimum.

4. Avoid a Local Building Boom—When an unusual amount of construction work is being carried on in a community, a local building "boom" is said to exist. Such a boom may exist in one part of the country, while conditions are normal or even subnormal in another part. If you acquire a home during such a local boom, you may expect some or all of the results listed below.

High Costs—Due to the inflated prices that exist locally during such a boom, your house will cost you much more than it will be worth when normal times are restored.

Poor Construction—If you *build* during a local boom, it will be difficult for you to obtain a properly constructed house. Much of the material that goes into your house will be of an inferior quality that has been rushed through its processing, especially the products of the local lumber mills. Furthermore, it may be difficult, if not impossible, to obtain the services of first-class workmen due to the law of supply and demand.

5. Select Proper Season for Building—To obtain the best construction, you should preferably select a time of the year when suitable weather conditions are apt to prevail in your locality, for a house built during the milder seasons of the year is almost sure to be superior to one built during freezing weather, or during periods of extreme or continuous rainfalls. Freezing weather is highly injurious to such materials as mortar (in masonry), concrete, wall plaster, paint, etc., and continuous or heavy rainfall is injurious to the wooden portion of the house, *unless suitable protective measures are used.*

Although an increasing amount of consideration is being given to continuous, year-round construction of residences (and rightly so), it appears that, as long as we continue to build with the present type of materials that are adversely affected by weather, the home builder has much to lose and little to gain by such a proceeding. He would probably save very little on construction costs, and might lose quite a bit in construction values. In some climates, of course, building construction may be carried on the year round; but in other climates the building season is relatively short. However, even though you may not intend to build until sometime during the period included between early spring and late fall, it may be advantageous for you, during the previous winter, to obtain *bids* and arrange for such construction. This will, no doubt, enable you to get a better price than if you wait until the spring rush.

GOOD CONSTRUCTION *VERSUS* COSTS

6. The Case for Good Construction Practices and Durable Materials—A few reasons for using good construction practices and durable materials are as follows:

(a) The maintenance or upkeep costs for your home will be greatly reduced.

(b) The physical depreciation of your house will be appreciably curtailed.

(c) Your home will be a greater source of satisfaction to you, as you will not be continuously annoyed by such defects as occur in a poorly built house (Par. 1).

(d) A large percent of the cost of a house is for labor. Therefore, the use of more durable materials may increase the cost of the house in a relatively small amount. In fact, the labor costs for installing inferior types of materials sometimes is in excess of the costs for installing a more desirable type of material (Par. 87, P. 133).

(e) The additional labor costs due to the employment of *good* construction practices, instead of poor construction practices, should be little or nothing, as the additional amount of labor required will be small.

7. A Word About Costs—The subsequent sections of this Guide outline the use of good, sound, "permanent" construction practices and materials that are applicable to present-day home building and which will insure the prospective home owner a well-built home having a low rate of physical depreciation, and requiring a minimum of upkeep costs.

It is natural and proper, however, that the average person should endeavor to build his home as economically as possible (Par. 1, P. 16). Therefore, when selecting construction materials for your home, the additional cost required for the more durable types of materials should be weighed against the benefits to be gained (Par. 6). From a purely *practical* standpoint, alone, the limit to which the more durable materials should be used is reached when the extra costs for such materials begin to be out of proportion to the saving in maintenance costs that will be effected by their use.

8. When Cutting Costs—The types of construction practices and materials that you specfiy for the construction of your new home will depend, of course, upon your personal desires, local costs, availability of certain materials locally, etc. When paring down costs, however, you are urged to do the following things:

(a) Economize on non-esentials, such as elaborate mechanical equipment and expensive interior finishes, rather than on those portions of the house that are exposed to the weather, decay, termites, corrosion, etc.

(b) Use the information in this Guide as a *pattern* for the proper procedure in obtaining an enduring home.

Finally, when planning the construction details of your home, remember that: "Only a rich man can afford 'cheap' construction".

TERMITE PREVENTION

1. What Termites Are — Termites are ant-like, wood-devouring insects that are closely related to the cockroach, but constructed very differently (Fig. 3).

2. Function of the Termite—The termite must be regarded as one of Nature's agents, whose function is to help Nature to reduce all dead wood to a "state of dust". This holds true whether such wood consists of a dead tree in a forest, a fence post on the farm, or the woodwork of a dwelling in the city.

3. Annual Damage by Termites — At the present time, termite damage in the United States is estimated to be about $50,000,000 annually, with such loss increasing at a steady rate. Some state legislatures are even considering making it compulsory to protect buildings against termites.

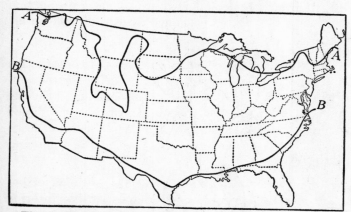

Fig. 1. Diagrammatic Map of the United States Showing Northern Limits of Damage by Subterranean Termites (A-A) and Non-subterranean or Dry-Wood Termites (B-B).

(Courtesy of the Bureau of Entomology of the U. S. Dept. of Agriculture)

4. Species and Distribution—There are fifty-eight species of termites in the United States, including the subterranean and non-subterranean types. Their distribution is shown by Fig. 1. This discussion will be confined to the subterranean type, as this type is more injurious and more prevalent; in fact, it is estimated that 99% of all house-dwelling termites are of the subterranean type.

5. Location of Nests or Colonies — The subterranean termites build their nests or colonies either in the ground, or in wood that is in contact with the ground. Fig. 2 shows, graphically, a colony of ter-

mites in the earth. There may be any number of such colonies in contact with the woodwork of a dwelling, and tens of thousands of termites may inhabit each colony.

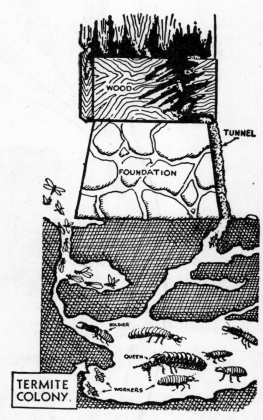

Fig. 2. How Subterranean Termites May Attack the Woodwork of the Foundation of a Dwelling.

(Courtesy of the American Building Association News)

6. Life Cycle of the Termite—Fig. 3 shows the life cycle of the termite. There are three stages in the life of termites—the egg, the nymph, and the adult. The adults are of two kinds—sterile and fertile. There are two types of sterile adults—soldiers and workers. There are three types of fertile adults—the winged type, or potential kings and queens, and two other types that are wingless and never emerge from the colony. All three types of fertile adults have the power of reproduction. Once each year (usually in the spring) the black or brown-bodied, white-winged, fertile adults of both sexes emerge from the nest to swarm. At this time they quickly mate, lose their wings, enter holes or cracks in the earth or wood, and start a new colony. When the colony is once started, both the queen and the supplementary reproductives produce eggs (Fig. 3). The queen, alone, is capable of laying 35,000 eggs per day or about 12,775,000 eggs per year. The average life of the queen is from 5 to 15 years. The death of the queen does not seriously affect the colony, for she is soon replaced.

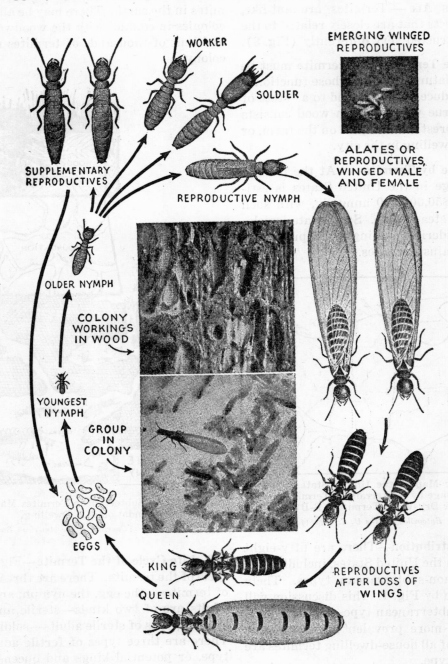

Fig. 3. The Life Cycle of the Termite.

(Reproduced from "Termites and Termite Control" by Kofoid et al, through the courtesy of the publishers, the University of California Press)

7. The Destructive Forms of Termites—The sterile workers are the destructive forms of termites. Here are some important facts to remember about them:

Size and Appearance—They are small (about the size of a grain of rice), cream-colored, wingless, ant-like, and blind. See Fig. 3 for enlarged view.

Physical Characteristics—They are soft-bodied, and able to squeeze through cracks and openings that are only sufficiently wide to permit water to seep through. They are able to penetrate the hardest of woods, and to disintegrate lime mortar and poor grades of concrete, provided they have their customary contact with the earth or with other sources of moisture supply.

Habits—They work under cover in the dark; shun light; and always remain concealed in the earth, in wood, or in their shelter tubes.

Food—They eat wood, by-products of wood, all cellulose materials, and many other similar materials.

Water—They require considerable moisture in order to exist. This moisture must be supplied through contact with the earth or by artificial means, such as a leaky pipe, leaky roof, condensation from metals or masonry materials in direct contact with wood, etc. *When their supply of moisture is permanently cut off, termites die.*

8. How Termites Get Into Dwellings — Termites may get into dwellings in any of the following ways:

Through Ventilators and Openings—Winged, reproductive termites may gain access under the house, or in unfinished attics, due to a lack of 18-mesh screens in the ventilators and openings, or by passing through cracks, etc.

Through Earth—Termites may work their way up from their foraging tunnels in the earth into the woodwork of the dwelling by either of two methods: (1) By working their way up through a crack in the foundation. (2) By building shelter tubes up the faces of foundation walls, pipes, etc. (Fig. 2).

9. Importance of Termite Prevention — With our present-day knowledge of the presence of termites and the damage that they are causing, it is essential for the prospective home owner to *know* that the house he builds or buys is fully protected against their destructive attacks. The time to make a house termite-proof is when it is being built—not afterwards. Here, indeed, is a case where the proverbial ounce of prevention is worth a pound of cure.

Fortunately, it is fairly simple to *build* a new dwelling so that it will be proof against termites. A description of these methods is given below.

METHODS OF TERMITE PREVENTION

10. Termite Shields (General) — Non-corrosive, metal termite shields are considered the simplest and most effective protection (Pl. 19). These shields, when properly installed, prevent termites from reaching the woodwork from the earth. Also, even if winged termites, of the subterranean type, do enter the woodwork and try to start a colony, they will quickly die because their necessary moisture supply from the earth will be cut off (Par. 7).

Type of Shields — It is recommended that all shields, in general, be of the type that is placed *over* the foundation walls. However, for masonry and brick veneer construction (Pl. 7), where the use of a shield placed over the foundation wall would destroy the bond between the masonry wall and the foundation wall, the shield should be of the inserted type. Where basement walls are of solid monolithic concrete construction, and exposed for ready detection of termite "tunnels", the shields may be omitted.

Material—16 oz. copper is preferable, especially for shields exposed to the weather. However, No. 26 Gage galvanized, copper-bearing steel will suffice for low-cost houses (Table 1, P. 75).

11. Shields for Masonry Steps, Etc.—The design and installation of shields at miscellaneous vulnerable points, such as the points where concrete or masonry steps, stoops, porches, etc., join the dwelling, should be watched with the utmost care. These junction points should be made absolutely and permanently termite-proof at the time of construction, because, when once the work is covered up, it will be too late to take precautions. The following recommendations are offered:

(a) Build all such steps, stoops, and porches hollow (without dirt fills), and with access openings as recommended by Par. 49, P. 82, if possible, and use inserted type shields.

(b) Where the above construction is not possible, use a suitable special shield, such as shown by Pl. 19, Fig. 5, that will prevent termites from entering the dwelling under the shield and prevent storm water from entering over the shield.

12. Solid Foundation Walls—Foundation walls and supporting piers so designed and constructed as to be free from present or future cracks or fissures, through which termites can secretly attack, form a first line of defense against the termites. Such walls and piers (Sec. 17, P. 95) should preferably be of concrete, with sufficient steel reinforcing at corners, intersections, and top surfaces to prevent cracks or fissures.

13. Treated Wood—All wood in contact with the ground, or exposed to termite infestation, should be either pressure-treated with coal-tar creosote or zinc chloride, or should be of a naturally durable wood such as heart tidewater red cypress or heart redwood (Table 1, P. 106), as such wood is inedible for termites.

14. Ventilation — Provide sufficient cross ventilation for unexcavated areas under house (Par. 11, P. 95).

15. Ventilator Screens—Provide all openings for ventilating under the house, or in the attic, with 18-mesh bronze screening.

16. Removal of Stumps, Etc. — All stumps, wood scraps, etc., should be removed from the soil under, and near, the dwelling.

17. Height of Wood Construction Above Ground— Such construction should be as follows:

(a) Wooden floor joists of dwelling should be at least 24″ above ground.

(b) Wooden construction on exterior of building should be at least 6″ above ground.

(c) Carriages for wooden steps should rest on a concrete slab and be insulated from the porch as shown by Pl. 19, Fig. 7.

DECAY PREVENTION

1. What Decay Is—Decay in wood is caused by the action of certain low forms of plant life, called fungi, which grow and feed upon the substance of the wood, and finally destroy it. These fungi consist, for the most part, of very fine, threadlike filaments that penetrate the wood in all directions, and finally grow out to the surface to form compact masses called fruiting bodies. The presence of a fruiting body indicates that decay has made considerable progress in the wood.

2. The Function of Decay Fungi—Decay fungi, like termites, the "weather", etc., must be regarded as one of Nature's ever-present, disintegrating agencies.

3. Annual Damage from Decay—According to authorities on the subject, the annual loss of timber in service because of decay alone, amounts to about one-fifth of the annual cut of lumber. This amounts to about 7,000,000,000 board feet of lumber annually.

4. Conditions Essential for Decay—The following conditions are essential for the existence and growth of practically all fungi:

Moderate Temperature—Extreme heat or cold will retard or kill the fungi.

Air—The fungi require a certain amount of air. A sluggish circulation of air is favorable to their growth, as it promotes moisture.

Moisture—The fungi require a moderate amount of moisture. Most decay occurs in wood that contains moisture in excess of the fiber saturation point. Wood continuously immersed in water or wood continuously dry (having less than 20% moisture content) will not decay.

Food—The fungi must have food, which usually consists of the substance of the wood itself.

5. How Decay Spreads—The fruiting bodies of decayed wood produce millions of microscopic spores which are to the fungus what seed are to higher plants. These spores float through the air for long distances; and when one makes contact with a piece of wood where conditions are favorable, it germinates and the fungus begins its destructive action. Decay may be also started by the fungus growing from one piece of wood to another, as when a piece of decaying wood is in contact with a piece of sound, untreated wood.

6. Molds and Stains—The *sapwood* of lumber is sometimes affected by fungi that produce molds and stains. These molds are cottony or powdery and are easily brushed off. The stains, however, penetrate into the wood and cannot be removed. The so-called blue stain is the most common of the stains. These molds and stains should not be confused with decay, as they do not cause disintegration of the wood, nor do they materially affect the strength of the wood. However, such stains and molds on new wood for a dwelling are unsightly, and indicate that the wood has been subjected to improper moisture and temperature conditions.

7. Importance of Decay Prevention—As decay ranks even higher than termites as a destroyer of dwellings, it is esential that the prospective home owner makes sure that the house he buys or builds is designed and built in a decay-proof manner.

METHODS OF DECAY PREVENTION

8. Outline of Methods—Just as it is fairly simple to *build* a house proof against termites, it is also fairly simple to *build* a house proof against decay. In fact, the methods used for combating termites and decay are the same in a good many instances; thus, figuratively speaking, we are enabled to "kill two birds with one stone". The best and surest methods of decay prevention are to deprive the decay fungi of either moisture or food, or both.

9. Depriving Fungi of Moisture—This may be accomplished by designing and building a dwelling in such a manner that the woodwork will remain permanently dry. This is the simplest and least expensive method. The following points should also be given careful consideration.

(a) Sufficient ventilation should be provided (Par. 11, P. 95).

(b) The height of wood construction above the ground should be as recommended by Par. 17, P. 70.

(c) A layer of sand (Par. 6, P. 77) should preferably be spread over the unexcavated areas under the house to serve as a permanent "mulch", and to thus prevent dampness caused by excessive evaporation of moisture from the earth.

(d) All lumber should be well-seasoned, and should be *kept* dry before and after installation in the building.

(e) All roofing, flashing, piping, and similar items should be carefully installed to prevent leaks and subsequent decay.

10. Depriving Fungi of Food—This may be accomplished by using either the heart portion of naturally durable wood (Table 1, P. 106) in its natural state or the sap portion of ordinary wood that has been impregnated with coal-tar creosote or zinc chloride. Either type of wood is practically decay-proof, as it is unsuitable for fungi food.

11. Prevention of Fungi Growths — All stumps, wood scraps, etc., should be removed from the soil, and from unexcavated areas under the house, so as to prevent the growth and possible spreading of decay fungi.

12. Cost of Decay Prevention—The added cost of building a house permanently decay-proof should be only a small percent of the total cost of the house. Any good lumber mill or wood preserving plant can readily supply you with this cost data. As in the case of termite prevention, this added cost will prove to be cheap insurance over a period of years from a standpoint of minimized upkeep costs, alone.

WOOD PRESERVATIVE METHODS

13. Coal-Tar Creosote — This is one of the best known wood preservatives, and consists of a heavy, brownish-black oil that is distilled from coal, and is practically *insoluble in water*. It has the disadvantages of being dark in color, of giving off a strong odor, and of not taking paint well. The serviceability of creosotes distilled from substances other than *coal* has not been thoroughly established, as yet.

14. Zinc Chloride—Zinc chloride is another valuable preservative for wood. Zinc chloride salts are obtained by dissolving metallic zinc in hydrochloric acid. A water solution of 3% to 5% is prepared from the salts and injected into the wood. Zinc chloride has several advantages, as it is colorless, odorless, takes paint well, and is slightly fire-retardant. The disadvantages of this preservative is the fact that it is soluble in water. It is necessary, therefore, that all zinc chloride treated wood that is exposed to rain or water be kept painted so as to prevent the preservative from being slowly dissolved out of the wood.

15. Pressure Treatment (General)—The pressure treatment method for injecting either creosote or zinc chloride into wood is by far the best method, and is the method recommended by this Guide. This method consists of placing the wood upon steel cars which are run into long cylindrical tanks into which the preservative is pumped in liquid form, and maintained under pressure for a sufficient time to insure that the preservative is forced into the pores of the wood.

16. Hot and Cold Bath Method (Creosote)—This method consists of placing the material, or the *ends* of posts, joists, etc., requiring treatment, in a bath of hot creosote (maintained at about the boiling temperature of water) for an hour or more. The material is then *quickly* removed to a bath of lukewarm creosote (about 100°F.) and allowed to remain for another hour or more. In this treatment, the hot bath drives out some of the air and moisture in the cells of the wood, and the sudden cooling of the other bath causes the remaining air to contract and draw in a considerable amount of the preservative. This Guide recommends this treatment for ends of untreated joists that are embedded in masonry, ends of untreated posts that are subject to decay, etc. This treatment is not as satisfactory as the pressure method, but is considered to be the best practicable field method. For further details of this method, see Ref. R24-13, Sec. 38.

17. Dipping—This method consists of dipping the ends of posts, joists, etc., in *hot* creosote maintained at about the boiling point of water and allowing them to remain for 15 minutes or longer. Although this method is not as good as the previous two methods, it will add considerably to the life of the material, and is certainly better than no treatment at all.

18. Brushing — This method consists of brushing *hot* creosote on the wood and allowing the wood to soak up as much of the preservative as possible. At least two coats are advisable, and all cracks and crevices should be carefully filled. This method is of questionable and *temporary* value.

CORROSION PREVENTION

1. General—Just as wood is disintegrated by termites and decay, metals are disintegrated by erosion, electrolysis (galvanic action), and corrosion.

2. Annual Damage—The annual monetary loss in the United States due to the deterioration of metals in dwellings is a stupendous amount. It is estimated that the deterioration of water pipes, alone, represents a loss of $86,000,000 a year.

3. Erosion—Erosion, for the purpose of this discussion, is the wearing away of metals, such as gutters, downspouts, metal roofs, flashings, pipes, etc., by the action of water flowing across or through them. Just as water "wears away the hardest stone", it will also eventually wear away the hardest metal exposed to it. This wear, of course, will ordinarily take place at a very slow rate, but should be considered when selecting thicknesses of plates and pipes.

4. Electrolysis — When dissimilar metals are in contact in the presence of an electrolyte (such as water that contains slight impurities, chemicals, etc.) galvanic action is set up, as in an electric battery, and one of the metals is deteriorated. This is known as electrolysis. The following table lists the more common metals according to what is known as the electro-chemical series:

1.	Aluminum	5.	Nickel
2.	Zinc	6.	Tin
3.	Steel	7.	Lead
4.	Iron	8.	Copper

How to Use the Table—When any two metals in the above table are in contact, with an electrolyte present, the one with the *lower* (lesser) number is corroded. For example, if number 3 and number 8 are in contact, the steel will be corroded. Such galvanic action, for the purpose of this discussion, *increases* as the metals are farther apart in the list. Thus aluminum would be more affected by copper than would nickel. Where the metals are close together on the list, as are steel and iron (3 and 4), or lead and copper (7 and 8), the potential is much less, so no injurious results are produced, especially if water is the electrolyte.

Electrolysis Prevention—Care should be taken that metals *far* apart in the above list are not connected together. For instance, don't allow galvanized nails to be used with copper or vice versa; don't allow steel or iron fittings to be used in a system of copper piping, as such fittings would be a weak point in an otherwise long-lived system; etc. Of course, there is a practical limit to the extent that this can be carried out. For example, if you have copper pipes for your heating system, they will ordinarily have to connect to a cast iron or steel boiler. Also, when iron or steel pipes are used, it is customary (and advisable) to use brass valves.

5. Types of Corrosion—The following three types of corrosion will be discussed here:

Atmospheric Corrosion—Metals exposed to the atmosphere, such as screens, gutters, flashings, etc., corrode mainly because of the combined action of oxygen (from the air) and of water which must be present in liquid form. This water may be present due to rain, snow, or the condensation of water vapor in contact with the cold metal surface. The most severely corrosive atmospheres are the "industrial" atmospheres (such as found in Pittsburgh) which contain dust, smoke particles, and sulphur oxides, resulting from the combustion of fuel. Seacoast atmospheres rate second as corrosive atmospheres, while the least corrosive atmospheres are found in rural locations where they are free from sulphur gases, smoke, and salt.

Underground Corrosion—Corrosion of metals buried in the ground, such as water and sewer pipes, etc., is due not only to the action of water and oxygen present in the ground, but to the action of certain salts or acids that may be present. Here are some facts about soils:

(a) The most corrosive soils are heavy, poorly drained soils which are either very acid, or contain excessive quantities of soluble salts.

(b) The slightly corrosive soils are soils that are porous and well-drained.

(c) The least corrosive soils are sandy soils, on account of their excellent drainage.

(d) The soils most destructive to copper or brass are soils containing sulphides.

(e) The soils most destructive to galvanized steel or iron are poorly drained, acid soils, and soils high in soluble salts.

Submerged or Semi-Submerged Corrosion—When metals, such as the inner surface of boilers, pipes, etc., are wholly or partly submerged (covered with water), the active corroding agents are water and oxygen; but the type and purity of the water determines the rate of corrosion to a great extent.

6. Corrosion of Non-Ferrous Metals—These metals have the following corrosion characteristics:

Atmospheric Corrosion—For exposure to atmospheric corrosion, copper is probably the most durable, all-around metal available; red brass is extremely durable; and yellow brass is very durable under average conditions.

Submerged Corrosion (Inside of Water Pipes, Etc.) —For exposure to submerged corrosion, copper is the most durable all-around metal; red brass is extremely durable; and yellow brass is durable, for average conditions, but should contain not less than 67% copper where the water is soft or is otherwise corrosive.

Underground Corrosion—Copper and red brass corrode slowly in most soils. Yellow brass shows a distinct tendency to dezincify. Lead tends to become badly pitted in some soils.

7. Corrosion of Ferrous Metals — These metals (wrought iron, steel, copper bearing steel, cast iron, etc.) have the following corrosion characteristics:

Atmospheric Corrosion—The ferrous metals corrode readily when exposed to the atmosphere. Steel or iron containing 0.15% to 0.30% copper is more durable than similar metal without the copper. A heavy (2 oz. per sq. ft.) coating of zinc prolongs the life of all ferrous metals several times. This zinc coating, however, is severely attacked by industrial and foggy seacoast atmospheres.

Submerged Corrosion (Inside of Water Pipes, Etc.) —In the submerged corrosion of steel and iron, the corrosion characteristics of the water is of more importance than the composition of the metal. Soft waters are usually more corrosive to ferrous metals than are hard waters, as hard waters are likely to form protective scales on the inside of the pipes.

However, such scales will gradually clog the pipes. The ferrous metals used in steam boilers and pipes suffer much more than those used in hot-water boilers and pipes.

Underground Corrosion—All ferrous metals (including wrought iron, copper bearing steel, and cast iron) corrode at about the same rate when buried in a given soil. An extra heavy zinc coating (2.8 oz. per sq. ft.) will prevent the metal from becoming pitted in most soils for 10 years or more. Cast iron frequently retains much of its usefulness even after severe corrosive attack, due to the formation of a heavy coating that fills the pits and often plugs the perforations.

8. Importance of Corrosion Prevention—Just as a chain is no stronger than its weakest link, a house is no more durable than the nails that hold it together, the shields that prevent the entry of termites, the flashings that keep out water, the pipes that are hidden in walls or the ground, or any of the other vital metal items that are necessary for its continued functioning as a dwelling.

9. Cost of Corrosion Prevention—In studying the cost of corrosion prevention, let us consider a few items separately:

Nails—The cost of nails is insignificant compared to labor costs. Rustproof nails will pay for themselves by merely preventing rusty streaks on paintwork, not to mention their other up-keep saving qualities.

Sheet Metal Work—Here again the cost of material is low compared to labor costs. If copper is used, it will never need painting, and should never need replacing.

Copper Tubing—It should be possible to install copper tubing, with soldered joints, at a cost not exceeding that for steel pipe, due to the fact that copper tubing costs only slightly more than the steel pipe and is much easier to install; also, the soldered joints are even superior to threaded joints, if properly made.

10. Selection of Metals—This Guide's recommendations in regard to the selection of metals are listed in Table 1. When selecting materials for pipes, it will be well to consult your local water-supply authorities as to the nature of the water and the soil in your locality.

TABLE 1.—Guide for the Selection of Metals Used in Residential Construction

Item No.	Item	Materials Recommended for Permanent Construction[1]	Alternate Materials (Not Permanent)
	Miscellaneous:		
1	Termite Shields	16-oz. Copper	26-Ga. Copper Bearing Steel, with 2-oz. Zinc Coating
2	Flashings and Gutters	16-oz. Copper	26-Ga. Copper Bearing Steel, with 2-oz. Zinc Coating
3	Metal Roofs	Copper	26-Ga. Copper Bearing Steel, with 2-oz. Zinc Coating
4	Nails	See Sec. 24, Table 20	
5	Screen Wire Cloth	Bronze (90% Copper, 10% Tin)	Copper Bearing Steel, With Heavy Zinc Coating
6	Plumbing: Cold-Water Pipes[2]	(1) Grade "A" Copper Tubing, Copper Fittings, Soldered Joints (2) Red Brass Pipe, Red Brass Fittings	(1) Galvanized Wrought Iron Pipe, Galvanized Malleable Iron Fittings (2) Galvanized Steel Pipe, Galvanized Malleable Iron Fittings.
7	Hot-Water Pipes	Same as for Item 6	(1) Wrought Iron Pipe, Malleable Iron Fittings (2) Copper Bearing Steel Pipe, Malleable Iron Fittings
8	Soil and Waste Pipes[3]	Galvanized Wrought Iron Pipe, with Galvanized Malleable Iron Fittings, for Pipes Up to 2" Diam. All Other Pipes and Fittings, Extra Heavy Cast Iron.	Galvanized Steel Pipe with Galvanized Malleable Iron Fittings, for Pipes Up to 2" Diam. All Other Pipes and Fittings Standard Weight Cast Iron.
9	Vent Pipes[4]	Same as for Item 8	Same as for Item 8
10	Traps (Exposed)	Extra Heavy Brass (Chromium Plated)	Brass (Chromium Plated)
11	Traps (Not Exposed)	(1) Extra Heavy Brass (2) Brass (3) Extra Heavy Cast Iron	Cast Iron
12	Heating: Piping (Hot-Water or Steam)	(1) Grade "A" Copper Tubing, Copper Fittings, Soldered Joints (2) Wrought Iron Pipe and Malleable Iron Fittings	Copper Bearing Steel Pipe, Malleable Iron Fittings

NOTES FOR TABLE 1—

[1] "Permanent", as here used, means having a life equal to the building, which may vary from 50 to 100 or more years.

[2] All underground piping should be of an extra heavy grade.

[3] No galvanized pipes should be used underground for plumbing. (Use extra heavy cast iron soil pipe, coated with asphaltum or coal-tar pitch.)

[4] Portions of galvanized steel vent pipes extending above roofs should preferably be of copper bearing steel.

Numbers (1), (2), etc., indicate first preference, second preference, etc., of Guide.

LAYOUT OF BUILDING, EXCAVATING, AND GRADING

1. Survey of Lot—Before a layout of building is made, the building lot should be accurately surveyed (Par. 4, P. 19) and the following additional requirements complied with:

(a) The surveyor should furnish owner with a map, showing the boundary lines of lot, and also grades.

(b) The surveyor should establish a "bench mark", which is simply a reference mark placed on a permanent object. Such a mark is located a certain known height above certain surroundings, such as the crown of a road bed, etc., and is useful for checking first-floor heights, grade lines, etc.

(c) The surveyor should establish the four corners of the lot with good substantial markers. The markers may consist of galvanized iron pipe, at least 2½ feet long, driven into the ground with the upper end about flush with the surface of the lot.

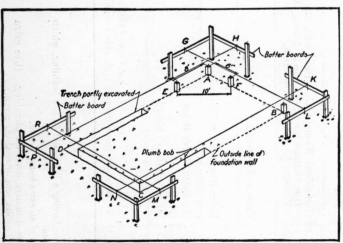

Fig. 1.—*One Method of Laying Out Foundations.*
(Reprinted from Reference R4-2, Sec. 38)

2. Layout of Building—A building is generally laid out by means of stakes and batter boards. See Fig. 1.

Preferred Method—This Guide recommends the use of surveying instruments for establishing the boundary lines of a building, as this method is the quickest, easiest, and most accurate.

Alternate Method—If surveying instruments are not used, the method known as the right-triangle method is recommended (Fig. 1). This method is based on the fact that a triangle with sides 6, 8, and 10 feet long is a right-triangle, and the 90 degree angle, or right angle, is opposite the longest side. This method is described below:

First, a base line is established, marking out one end or side of the new building. See line A-B in Fig. 1. Stakes are set at A and B on this line, locating two corners. In the top of Stake A a nail is driven near the center. This nail accurately locates the corner. On the line A-B another stake is driven at F, 6 feet from Stake A. A nail is driven in the top of this stake exactly 6 feet from the nail in Stake A. Stake E should be driven so that its center will be exactly 8 feet from Stake A, and exactly 10 feet from Stake F. The corner represented by the angle E-A-F is a right angle; the line A-E extended to D will form the second boundary line of the building, and D will represent the third corner. Other corners are located in a similar manner. After this has been done, strings are stretched over the corner stakes A-B-C-D and carried to outside supports called "batter boards" as indicated by G-H-K-L-M-N-P-R. The top of the horizontal batters should be set at first floor level or some other convenient "datum". The building lines may be projected from the strings to the ground by means of a plumb bob suspended as shown in the drawing. When the outside Stakes G-H-K-L, etc., have been set, and the strings indicating the layout of the building transferred to them, the corner Stakes A-B-C-D and Stakes E and F are removed so that the trench may be excavated. Nails should be driven in the batters where the strings are fastened so that, if strings are broken or removed, they can be replaced accurately. Having found the building lines, it is easy to locate piers, posts, columns, or other intermediate supports.

3. Removal of Top Soil—All top soil in area covered by dwelling, and extending at least 5 feet beyond dwelling on all sides, should be removed to a depth of approximately 12" and deposited at a suitable location on the lot so as to be available for finish grading.

4. Excavating for Foundations—Such excavations should extend to solid ground and have level, *undisturbed* bottoms. No fill should be allowed under any foundation.

Bottoms of excavations for the foundations supporting outside walls of a building should have a depth at least 6" below the local frost line. This will prevent the upheaval of the foundation when the ground freezes in winter.

5. Excavating Below Floor Joists—The minimum distance from floor joists to ground should be 24″. This will provide room for a person to crawl under the house when necessary, and will help prevent termite infestation and decay. If the land is low or poorly drained, this minimum height should not be obtained by excavating under the house, but rather by selecting a type of house that looks well if set several feet off the ground.

6. Treatment of Unexcavated Areas—Make sure that all unexcavated areas under the building are free from wood scraps of every kind. This Guide also recommends that such areas be covered with about 2″ of clean sand, as this will help prevent the escape of moisture from the ground, and thus help curtail termite infestation, decay, warped first floors, etc.

7. Tree Roots—All the roots adjacent to foundations, walks, and similar items should be removed to a sufficient depth and distance to prevent future injury to such foundations, walks, etc. by the roots.

8. Fills for Porches, Etc.—All such fills should consist of good bearing soil, and should be thoroughly tamped. Before allowing such fills to be placed for porches, etc., make sure that all surfaces of the walls, which will be covered by the fill, have been made proof against the entry of termites.

9. Removal of Debris from Soil—All debris incidental to the building operation, such as wood, bricks, mortar, cement, etc., should be removed from the soil before any grading is started. Otherwise, difficulty will be experienced when you landscape the building lot.

MONOLITHIC CONCRETE CONSTRUCTION

CONCRETE MATERIALS

1. Cement (General)—A reputable brand of Portland cement that conforms to A.S.T.M. (American Society for Testing Materials) Specifications should be used.

2. Waterproofed Cements — In general, these are not recommended as most waterproofing substances are only temporary in effectiveness, and some have harmful effects upon the concrete (Par. 3, P. 99).

3. High-Early-Strength Portland Cement — This cement sets quicker and has a higher initial strength than standard Portland cement. There are two types of this cement; in one type, the proportionate alumina content is increased; in the other type, standard Portland cement is reground to the fineness of flour. On account of its extra cost, the use of this cement is not warranted unless the time element is of great importance, such as when the weather is cold and it is desirable to reduce the time of protection from freezing weather by having the concrete set quicker.

4. Fine Aggregates for Concrete and Concrete Topping—Such aggregates should consist of natural sand or the screenings from crushed rock; and should be clean, hard, durable, uncoated, and free from injurious amounts of loam, organic (vegetable or animal) matter, saline (salt), alkali, or injurious amounts of other impurities.

As little as 1/10 of 1% of organic matter may prevent the concrete from hardening, or may cause its early disintegration. A slight amount of finely divided clay that is well distributed is not seriously objectionable.

All fine aggregates should be well-graded from fine to coarse, with all aggregates passing a 1/4" sieve, but not more than 30% (15% for topping) passing a No. 50 (.012" opening) sieve, and not more than 5% passing a No. 100 (.006" opening) sieve.

5. Coarse Aggregates for Concrete—These should consist of gravel, crushed stone, or blast furnace slag; and should be clean, hard, durable, uncoated, and free from injurious amounts of loam, organic (vegetable and animal) matter, saline (salt), alkali, or injurious amounts of other impurities. Laminated materials, shale, or stones laminated with shale, should especially be avoided.

As in the case of fine aggregates, as little as 1/10 of 1% of organic matter may prevent the hardening of the concrete or may cause its early disintegration.

Such aggregates should be well-graded from fine to coarse, with all aggregates passing a 1 1/4" sieve, but not more than 5% passing a 1/4" sieve.

6. Water—The water should be free from injurious amounts of oil, alkali, acid, vegetable or animal matter, or other impurities. In general, water for mixing concrete *should be clean and pure enough to drink*.

7. Coloring Materials—When mortar, cement topping, or concrete is to be colored, the use of some reliable brand of cement that has been colored at the factory is recommended, if available in your locality. If coloring matter is to be mixed on the job, the best type of material and workmanship must be used, or the results are sure to be disappointing and inferior. For list of recommended coloring pigments, see Table 1 below.

TABLE 1.—*Colors to Be Used in Concrete Floor Finish*

COLOR DESIRED	Commercial Names of Colors for Use in Cement	Pounds of color required per sack of cement to secure	
		Light Shade	Med. Shade
Grays, blue-black and black	Germantown lampblack[1] or	1/2	1
	Carbon black[1] or	1/2	1
	Black oxide of manganese[1] or	1	2
	Mineral black[1]	1	2
Blue Shade	Ultramarine blue	5	9
Brownish - red to dull brick red	Red oxide of iron	5	9
Bright red to vermillion	Mineral turkey red	5	9
Red sandstone to purplish-red	Indian red	5	9
Brown to reddish-brown	Metallic brown (oxide)	5	9
Buff, colonial tint and yellow	Yellow ochre or	5	9
	Yellow oxide	2	4
Green shade	Chromium oxide or	5	9
	Greenish blue ultramarine	6	

[1]Only first quality lampblack should be used. Carbon black is light and requires very thorough mixing. Black oxide or mineral black is probably most advantageous for general use. For black use 11 pounds oxide per sack of cement.

(Reprinted from Ref. R4-5 Sec. 38.)

FORMS FOR MONOLITHIC CONCRETE CONSTRUCTION

8. Types of Forms—When concrete is cast, as for footings, foundation walls, etc., suitable forms must be provided. The types most generally used for house construction are earth forms and wooden forms.

9. Earth Forms—These are usually suitable for monolithic concrete footings below grade. Earth forms are also often used for one or more faces of those portions of foundation walls that are below grade, for small structures, provided that the soil is suitably firm.

10. Wooden Forms—Wooden forms are preferable for the exterior faces of all foundation walls, and the exterior and interior faces of all basement walls. The use of exterior wooden forms permits inspection and waterproofing of exterior walls, and the proper laying of drain tile. See Pl. 1, Figs. 4 to 14.

REINFORCEMENT OF CONCRETE

11. Methods of Reinforcing Concrete—This is accomplished by embedding steel reinforcing bars, or steel wire mesh, in the concrete structure. See Fig. 1, C.

12. Why Steel Reinforcing Is Desirable—If a thick piece of rubber is supported and bent as shown by Fig. 1, A, it will be seen that the side on which the load is applied becomes shorter and is, therefore, in "compression", while the opposite side is stretched and is, therefore, in "tension". Now, the average ultimate strength of concrete, when 28 days old, is approximately 2,000 pounds per square inch in compression, but only about 400 pounds per square inch in tension. Therefore, when a piece of plain concrete is overloaded as shown by Fig. 1, B, it will fail in tension. When steel reinforcing is placed in the concrete on the *opposite side from which the load is applied*, as shown by Fig. 1, C, the steel takes the tension stresses, and the concrete takes the compression stresses. As steel has an ultimate tensile strength of about 60,000 pounds per square inch, it is evident that even a small amount of steel properly located in a concrete structure will greatly increase the strength of the structure.

13. Use of Steel Recommended—Steel is one of the cheapest of building materials; and it takes only a comparatively small amount of steel, properly placed in concrete, to make the concrete structure many times stronger. It is recommended, therefore, that every concrete item of any importance be suitably reinforced with sufficient steel to insure it against cracks.

14. Design of Reinforcing for Concrete—The following is recommended:

Simple Reinforcing—For simple reinforcing for items like sidewalks, which are not subjected to exceptional strains, the information given in other parts of this Section should suffice. Such reinforcing usually consists of steel bars or wire mesh laid straight, with no attempt made to follow exact theoretical practice as to alternate bent bars, etc. such as shown by Pl. 3, Figs. 1 and 2.

Special Reinforcement—Where special reinforcement is needed, as in floors and walls of basements subjected to extreme ground-water conditions, the following alternate suggestions are offered: (1) Seek the services of a competent local engineer or architect. (2) Consult a local contractor who has had experience in this line of work.

Reinforced Concrete Houses—The reinforcement for such houses should, by all means, be designed by a competent engineer; and such reinforcement should be clearly shown on the contract drawings.

15. Locating and Placing of Reinforcement in Concrete—Such reinforcement, when used to increase the load-bearing capacity of the concrete, should be placed in the side of concrete slab that is on the *opposite side from the direction of the load* (see Fig. 1, C). The location of "temperature" reinforcement, used to prevent cracks due to temperature strains, is not of as much importance. All reinforcement should be rigidly supported, and securely held in place in the forms prior to the placing of the concrete.

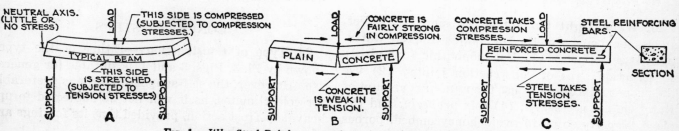

FIG. 1.—*Why Steel Reinforcement is Desirable in Concrete Structures*

MIXING, PLACING AND CURING OF CONCRETE

16. Ratio of Materials — The ratio of cement to aggregates varies according to requirements; a proportionately greater quantity of cement being used where greater strength and water-tightness is required. Use Table 2 for a general guide.

TABLE 2.—*Mixtures and Finishes for Monolithic Concrete Items*

ITEM	MIXTURE[1]	FINISH[2]
Basement Walls, and Wall Footings of Residence	See Sec. 18, P. 97	F1
Basement Floor	See Sec. 18, P. 97	F3
Miscellaneous Foundation Walls, and Wall Footings of Residence	1 – 2¼ – 3	F1
Miscellaneous Piers, and Pier Footings of Residence	1 – 2¼ – 3	F1
Miscellaneous Footings for Masonry Walls of Residence	1 – 2¾ – 4	F1
Chimney Footing	1 – 2¾ – 4	F1
Area Floors (See Par. 38)	1 – 2¼ – 3	F3
Area Walls (See Par. 38)	1 – 2¼ – 3	F1
Under-hearths (Slab for Supporting Hearth)	1 – 2¼ – 3	Rough
Base for Tile Floor	1 – 2¼ – 3	Rough
Door Sill	1 – 2¼ – 3	F3
Window Sills	1 – 2¼ – 3	F3
Lintels (Overhead of Windows)	1 – 2¼ – 3	F3
Chimney Cap	1 – 2¼ – 3	F3
Porch Floor	1 – 2¼ – 3	F4
Rear Stoop Floor	1 – 2¼ – 3	F3
Steps	1 – 2¼ – 3	F3
Foundation for Masonry Steps or Walk	1 – 2¼ – 3	Rough
Walks	1 – 2¼ – 3	F2
Foundation Walls and Footings for Garage	1 – 2¼ – 3	F1
Garage Floor	1 – 2¼ – 3	F3
Driveway or Runways for Garage	1 – 2¼ – 3	F2
Ramp for Garage	1 – 2¼ – 3	F2
Septic Tank and Distribution Box	1 – 2¼ – 3	F1
Grease Trap	1 – 2¼ – 3	F1

[1]The numerals "1–2¼–3", etc. = Proportionate amount of cement, fine aggregates (sand), and coarse aggregates (gravel) respectively, measured by Volume.

In general, the following rules may be used for selecting the concrete mixture:

(1) Use "1–2¼–3" mixture for concrete to be watertight or subjected to moderate wear and weather; and for all reinforced concrete.

(2) Use "1–2¾–4" mixture for concrete not subjected to water, wear, or weather.

[2]The symbols for type of "finish" are interpreted as follows:

F1 = Smooth, formed finish.
F2 = Smooth, wooden float finish.
F3 = Smooth, troweled finish.
F4 = Monolithic topping, smooth troweled finish, colored.

17. Water-Tight Concrete—The simplest, safest, and least expensive method of making concrete watertight is as follows: (1) Use monolithic (one-piece) construction, free of construction joints; (2) use the proper mixture; (3) use the *minimum* amount of water that is necessary; (4) mix *properly;* and (5) place *properly* so as to avoid honeycombed, porous surfaces.

18. Mixing Concrete—Proportionate quantities of concrete materials should be accurately *measured*—not guessed at—and only machine mixing should be allowed.

Amount of Water—For strong, water-tight concrete, *only the necessary amount of water to give a workable mixture should be used.* This is of the utmost importance, as excessive water makes concrete porous and weak.

Time of Mixing—For strength, water-tightness, and increased workability, the concrete should be thoroughly mixed for *at least* 1 minute (preferably 2 minutes) after all materials, including the water, are in the mixer.

19. Placing Concrete — Concrete should be transported from the mixer and placed in the forms, in such a manner as to avoid segregation of the materials. The placed concrete should be spaded only enough to prevent air pockets and honeycombing as excessive tamping, puddling, or spading will cause separation of the materials.

20. Curing Concrete—The hardening of concrete is of a chemical nature, and is due to the chemical reactions between Portland cement and water. All concrete should be "moist cured" during the early hardening period as this will add materially to its strength.

FINISHES FOR MONOLITHIC CONCRETE

21. Finish for Miscellaneous Concrete Items—See Table 2.

22. Finish for Porch Floors—A monolithic topping, colored and laid off in squares to imitate tile, should prove satisfactory and durable for average use. Such a floor may be maintained in good condition by periodic waxing.

Where a terrazzo floor finish is desired, a pattern may be selected from one of the bulletins issued by the various cement manufacturers.

23. Finish for Interior Floors—Concrete floors for living rooms, bedrooms, etc., unless covered by a carpet, should have an insulating covering of linoleum, wood flooring, etc., to make them more comfortable.

CONCRETE STEPS

24. Type of Construction — Either of the types shown by Pl. 3, Figs. 3 and 4, is suitable for general use. However, the self-supporting type is preferable for cold climates, as it will not be subjected to upheaval by frost action, provided that its footings are of proper depth.

25. Base (for Soil-Supported Type)—The supporting soil under the center of the steps may be sloped, as shown, as this portion serves primarily as a form for the concrete, since the bearing loads are supported by the horizontal undersurfaces of the lower step and the end walls. Where the soil is of a water-retaining type, such as clay, the supporting soil under the center of the steps, the bottom step, and the end walls should be covered by a 4" or 5" base of well-tamped cinders or gravel as shown by Pl. 3, Fig. 3.

26. Thickness—The thickness of weakest point of steps should be 6" for soil-supported type, and in accordance with Table 3 for self-supporting type.

27. Reinforcement—The minimum reinforcing used should be ⅜" diameter bars, spaced 18" center to center, for the soil-supported type, and bars of size and spacing indicated in Table 3, for the self-supported type. The bars in Table 3 are spaced only in one direction (lengthwise the treads), and temperature bars are used in the other direction as shown by Pl. 3, Fig. 4.

TABLE 3.—*Thickness and Reinforcing for Self-Supported Type Concrete Steps.*

WIDTH OF STEPS	THICKNESS AT WEAKEST POINT (Pl. 3, Fig. 4)	SIZE AND SPACING OF REINFORCING BARS
4' - 0"	4"	¼" Diam., 8" c. to c.
5' - 0"	4½"	¼" " 6" "
6' - 0"	5"	⅜" " 8" "
8' - 0"	5"	⅜" " 6" "
10' - 0"	6"	⅜" " 4" "

28. Treads and Risers—The treads of all masonry steps that have no projecting noses should be at least 10" wide, and should pitch forward about ⅛" in total width for drainage purposes. The risers for such steps may be from 6" to 7½" high. Risers exceeding 7¾" are considered too steep.

29. Termite-Proof Construction—This is very essential. See Par. 11, P. 69.

30. Removal of Forms—All wooden forms should be removed from under, or around, the steps as a precaution against termites.

CONCRETE WALKS AND DRIVEWAYS

31. Dimensions for Walks—Sidewalks are usually 5'-0" wide (6'-0" is preferable) and should be 5" to 6" thick. Private walks may be from 2'-0" to 5'-0" wide, depending upon architectural requirements, and should also be from 5" to 6" thick.

32. Dimension for Driveways and Runways—The minimum dimensions for these items should be as shown by Pl. 3. For curved driveways, the overall widths shown by Pl. 3, Figs. 6 and 8, should be increased from 8'-0" to 9'-0", or more.

33. Base—If soil is of a water-retaining type, such as clay, the concrete should be supported by a 6" to 8" bed of well-compacted cinders, or gravel, for drainage purposes.

34. Drainage—Where unusually wet soils are encountered in cold climates, a line of open-jointed drain tile should be provided to carry off the water from under the walk or driveway, and thus prevent damage due to the freezing of the ground water.

35. Reinforcement—A No. 10 Gage (.135" diameter) wire fabric with 6" x 6" square mesh should prove satisfactory for walks or wide driveways. For narrow driveways (18" to 24" wide), the use of three ¼" diameter (or larger) steel reinforcing bars are recommended.

36. Slope—Walks and driveways should ordinarily slope endways, towards the street. Sidewalks should slope sideways, toward the curb.

37. Joints—Joints should be provided for expansion and contraction of the concrete. Such joints generally improve the appearance of the walk or driveway.

AREAS FOR BASEMENT WINDOWS

38. Definition—An area, as discussed here, is an uncovered enclosure on the exterior of basement wall, partially surrounding a basement window that is wholly or partly below the grade line (Pl. 2, Fig. 15).

39. When Required—Areas are necessary for basement windows that are wholly or partly below the grade line. Sometimes the above type of basement window is necessary, due to the house being "low to the ground"; but such windows are often used for the sake of appearance, as they are practically hidden from view and therefore eliminate the "factory" appearance given to a house by basement windows that are exposed to view.

40. Material and Type of Construction — Reinforced, one-piece, monolithic concrete construction, as shown by Pl. 2, Fig. 15, is recommended.

41. Minimum Thickness of Walls — Referring to Pl. 2, Fig. 15, where the depth "H" (from top of wall to top of floor) is less than 4'-0", the wall thickness may be 6"; where "H" is from 4'-0" to 6'-0", the wall thickness should be 8"; for greater depths of "H", increase wall thickness 1" for each additional 1'-0" of depth.

42. Minimum Thickness of Floor — A minimum floor thickness of 4½" for well-drained soils, up to 6" for water-retaining soils, is recommended.

43. Reinforcement—Size and spacing of reinforcement required for walls and bottom varies with soil conditions. For well-drained soils, ¼" diameter bars 18" center to center, both ways, should suffice. For water-retaining soils, ⅜" diameter bars 8" center to center, both ways, are recommended as the minimum.

44. Minimum Depth of Area Walls—The depth "D" of area walls below upper surface of area floor should be not less than the dimensions given in Table 1, P. 91.

45. Drainage—Drainage is essential, as the area will be exposed to storm water.

CONCRETE PORCHES AND STOOPS

46. General Type of Construction — The self-supported type of construction (Pl. 3, Figs. 1 or 2) is recommended whenever the porch or stoop is as much as 18" above the mean grade line, as better termite protection may be obtained with this type of construction.

47. Treatment of Edges—Overhanging edges are more economical, and are satisfactory for average use. Concealed edges have a better appearance, especially for use with brick dwellings.

48. Thickness and Reinforcement—The thickness of slab, and size and spacing of reinforcement, depends on the width of porch or stoop. Table 4 gives this Guide's minimum recommendations, which apply to both the self-supported and the soil-supported type of construction. The bars in Table 4 are spaced in only one direction, as temperature bars are used in the other direction as shown by Pl. 3, Figs. 1 and 2.

TABLE 4.—*Thickness and Reinforcing for Concrete Porches and Stoops.*

WIDTH OF SLAB	THICKNESS OF SLAB	SIZE AND SPACING OF REINFORCING BARS
4' – 0"	4½"	¼" Diam., 8" c. to c.
5' – 0"	4½"	¼" " 6" "
6' – 0"	4½"	⅜" " 9" "
8' – 0"	5"	⅜" " 6" "
10' – 0"	5"	⅜" " 4" "

49. Access Openings — If the self-supported type of construction is used (with dirt fill omitted), at least one access opening, approximately 2'-0" x 2'-0", should be provided for the purposes of removing the necessary wooden forms, and inspecting for termites during the ensuing years (Pl. 3, Figs. 1 and 2).

50. Termite-Proof Construction — Such construction is very essential (Par. 11, P. 69), and can readily be obtained in the self-supported type of construction by the use of termite shields anchored in the foundation walls beneath the slab.

51. Removal of Forms—All wooden forms should be removed from under the porch or stoop as a precaution against termites.

52. Base—Where the soil-supported type of construction is used, it is well to use 4" or 5" of well-compacted cinders or gravel under the concrete to prevent dampness and possible damage due to the freezing of moisture in the supporting soil.

53. Bonding of End Walls—The end walls of the supporting foundation should be bonded into the foundation wall of the dwelling securely to prevent a future crack at this junction point through which termites may enter (Pl. 3, Figs. 1 and 2).

FLOOR, FOUNDATION WALLS, AND FOOTINGS FOR GARAGE

54. Materials and Type of Construction — Monolithic concrete construction, as shown by Pl. 2, Figs. 1 to 6, is recommended.

55. Thickness of Floor—A floor thickness of 5" to 6" is recommended.

56. Base for Floor—A 4" to 6" base of well-compacted cinders or gravel is recommended as a precaution against the freezing of the supporting soil.

57. Reinforcing — For the floor, a No. 10 Gage (.135" diameter) wire fabric with 6" x 6" square mesh is recommended to stiffen the floor and to prevent cracks due to temperature stresses. For the foundation wall footings, ¼" diameter bars, spaced as shown by Pl. 2, Fig. 2, are advisable on account of temperature stresses.

58. Foundation Wall Widths—See Sec. 17, P. 95, for general discussion. Recommended foundation wall widths for different types of side walls are shown by Pl. 2, Figs. 3 to 5.

59. Footings—See Sec. 15, P. 91, for general discussion. Due to the light loads on the footings of the average garage, the width of the footing in most cases may be made only 1½ times the width of foundation wall or omitted entirely. It is very important, however, that the bottoms of footings are at least 6" below the local frost line.

60. Inside Dimensions of Garage — The recommended minimum inside dimensions for garages (see Pl. 2, Fig. 1) are as follows:

Single garage: L = 20'-0"; W = 10'-0"; 0 = 8'-0"
Double garage: L = 20'-0"; W = 18'-0"; 0 = 8'-0"
(for each door). If a work bench is desired, add width of bench to "L" dimension.

61. Drainage—A floor drain will prove useful for washing the car or floor, draining radiator of car, etc.

CONCRETE SEPTIC TANK, SIPHON TANK, DISTRIBUTING BOX, AND GREASE TRAP

62. Material and Type of Construction — Reinforced, one-piece, monolithic concrete construction, as shown by Pl. 2, Figs. 7 to 14, is recommended where permanency is desired.

TABLE 5.—*Dimensions for Disposal Plant (Refer to Pl. 2, Figs. 7 and 8.)*

| No. of Persons Served | Capacity of Septic Tank (Gallons) | DIMENSIONS | | | | LINEAR FEET OF 4" DRAIN TILE REQUIRED | | |
| | | SEPTIC TANK | | SIPHON TANK | | | | |
		L (Length) Ft. In.	W (Width) Ft. In.	L (Length) Ft. In.	W (Width) Ft. In.	Sandy Soils	Medium Soils	Clay Soils
5-9	450	6 0	2 6	3 0	2 6	200	350	700
10-14	720	7 0	3 6	3 6	3 6	340	500	1,000
15-20	1,000	8 0	4 0	4 0	4 0	475	650	1,250

63. General Dimensions — These should be as shown by Pl. 2. For dimensions not shown, refer to Table 5. In general, a septic tank having a capacity of 50 gallons per person served, is sufficiently large; but one having a capacity of 60 to 70 gallons per person served, is preferable. For dimensions for systems of larger capacity than given in Table 5, see Ref. R18-6, Sec. 38.

64. Reinforcing — As the internal and external pressure should practically equalize each other, reinforcing of the walls and bottoms of the structures is advisable mostly from a standpoint of temperature stresses. For recommended reinforcing, see Pl. 2.

65. Siphon Tank—A siphon and siphon tank (Pl. 2, Figs. 7 and 8) are generally not necessary for tanks having a capacity of less than 1000 gallons.

66. Grease Trap—See Par. 10, P. 159, for discussion of this item, and Pl. 2, Fig. 14 for construction details.

MASONRY CONSTRUCTION

MASONRY MATERIALS

1. Cement—A reputable brand of Portland cement that conforms to A.S.T.M. (American Society for Testing Materials) Specifications should be used.

2. Sand — All sand for mortars should be clean, hard, durable, uncoated, and free from injurious amounts of loam, vegetable matter, organic matter, saline (salt), and alkali. All sand should be well-graded from fine to coarse, with all sand passing a ¼″ sieve but not more than 30% passing a No. 50 (.012″ opening) sieve, and not more than 5% passing a No. 100 (.006″ opening) sieve.

As little as 1/10 of 1% of organic (vegetable or animal) matter may prevent the mortar from hardening, or may cause its early disintegration. Salt in the sand will cause efflorescence (formation of a white, powdery crust) on the masonry. The sharpness of the sand is of little consequence.

The use of pure quartz, or other highly siliceous sand, for chimneys should be prohibited.

3. Colored Sand—Colored sand used for coloring mortar (Par. 12) may consist of ground granite, marble, or other colored stone. Sand for white mortar may consist of natural white sand, ground limestone, or ground marble. The color of the mortar joint will be modified somewhat by the cement and lime, however.

4. Water—See Par. 6. P. 78.

5. Hydrated Lime — Hydrated lime is essentially slaked lime. It is more quickly and accurately proportioned than quicklime as it does not require slaking. Therefore, it is preferable to quicklime when the time and skill necessary to prepare lime putty from quicklime is not available.

6. Quicklime—When a fairly large amount of lime is required for mortars or plasters, it is well to give the contractor the option of using hydrated lime *or* quicklime. Quicklime (lime putty) has slightly better working qualities than hydrated lime; and, when used in quantity, may cost slightly less than hydrated lime. However, only a brand of known quality should be specified, and it should be thoroughly slaked for not less than 15 days before it is used.

MORTARS

7. Cement Mortar—This mortar should be mixed in the proportions by Volume of 1 part Portland cement and not more than 3 parts sand, to which may be added hydrated lime to an amount not exceeding 15% of the cement content.

Cement mortar is more difficult to use than lime mortar, due to its lack of plasticity. However, due to its durable qualities and strength, it should be used for all masonry exposed to dampness, heat, and heavy loads.

8. Cement-Lime Mortar — This mortar should be mixed in the proportions by Volume of 1 part Portland cement, 1 part hydrated lime or lime putty, and not more than 6 parts sand.

This mortar is economical and strong; and it works smoothly and easily, thus facilitating the filling of all joints. Due to these good qualities it is the most universally endorsed mortar at the present time, and is recommended by this Guide for all exterior masonry work above grade, provided such mortar *is very thoroughly mixed.*

9. Prepared (Patent) Mortars—Before using these mortars, the owner should be sure of their composition, and of their performance over a reasonable period of time. Such mortars should be used in strict accordance with the manufacturer's directions. The cost of these mortars usually exceeds the costs of mortars mixed on the job, but their quality may be more uniform.

10. Fire-Clay Mortar—Such mortar should consist of ground fire clay mixed with water, and should be used for laying fire bricks of fireplaces, *only.*

11. Waterproofed Mortars—See Par. 3, P. 99.

12. Colored Mortar—A slight change in the color of mortar will change the whole appearance of a brick wall. So, after the face brick has been selected, the color of the mortar that will set the bricks off to the best advantage should be chosen. This can usually be done by examining the color of mortar used in existing dwellings where the same brick (as that selected) has been used to construct attractive walls.

Methods of Coloring Mortar—Mortars may be colored by the use of mineral pigments, or by the use of naturally colored sand. Colored sand (Par. 3) should be used, if practicable, as the colors will be permanent, whereas mineral colors are apt to fade.

Coloring Materials—See Par. 7, P. 78.

13. Proportioning and Mixing of Mortars — The proportioning and mixing of mortar is often a combination of guesswork and carelessness on the average small job. As sand is relatively cheap, the amount added to the mortar is often in excess of the amount specified. This Guide recommends that proportioning and mixing of mortars be carefully supervised.

14. Amount of Water — An excessive amount of water is harmful to mortar and concrete, and will cause both to be weak, porous, and permeable.

15. Retempering Mortar—The practice of retempering (adding water to) mortar that has taken any degree of initial set should be strictly prohibited, as the strength of the mortar will be impaired.

MASONRY UNITS

16. Brick (General)—All brick should have sufficient strength for the loads imposed, should be well-burned, and should not have excessive absorptive properties.

Strength—Bricks exposed to the weather, or used below grade, should have a minimum compressive strength of 2,500 pounds per square inch when tested flat. Bricks not exposed to the weather should have a corresponding strength of 1,500 pounds per square inch.

Well-Burned Bricks—All bricks should be well-burned; otherwise, they will be more susceptible to frost action. By striking a brick with a trowel, or by striking two bricks together, a resonant metallic sound should usually be produced if the bricks are well-burned.

Absorptive Properties of Bricks—The absorptive property of brick, if excessive, will result in damp walls and greater likelihood of disintegration by frost action (freezing and thawing). However, a moderate amount of absorption (5 to 15%) is considered helpful in securing a good mortar bond. The A.S.T.M. (American Society for Testing Materials) Specifications state the permissible absorptive properties.

17. Salmon or Soft Brick—This type of brick is not recommended, as it has too many points of inferiority.

18. Common Brick (Definition) — Common brick is brick made from clay or shale, and having natural surfaces.

19. Face Brick — The following information and recommendations are offered:

Definition—Face brick, as designated in this Guide, is brick made from surface clay, shale, or fireclay, and having its exposed surfaces treated to produce certain effects in color or texture. Very often selected common brick is used for facing purposes.

Selection of Face Brick—Face brick should be selected in accordance with one's personal tastes and the architectural requirements, insofar as the color and texture of the brick are concerned. Bricks with rough textures bond better than those with smooth textures, everything else being equal.

Allowance for Face Brick by Contractor—Very often the specifications arrange for the contractor to allow (in his bid) a certain amount per thousand for face brick, which are to be selected by the owner. This gives the owner more time to make his selection.

20. Concrete Masonry Units — As these units are relatively easy to manufacture, they are made and sold by many small concerns. Therefore, one should be sure that all such units are made by reliable people, and not by an irresponsible, fly-by-night type of organization.

21. Structural Clay Tile — A "hard" class of tile should be used for all tile in the outer surface of exterior walls; a "hard" or "medium" class should be used for all bearing walls; and a "soft" class may be used for non-bearing, interior partitions.

MASONRY WALLS (GENERAL)

22. Leakproof Construction — The following precautions will help prevent leaks:

Masonry Unit—Be sure that the unit selected has low water-absorptive properties.

Mortar—Use types of mortars described by Pars. 7 and 8.

Type of Joint—For types of joints, see Pl. 5, Figs. 9 to 15. A tooled "concave" joint as shown by Pl. 5, Fig. 9, or a tooled "V" joint as shown by Pl. 5, Fig. 10, are recommended, as they are the most weatherproof types.

Filling of Joints—Make sure that each and every joint is thoroughly filled.

23. Protection Against Leaks—It is essential that precautions are taken to prevent damage to beams, wall plaster, etc., due to water being driven through the exterior walls by sustained wind and rain, or damage due to water collecting on the inner surface of exterior walls by condensation. The following precautions are especially necessary:

Protection of Wall Plaster—Use furring strips between inside of exterior walls and plaster base. See Pars. 123 to 130, P. 127.

Flashings — Flash thoroughly throughout. See Pars. 1 to 7, P. 138.

Protection of Wood Beams, Etc., Embedded in Masonry—All wood embedded in masonry should be thoroughly treated with an approved wood preservative, or should be of a naturally decay resistant species.

Protection of Metal Embedded in Masonry—All such metal should be of a non-corrodible type, where practicable. All such iron and steel should preferably be hot-dipped galvanized; otherwise, it should be given a good coat of red lead and linseed oil.

24. Chases in Masonry Walls

— Chases (openings for pipes, etc., to pass through) should not be permitted in 8″ masonry walls; and in thicker walls, the backs of chases should not be less than 8″ thick. Chases should always be *built* in, and should never be cut in, as the cutting is sure to damage the walls.

25. Wood Inserts in Masonry Walls

— No nailing blocks longer than 8″ horizontally, or nearer together than 2 feet, should be built into a masonry wall. All wood inserts should be pressure-treated with an approved preservative, or should be of a naturally decay resistant species.

26. Arches and Lintels

— The masonry over windows, exterior doorways, and similar openings in masonry walls, must be supported by either a masonry arch or a flat supporting member, called a lintel. Pl. 16, Figs. 3 to 7, shows various types of lintels.

Lintels Generally Preferable — Lintels are preferred to arches in small houses, for the sake of appearance. These lintels are generally made of steel angles; and, where the atmosphere is exceptionally corrosive, such lintels should preferably be hot-dipped galvanized.

Design of Lintels—As brickwork tends to arch itself over (form an arch), the only actual weight usually carried by a lintel in brick walls is a section of brickwork (above the lintel) forming an equilateral triangle, each side of which has the same length as the width of the opening. Of course, when the ends of floor joists or some similar load is carried by the brickwork directly above the lintel, the size of the lintel must be increased in proportion (Table 1).

Size of Lintel—The size of lintel (see Table 1) should be specified on the contract drawing, above each opening requiring a lintel. The length should be 8″ longer than opening, to provide a 4″ bearing at each end.

TABLE 1.—*Minimum Quantity and Sizes[1] of Steel Angle Lintels Required Over Openings in Masonry Walls*

WIDTH OF OPENING	4″ BRICK VENEER WALL	8″ MASONRY WALL		12″ MASONRY WALLS	
		Masonry Only	Masonry Plus Floor Loads[2]	Masonry Only	Masonry Plus Floor Loads[2]
2′ – 0″	1 Angle— $3\frac{1}{2}″$ x $2\frac{1}{2}″$ x $\frac{1}{4}″$	2 Angles— $3\frac{1}{2}″$ x $2\frac{1}{2}″$ x $\frac{1}{4}″$	2 Angles— $3\frac{1}{2}″$ x $2\frac{1}{2}″$ x $\frac{1}{4}″$	3 Angles— $3\frac{1}{2}″$ x $2\frac{1}{2}″$ x $\frac{1}{4}″$	3 Angles— $3\frac{1}{2}″$ x $2\frac{1}{2}″$ x $\frac{1}{4}″$
2′ – 6″	"	"	"	"	"
3′ – 0″	"	"	"	"	"
3′ – 6″	"	"	2 Angles— $3\frac{1}{2}″$ x $3″$ x $\frac{1}{4}″$	"	"
4′ – 0″	"	"	2 Angles— $3\frac{1}{2}″$ x $3\frac{1}{2}″$ x $\frac{1}{4}″$	"	3 Angles— $3\frac{1}{2}″$ x $3″$ x $\frac{1}{4}″$
4′ – 6″	"	"	"	"	3 Angles— $3\frac{1}{2}″$ x $3\frac{1}{2}″$ x $\frac{1}{4}″$
5′ – 0″	"	"	2 Angles— $3\frac{1}{2}″$ x $4″$ x $\frac{5}{16}″$	"	"
5′ – 6″	1 Angle— $3\frac{1}{2}″$ x $3″$ x $\frac{1}{4}″$	2 Angles— $3\frac{1}{2}″$ x $3″$ x $\frac{1}{4}″$	"	3 Angles— $3\frac{1}{2}″$ x $3″$ x $\frac{1}{4}″$	3 Angles— $3\frac{1}{2}″$ x $4″$ x $\frac{5}{16}″$
6′ – 0″	"	2 Angles— $3\frac{1}{2}″$ x $3\frac{1}{2}″$ x $\frac{1}{4}″$	2 Angles— $3\frac{1}{2}″$ x $5″$ x $\frac{5}{16}″$	3 Angles— $3\frac{1}{2}″$ x $3\frac{1}{2}″$ x $\frac{1}{4}″$	"

[1]The figures in above table are: Quantity of steel angles required, size of **horizontal** leg of angle, size of **vertical** leg of angle, and thickness of angle, respectively.
[2]**"Floor load"** of above table is assumed to be 600 lbs. **per foot width of opening**, as follows: 20 lbs. dead load + 40 lbs. live load × ½ of 20 ft. span = 60 × 10 = 600.
The sizes of the steel angles given in Table 1 **must be increased** for load bearing walls when the distance from the **bottom surfaces** of the floor joists (or other load-carrying members) to the **top** of the vertical leg of the angle **is less** than 7″ for 8-inch masonry walls, or less than $13\frac{1}{2}″$ for 12-inch masonry walls.

Soldier Course Over Lintel (Brick Construction)—Where a soldier course of "brick-on-end" is desired over the lintel, such a course should *not* be longer than the width of the opening. See Pl. 6, Fig. 10.

27. Window Sills—See Pl. 6, Fig. 11, and Pl. 16 for types of masonry sills. Brick *or* concrete sills are satisfactory for brick construction. Concrete sills should be reinforced with steel bars.

28. Door Sills—Such sills often consist of monolithic concrete poured in place. Special attention should be given to construction at door sill to prevent termite infestation and decay. See Pl. 17, Figs. 1 to 3, and Pl. 19, Fig. 5.

29. Floor and Roof Anchors—Floor joists and roof plates should be anchored to masonry walls at intervals of not more than 6 feet. See Pl. 7, Figs. 1 and 2.

30. Ends of Floor Joists—The ends of all joists resting in masonry should be splayed or "fire cut" as shown by Pl. 7, Figs. 1 and 2, to allow the joist to drop out, in case of fire, without damaging the masonry. Also, a narrow space should be left at ends and on each side of joists to allow air to circulate around them, and thus help prevent dry rot.

31. Intersecting Walls—It is very important that each course of all intersecting walls be carried up together. The practice of building one wall up several courses, or several feet, and then bonding the intersecting wall into it should not be allowed, for the joints at the intersection are sure to be weak and poorly filled. See Pl. 6. Figs. 8 and 9.

BRICK WALLS

32. Types of Brick Walls—The two types of brick walls are the "solid" type, as shown by Pl. 5, Figs. 16 and 17, and the "hollow" type, as shown by Pl. 5, Figs. 18 to 24.

The "solid" type are preferable, as they offer maximum stability, strength, durability, weather resistance, fire resistance, soundproofness, and adaptability to future alterations. The "hollow" types should be considered as substitutes for solid walls.

33. Thickness of Walls—The thickness of all exterior walls should be clearly shown or noted on the contract drawings.

Solid Brick Walls—The *minimum* thickness should be 8″ for a height not exceeding 35 feet. For walls of greater height, the thickness should be at least 12″ for the uppermost 35 feet; and should be increased 4″ for each successive 35 feet or fraction thereof, all measurements taken *downwards* from the top of the wall. A 12″ wall is much superior to an 8″ wall, and should certainly be used in preference to an 8″ wall in localities subject to high winds or severe earthquake shocks, inasmuch as such walls possess superior stability, water-tightness, and insulating qualities; and provide sufficient space in walls for chases (openings for pipes, etc.).

Hollow Walls of Brick—Thickness of these walls should be in accordance with Par. 46.

34. Height of Walls—Height of solid brick walls should be in accordance with Par. 33, above; and height of hollow walls of brick should not exceed 50 feet above the top of foundation walls.

35. Selection of Bond for Brickwork—For various types of bonds, see Pl. 5, Figs. 1 to 8. A type of bond should be selected that will suit one's personal taste and fulfill all of the architectural requirements, insofar as possible. Examination of the bond used in existing attractive brick dwellings will prove helpful. However, the selection should be governed by the considerations listed below.

Most Popular Bonds—The common bond is used most, with the Flemish bond a close second.

Bonds Suited to Solid Brick Walls—All types of bonds.

Bonds Suited to Hollow Rolok-Bak Walls—All types of bonds.

Bonds Suited to Hollow All-Rolok Walls—See Pl. 5, Figs. 21 to 24, and Pl. 6, Figs. 1, 2, 6, and 7.

Minimum Headers for Solid and Hollow Brick Walls—For such walls every sixth course should be a header course, or there should be at least one full header in every 72 square inches of wall surface.

36. Sample Panels of Brickwork—It is advisable to have the contractor construct one or more sample panels of brickwork, before actual construction is begun on a brick wall. These panels will help you to decide upon the color of mortar, type of bond, and type of mortar joint.

37. Wetting of Bricks — All brick, except glazed brick, should be thoroughly wetted, before laying, so as to prevent the brick from absorbing water from the mortar, and thereby producing a poor bond. However, the brick should not be soaked to the point of saturation; and wetting should be omitted in freezing weather.

38. Filling of Joints—This is absolutely essential, and is usually best obtained in brickwork by using a "shoved" joint.

39. Skintled Brickwork — This consists of brickwork in which the exterior bricks are laid in such a manner that their exposed faces are set "in and out" (at random) from a true vertical plane. Also, the mortar is "squeezed" out of joints and all such projecting mortar is allowed to remain, without cutting or tooling of the mortar joints.

The whole idea of skintled brickwork is to obtain an artistic appearance. However, as the rough, untooled mortar joints and the numerous ledges formed by the brickwork increases the possibility of leaks, damage from frost action (freezing), etc., this type of brickwork should be used only after the most careful consideration.

40. Cleaning Brickwork—All exposed exterior and interior brickwork should be thoroughly cleaned, and all voids neatly filled, as soon after completion as practicable.

Only a neutral soap and pure water should ordinarily be used for cleaning masonry. In extreme cases, however, water containing not more than 5% muriatic acid may be used, provided that such cleaning is immediately followed by a copious bath of fresh, clear water.

HOLLOW MASONRY WALLS

41. Walls of Structural Clay Tile — Such walls usually cost less than solid masonry walls, and will have slightly better insulating properties than solid masonry walls (Tables 4 and 5, P. 136). However, they have the following disadvantages: (1) The theoretical sizes of the tile varies in actual practice, and thus increases the cost of laying. (2) The tile is easily broken during shipment or when handling. (3) Such tile requires an exterior facing of stucco or brick for the sake of appearance. (4) Although sufficiently strong for the average dwelling, such walls are relatively weaker than solid masonry walls of the same thickness.

42. Walls of Concrete Masonry Units—Such walls usually cost less than solid masonry walls, and will have slightly better insulating properties than solid masonry walls (Tables 4 and 5, P. 136). However, such walls usually require an exterior facing of stucco or brick; and, although they are sufficiently strong for the average dwelling, such walls are relatively

weaker than solid masonry walls of the same thickness.

43. Type of Facing—A facing of Portland cement stucco is somewhat more resistant to the penetration of water than is a facing of medium absorptive bricks.

44. Hollow Walls With Brick Facings—The types shown by Pl. 5, Figs. 25 to 39, are recommended, as these walls are thoroughly bonded together; also, the hollow units are erected "on end", in most of the cases illustrated, which is the preferred manner of erection for most types of tile from a standpoint of strength and watertightness.

45. Hollow Walls With Stucco Facing—The following points should be considered:

Erection of Structural Clay Tile—Most types of tile are stronger and less permeable when erected with the cells vertical (Pl. 6, Fig. 14). However, as it requires more skill to erect tile in this manner, the tile is often erected with the cells horizontal as shown by Pl. 5, Fig. 40. Either manner of erection should prove satisfactory if properly done.

Erection of Concrete Masonry Units—These units should be erected with cells vertical, as shown by Pl. 5, Fig. 41.

46. Thickness of Walls—Such walls should have a minimum thickness of 8″ for walls not exceeding 35 feet in height. For walls of greater height, the minimum thickness should be 12″ for the uppermost 35 feet, and 16″ for the remaining lower portion of wall.

47. Height of Walls—Such walls should not exceed 50 feet in height above the top of foundation walls.

48. Concentrated Loads — Where a floor beam, joist, girder, or other item delivers a concentrated load to the wall, the hollow masonry unit directly under the load should be filled solidly with concrete, unless 3 courses of solid brickwork or suitable, approved support slabs are provided to bear the load. See Pl. 6, Fig. 14.

49. Openings—Window, door, and similar openings in walls of hollow units should be so formed as to close all cells; otherwise, the open cell-ends should be filled with masonry at least 4″ thick or, the opening should be laid up with 4″ of brick.

50. Partitions—All intersecting or abutting walls of hollow units should be regularly bonded, and continuous perpendicular joints should be avoided. Walls of hollow units intersecting or abutting other types of walls should be secured with wall ties spaced not more than 12" apart in any direction, and should also be bonded to the wall with mortar, if possible.

51. Backing for Brick, Etc.—Where hollow units are used for backing brick or other masonry facing, the hollow unit and facing should be securely anchored together. The headers of all brick facing should be bonded into the hollow unit backing at least every 7th course of brickwork, as shown by Pl. 5, Figs. 25 to 39 inclusive. Where headers or other satisfactory bonding units cannot be used, the bonding should be made with wall ties spaced 12" in each direction in staggered rows. The facing and backing should be further bonded together with mortar which should completely fill the space between them. All joints should be completely filled with mortar, and all walls (both facing and backing) should be carried up together.

BRICK VENEER WALLS (ATTACHED TO WOODEN FRAME)

52. Type of Frame Construction—The type shown by Pl. 10 is recommended, as it has a minimum amount of shrinkage. This is an essential feature for any frame used with brick veneering. See Par. 11, P. 15.

53. Protection Against Leaks—Special precautions must be taken to protect the inner frame construction from the possible seepage of water through the brick veneering. The following special recommendations are offered:

Building Paper—When water seeps through the brick veneer, due to prolonged, driving rains, the building paper attached to the sheathing is depended upon to keep the wood sheathing dry, and thus prevent decay. As any decay or damage to this woodwork cannot be repaired, it is needless to say that the quality of the building paper, and the manner in which it is applied, is of the utmost importance. This paper should at least consist of a good grade of asphalt saturated, rag felt, weighing not less than 15 pounds (preferably 30 pounds) per 100 square feet; and it should be applied in the most careful manner. The practice of bringing the top of the brick wall up to, or over, the top edge of the uppermost layer of paper before applying another layer of paper should be strictly prohibited.

Sills—As the sills will be subjected to dampness due to water trickling down the 1" airspace, the sills should be decay-proof (Pars. 4 to 13, P. 116). Also, it is well to provide drain tubes as shown by Pl. 7, Fig.

4, so as to prevent the possibility of water damming up behind sills and causing excessive dampness.

Flashing—It is advisable to flash *over* every piece of wood that extends into, or through, the 1" airspace. This includes window and door frames, porch framing, etc. See Pl. 16, Fig. 3; Pl. 17, Fig. 2; and Pl. 20, Figs. 18 to 20.

54. Bond—Brick veneer is often laid up in a running stretcher bond, as shown by Pl. 6, Fig. 20. If other types of bonds (Pl. 5, Figs. 1 to 8) are used, it means the cutting of bricks, for use as headers, thus resulting in a slight increase in cost, and the possibility of having a lot of cracked and chipped headers in the wall.

55. Workmanship — Supplementing other miscellaneous recommendations for "Masonry Walls", etc., the following special recommendations are given here:

Wall Ties—These ties should be of a non-corrodible material, or should be heavily coated with zinc by the hot-dipped galvanizing process. If ties having an inferior protective coating are used, they are very apt to rust out in a few years, and thus leave the wall unsupported. These ties should be spaced so as to have at least one tie for every 144 square inches. See Pl. 7, Fig. 4.

Placing Uppermost Bricks—The brick wall should be carried up its entire required height before the cornices or eaves boards are nailed in place. This allows the mason to fill the joints of the uppermost courses properly. See Pl. 6, Fig. 20.

56. Skintled Brickwork—This Guide advises against the use of skintled brickwork (Par. 39) for brick veneer construction.

BRICK WALKS

57. Type of Construction—The types shown by Pl. 4, Figs. 3 to 6, are recommended.

58. Patterns for Walks—See Pl. 4, Figs. 8 to 14. The patterns in which the bricks are laid flat are the least expensive, of course.

59. Bricks—Grade "A" or "B" common, or face brick, are recommended. Bricks should be hard burned, with low absorptive properties.

60. Mortar—Use only a cement mortar.

61. Base—The concrete base may be a lean 1:8 mixture (1 part cement to 8 parts of cinders or aggregates) but should preferably be a 1-2¼-3 concrete mixture, reinforced as shown by Pl. 4, Figs. 3 to 6, and having a minimum thickness of 4".

62. Sub-Base—If the soil is of a water-retaining type, such as clay, the concrete base should be supported by a 4" or 5" bed of well-compacted cinders or gravel.

63. Drainage—Where the soil is of a water-retaining type (such as clay), and the climate is cold, suitable drainage should be provided to prevent damage that might be caused by the freezing of the ground water.

64. Crowned Surface—Surface of the walk should be slightly crowned so as to shed water (Pl. 4, Figs. 3 to 7).

65. Joints — A broad, slightly concave "thumb" joint should be used. The vertical joints between bricks should be completely filled with mortar by the use of a trowel and a "shoved" joint. The practice of making the mortar "soupy", and pouring it in the joints, should be prohibited.

66. Cleaning Bricks—All bricks should be wiped clean before the mortar has set.

BRICK STEPS

67. Type of Construction—The type shown by Pl. 4, Fig. 1, is recommended because such "brick-on-edge" construction is more durable.

68. Bricks—Grade "A" or "B" common, or fac brick, are recommended. Bricks should be har burned, with low absorptive properties.

69. Mortar—Use only a cement mortar.

70. Base—See Table 2, P. 80. A 1-2¼-3 concret base, at least 6" thick at its weakest point, should b used. The undersurface of base should never be slope (unless constructed as shown by Pl. 3, Fig. 3), bu should consist of a horizontal slab, as shown by Pl 4, Figs. 1 and 2, *or* of horizontal steps, to prevent i from slipping.

71. Reinforcement of Base—This may not be nec essary in some cases. However, as reinforcement i relatively inexpensive and adds so much to th strength of the structure, its use is recommended.

72. Sub-Base—See Par. 62.

73. Treads—Treads should never be less than 12 wide and should have a forward, downward slope o about ¼" per foot (see Pl. 4, Figs. 1 and 2).

74. Types of Joints — A broad, slightly concav "thumb" joint should be used.

75. Termite-Proof Construction—This is very es sential. See Par. 11, P. 69.

FOOTINGS FOR FOUNDATION WALLS, CHIMNEYS, AND PIERS

GENERAL RECOMMENDATIONS

1. Importance of Footings—Footings (Figs. 1 and 2) rest upon the soil and carry the weight of the house. It is evident, therefore, that the first requirement for a properly constructed house is strong,

durable footings of ample size to prevent settlement of the house with resultant cracked basement, cracked plaster on walls and ceilings, sloping floors, binding doors and windows, etc.

2. Types of Construction—The types shown by Pl. 1 are recommended.

3. Material—Monolithic concrete footings are recommended (Table 2, P. 80).

4. Area of Footings—Ascertain loads (Pars. 11 to 15), and make footings of proper area to suit soil. Use Figs. 1 and 2 as a guide for *minimum* dimensions. Special attention should be paid to footings for piers and columns, as these ordinarily carry a *very heavy* load.

5. Thickness of Footing—Refer to Figs. 1 and 2 for proportional thicknesses. Large footings for heavily loaded piers or columns should be "stepped down", as shown by Fig. 2 and Pl. 1, Fig. 15.

6. Depth of Bottoms Below Frost Line—Be guided by local Building Code requirements. The *minimum* depth (distance "D", Figs, 1 and 2) should be at least 6" below local frost line. For further guidance, refer to Table 1.

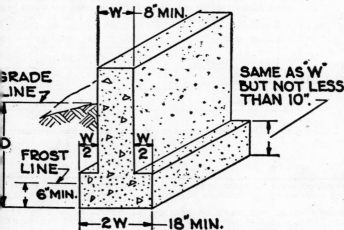

FIG. 1.—*Typical Footing for Foundation Walls*

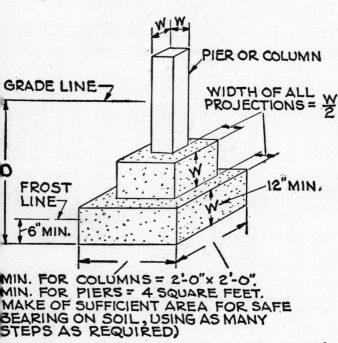

FIG. 2.—*Typical Footing for Piers or Columns*

TABLE 1.—*Recommended Minimum Depths of Footings and Area Walls Below Finish Grade.*

Minimum Local Temperature	Depth of Footing (See D, Figs. 1 and 2)	Depth of Area Wall (See D, Pl. 2, Fig. 15)
No Freezing Weather	1′ – 6″	0′ – 0″
+20°	2′ – 6″	1′ – 0″
+10°	3′ – 0″	1′ – 6″
0°	3′ – 6″	2′ – 0″
−10°	4′ – 0″	2′ – 6″
−20° (or Colder)	4′ – 6″	3′ – 0″

7. Bearing for Footings—Footings should rest on soil that is firm, level, and *undisturbed*. No building should be erected on filled land that is less than two years old, and even then the fill should be composed of good, solid earth that is free from rubbish, voids, etc., and such footings should be from 1½ to 2 times normal size.

8. Chimney Footings — Such footings should extend down to the level of adjacent foundation walls; and where chimneys occur in outside walls or inside bearing walls, the footings should be an integral part of the wall footing. (Pl. 1, Fig. 3.)

9. Reinforcing of Footings—Footings that rest on soft or filled ground should be reinforced with steel bars as shown by Pl. 1. Where footings rest on firm, soil, the reinforcing may be omitted from all portions except those portions that span trenches or similar excavations.

10. Drainage—See Pars. 8 to 10, P. 98.

USEFUL DATA FOR FOOTING COMPUTATIONS

TABLE 2.—*Safe Load-Bearing Capacity of Various Soils*

CHARACTER OF SOIL	BEARING CAPACITY (Tons Per Sq. Ft.)
Soft Clay	1
Wet Sand and Firm Clay	2
Fine and Dry Sand	3
Hard Dry Clay	4
Coarse Sand	4
Gravel	6

TABLE 3.—*Weights of Materials for Footings and Foundation*

MATERIAL	Lbs. Per Sq. Ft.
8″ Brickwork, Solid	80
12½″ Brickwork, Solid	125
8″ Concrete, Stone	100
10″ Concrete, Stone	125
12″ Concrete, Stone	150

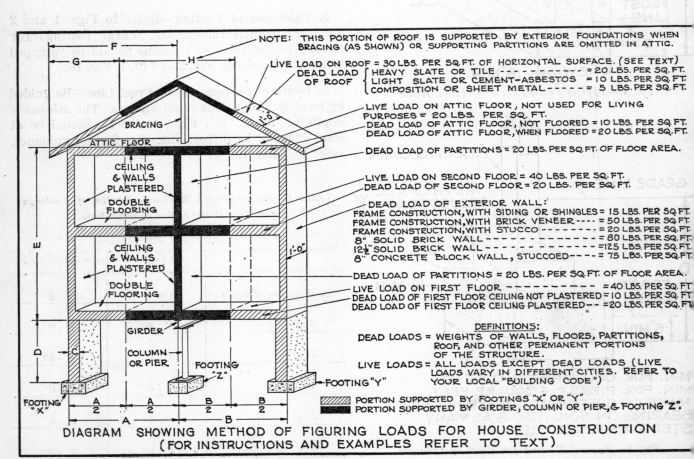

NOTE: THIS PORTION OF ROOF IS SUPPORTED BY EXTERIOR FOUNDATIONS WHEN BRACING (AS SHOWN) OR SUPPORTING PARTITIONS ARE OMITTED IN ATTIC.

LIVE LOAD ON ROOF = 30 LBS. PER SQ. FT. OF HORIZONTAL SURFACE. (SEE TEXT)

DEAD LOAD OF ROOF { HEAVY SLATE OR TILE ---------- = 20 LBS. PER SQ. FT. / LIGHT SLATE OR CEMENT–ASBESTOS = 10 LBS. PER SQ. FT. / COMPOSITION OR SHEET METAL---- = 5 LBS. PER SQ. FT. }

LIVE LOAD ON ATTIC FLOOR, NOT USED FOR LIVING PURPOSES = 20 LBS. PER SQ. FT.
DEAD LOAD OF ATTIC FLOOR, NOT FLOORED = 10 LBS. PER SQ. FT.
DEAD LOAD OF ATTIC FLOOR, WHEN FLOORED = 20 LBS. PER SQ. FT.

DEAD LOAD OF PARTITIONS = 20 LBS. PER SQ. FT. OF FLOOR AREA.

LIVE LOAD ON SECOND FLOOR = 40 LBS. PER SQ. FT.
DEAD LOAD OF SECOND FLOOR = 20 LBS. PER SQ. FT.

DEAD LOAD OF EXTERIOR WALL:
FRAME CONSTRUCTION, WITH SIDING OR SHINGLES = 15 LBS. PER SQ. FT.
FRAME CONSTRUCTION, WITH BRICK VENEER ---- = 50 LBS. PER SQ. FT.
FRAME CONSTRUCTION, WITH STUCCO ------- = 20 LBS. PER SQ. FT.
8″ SOLID BRICK WALL ---------- = 80 LBS. PER SQ. FT.
12½″ SOLID BRICK WALL ---------- = 125 LBS. PER SQ. FT.
8″ CONCRETE BLOCK WALL, STUCCOED---- = 75 LBS. PER SQ. FT.

DEAD LOAD OF PARTITIONS = 20 LBS. PER SQ. FT. OF FLOOR AREA.
LIVE LOAD ON FIRST FLOOR ---------- = 40 LBS. PER SQ. FT.
DEAD LOAD OF FIRST FLOOR CEILING NOT PLASTERED = 10 LBS. PER SQ. FT.
DEAD LOAD OF FIRST FLOOR CEILING PLASTERED-- = 20 LBS. PER SQ. FT.

DEFINITIONS:
DEAD LOADS = WEIGHTS OF WALLS, FLOORS, PARTITIONS, ROOF, AND OTHER PERMANENT PORTIONS OF THE STRUCTURE.
LIVE LOADS = ALL LOADS EXCEPT DEAD LOADS (LIVE LOADS VARY IN DIFFERENT CITIES. REFER TO YOUR LOCAL "BUILDING CODE")

PORTION SUPPORTED BY FOOTINGS "X" OR "Y".
PORTION SUPPORTED BY GIRDER, COLUMN OR PIER, & FOOTING "Z".

BRACING
ATTIC FLOOR
CEILING & WALLS PLASTERED
DOUBLE FLOORING
CEILING & WALLS PLASTERED
DOUBLE FLOORING
GIRDER
COLUMN OR PIER
FOOTING "Z"
FOOTING "Y"
FOOTING "X"

DIAGRAM SHOWING METHOD OF FIGURING LOADS FOR HOUSE CONSTRUCTION
(FOR INSTRUCTIONS AND EXAMPLES REFER TO TEXT)

FIG. 3

DETERMINING FOOTING WIDTH FOR FOUNDATION WALLS

11. General Procedure—The procedure is divided into three general steps, as outlined below.

First Step—Determine the load imposed upon a typical *linear foot* of footing (Fig. 3 and Par. 12).

Second Step—Ascertain the safe bearing capacity of the soil (Table 2).

Third Step—Determine the width of the footing by using the following formula:

$$\frac{\text{Total load per linear foot on footing, in lbs. x 12}}{\text{Safe bearing capacity of soil, in lbs. per sq. ft.}} = \text{Width of}$$

footing, in inches.

12. Determining Load Per Linear Foot on Footing—This may be accomplished in the following six simple steps.

First Step—Refer to Fig. 3 as a general guide, and jot down actual dimensions opposite the symbols A, B, C, etc., of Fig. 3. It should be borne in mind that all loads are calculated for only *one* linear foot of building length, as indicated by Fig. 3.

Second Step—Determine the weight per linear foot of the foundation wall. This weight is obtained by multiplying weight per square foot of wall (Fig. 3 and Table 3) by dimension D of Fig. 3.

Third Step—Determine the weight per linear foot of super-structure wall. This weight is obtained by multiplying weight per square foot of wall (Fig. 3) by height E of Fig. 3.

Fourth Step—Determine the combined live and dead loads per linear foot of floor area for the first, second, and attic floors. These loads are obtained by multiplying the combined live and dead loads of each floor by the distance A/2 or B/2 of Fig. 3.

Fifth Step—Determine the combined live and dead load per linear foot of roof area. This load is obtained by multiplying the combined live and dead loads by the distance G or F of Fig. 3. (The distance used depends upon whether or not the roof is braced, as indicated by Fig. 3.)

Sixth Step—Total up the various loads previously obtained to ascertain the total load per linear foot on footing.

13. Typical Example—The following example will illustrate the method of determining the footing width for a house:

Assume that the house is a two-story, brick veneer dwelling having a full basement, but *not* having the roof bracing shown by Fig. 3. Also, referring to Fig. 3, assume that A/2=6'—0";

C=10" concrete; D=8'—0"; E=18'—0"; and F=13'—0". The supporting soil is soft clay. Using this data in combination with the loads indicated by Fig. 3, a typical example is as follows:

10" basement wall, 8'—0" high, 8 x 125 lbs.	=1000 lbs.
Brick veneer super-structure walls, 18'—0" high, 18 x 50 lbs.	= 900 lbs.
1st floor load, 6 x 50 lbs.	= 300 lbs.
2nd floor load, 6 x 60 lbs.	= 360 lbs.
Attic floor, not floored, 6 x 30 lbs.	= 180 lbs.
Roof, light slate shingles, 13 x 40 lbs.	= 520 lbs.

TOTAL LOAD ON FOOTING PER LINEAR FOOT....=3260 lbs.

Table 2 indicates that the safe load-bearing capacity of soft clay is 2,000 pounds per square foot. Therefore, the minimum width of the footing should be: $\frac{3260 \times 12}{2000} = 19.56''$ or, say, 20".

DETERMINING FOOTING SIZE FOR PIERS OR COLUMNS

14. General Procedure—The procedure is divided into four general steps, as outlined below.

First Step—Determine the *total load per linear foot of girder length*. See Par. 22(a), "First Step" and "Second Step", P. 117; and Par. 22(b), P. 118.

Second Step—Determine the load on each pier or column. See "Second Step", Par. 32, P. 120.

Third Step—Ascertain the safe bearing capacity of the soil. See Table 2.

Fourth Step—Determine the required area of the footing by using the following formula:

$$\frac{\text{Total load on pier or column footing, in lbs.}}{\text{Safe bearing capacity of soil, in lbs. per sq. ft.}} = \text{Required}$$

area of footing, in *square feet*.

15. Typical Example—Assume that upon following the procedure outlined above, the load imposed upon a column footing is found to be 12,000 pounds; also, assume that the soil is soft clay. As the safe bearing capacity for soft clay is 2,000 pounds per square foot, the required area of the footing will be:

$\frac{12,000}{2,000} = 6$ square feet. By extracting the square root of 6, we find that a pier approximately 2'—6" x 2'—6" in size will be required.

PIERS

1. Definition — A pier is a bearing (supporting) wall having a horizontal cross section not exceeding 4 square feet, and not bonded at the sides into the adjoining masonry. See Pl. 1, Figs. 1 and 2.

2. Importance—This Guide recommends that special attention be given to piers and their footings on account of the heavy loads that they must carry.

3. Types of Construction—The types shown by Pl. 1, Figs. 1 and 2 are recommended.

4. Material—A monolithic concrete pier and footing is preferable from a standpoint of permanence (Pl. 1, Fig. 1). Where masonry piers are used, the footings should be monolithic concrete; and the masonry should consist of hard-burned brick, stone, or other *solid* (not hollow) units, laid up in Portland cement mortar.

5. Minimum Sizes—The minimum sizes should be as follows: 8″ x 8″ for reinforced concrete piers; 10″ x 10″ for plain concrete piers; and 12″ x 12″ for brick piers. Height of pier should not exceed 10 times its smallest horizontal dimension.

6. Spacing — Spacing should suit load (Par. 31, P. 120), but should never exceed 10′-0″ center to center of piers.

7. Termite Shields—These are essential. See Sec. 9, P. 67 and Pl. 19, Figs. 1 and 2.

FOUNDATION WALLS

1. Definition—Foundation walls of a house are, usually, the portion of the building walls that are below the first floor. See Pl. 1.

2. Type of Construction—The two general types of foundation walls that are in common use today are shown by Fig. 1, and are designated as Type 1 and Type 2 for convenience when discussing them.

Either type will prove satisfactory if *properly* constructed. Type 1 is cheaper, but is more susceptible to termite penetration than Type 2. Type 2 usually requires an exterior facing of stucco or masonry veneer above grade for the sake of appearance.

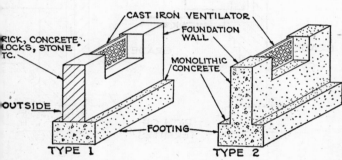

FIG. 1.—*Usual Types of Foundation Walls and Footings*

2. Material—Hard-burned brick, stone, or other solid (not hollow) masonry units, laid up in Portland cement mortar, should preferably be used for Type 1 foundation walls; and monolithic concrete should be used for Type 2 foundation walls (see Table 1, P. 30).

4. Wall Width—The width should never be less than 8″, and should generally be thicker, as noted below:

Walls for Supporting Frame Construction—Width below grade, not less than 10″. Width above grade, not less than 8″.

Walls for Supporting Masonry Veneer over Wood Framing—Width not less than total combined width of sill, sheathing, air-space, etc., *plus* veneering.

Walls for Supporting Masonry Construction—Width below grade, not less than 10″, nor less than 2″ thicker than the walls supported above.

Rubble Stone Walls—Width below grade, not less than 18″, nor less than 4″ thicker than the wall supported above

5. Top Construction—For recommended construction at tops of foundation walls, see Pl. 1, Figs. 6 to 10. This Guide recommends the type shown by Figs. 6 or 9 for brick veneer construction; the type shown by Fig. 10 for brick, hollow tile, and similar types of construction; and the types shown by Figs. 6, 7, 8, or 9 for frame construction.

6. Height of Top Above Grade—Top of foundation wall should be not less than 8″ above grade for supporting frame construction.

7. Reinforcing at Top of Wall—Pl. 1, Figs. 6, 7, 8, and 10, shows reinforcing bars in top of monolithic concrete foundation walls. While such reinforcement cannot be considered essential, it is good insurance against future cracks in the wall, with subsequent termite infestation, and is therefore recommended.

8. Facing for Walls—All facings for portions of foundation walls above grade should terminate slightly above grade as shown by Pl. 1, Figs. 6 to 9, so as to minimize the possibility of termites working their way up behind the facing.

9. Anchor Bolts—Anchor bolts, spaced not greater than 12″ from each corner and not greater than 8′-0″ apart, should be provided in the tops of all foundation walls for residences and garages of frame or veneer construction (see Pl. 1). Such bolts may be 5/8″ or 3/4″ diameter for monolithic concrete walls, but should preferably be 1/2″ diameter for masonry type walls as 1/2″ is the usual maximum width of mortar joints, between which the bolts must fit. Bolts should extend into the foundation walls at least 18″.

10. Bonding of Walls—Foundations for areaways, terraces, porches, steps, and similar items should be adequately bonded or anchored to main walls.

11. Ventilation—All unexcavated areas should be cross ventilated by through wall vents (see Fig. 1). At least 2 square feet of vent area should be provided for each 25 linear feet of exterior wall; and one opening, at least 1 square foot in area, should be provided within 5 feet of each corner. The various standard sizes of cast iron ventilators may be seen at a local hardware store.

12. Manholes—An opening not less than 2'-0" x 2'-0" should be provided in each basement or foundation wall, where such openings are necessary to obtain access to unexcavated areas.

13. Termite Shields—See Pars. 9 to 11, P. 69.

14. Drainage—See Pars. 8 to 10, P. 98.

15. Important Pointers for Masonry Foundation Walls—Where the wall is of Type 1 (Fig. 1), the following suggestions are offered:

(a) Use only Portland cement mortar for joints below grade.

(b) Make sure that all joints are completely filled and finished with a "concave", "vee", or "weathered" joint. See Pl. 5, Figs. 9 to 11.

(c) For damp locations, have exterior portions below grade waterproofed. This will give added protection against termites and frost action. See Sec. 19, P. 99, and Pl. 1, Figs. 5 and 12.

(d) Have the necessary termite shields provided.

(e) Use only a hard-burned, dense brick below grade for foundation walls of brick. See Par. 16, P. 85.

(f) Do not use hollow units below grade, or for any foundation work, unless all woodwork above such walls are adequately protected from termites.

(g) Do not use the types of foundation for brick veneer that are shown by Fig. 2. The type shown by Fig. 2, A, is weak and unsafe. The type shown by Fig. 2, B, is also weak and unsafe; and will make the house liable to infestation by termites, which are likely to work through cracks in the brick veneer wall, up the 1" airspace, and into the woodwork; furthermore, water beating through the veneer wall will tend to collect in the bottom of the 1" airspace and cause dampness, molds, and decay.

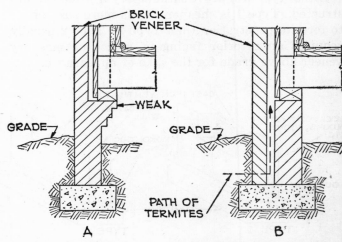

FIG. 2.—*Common Defects of Foundation Walls for Brick Veneer Construction*

BASEMENTS

1. Advantages of Basement — A basement in a home, *when properly designed and constructed,* offers the following advantages:

(a) Provides an ideal condition for the installation of practically any kind of heating system, at the time of building or in the future.

(b) Insures more efficient functioning of heating system, and better utilization of waste heat from pipes, ducts, etc. of heating system under first floor.

(c) Lessens danger of water pipes freezing under house.

(d) Makes the installation, control, and repair of pipes, valves, wiring, etc., installed under house a much easier task.

(e) A *full* basement offers practically complete control over termites and decay, due to lack of dampness and darkness, ease of inspection, etc.

(f) A *full* basement provides ample room for heating system, laundry, recreation and hobby rooms.

(g) Where the walls of a basement are of good, solid-walled monolithic concrete, termite shields may be eliminated from such walls, and the cost of shields may be applied to cost of basement.

(h) The value of the house will very likely be enhanced by an amount *greater* than that spent for basement.

2. Good Construction Necessary — It costs much less to *build* a basement properly than to repair leaky walls, and repair (or replace) a cracked and leaky floor. Therefore, this Guide recommends that basement be designed to suit local soil conditions, and be built proof against leaks, cracks, etc.

3. Materials and Workmanship—This Guide recommends the use of monolithic concrete for water-tight basements. The concrete should be of the mixtures hereinafter recommended, and should be properly mixed, placed, and cured.

4. Basement in Well Drained Soil — The types shown by Pl. 1, Figs. 11 or 12, may be used. The type shown by Pl. 1, Fig. 11, is preferable as it is safer, more durable, and more proof against termites.

Concrete Mixture—Mixture may be 1 part Portland cement, 2¾ parts sand, and 4 parts coarse aggregates (1-2¾-4 mixture), with mixing water *not exceeding* 7 gallons per sack of cement.

Thickness of Floors—Floors should be *at least 4"* thick, to prevent cracking. A 5" floor is safer.

5. Basements in Poorly Drained Soil—The same types listed in Par. 4 may be used, with modifications indicated below:

Concrete Mixture—Mixture should be 1 part Portland cement, 2¼ parts sand, and 3 parts coarse aggregates (1-2¼-3 mixture), with mixing water *not exceeding* 6 gallons per sack of cement.

Thickness of Floors—It is advisable to make floors 5" or 6" thick.

6. Basements in Soil Where Ground Water Is Present—Under these conditions, the types shown by Pl. 1, Figs. 13 or 14, are recommended. The type shown by Pl. 1, Fig. 13, is simpler and less expensive to build, and will prove satisfactory for light or moderate ground-water conditions.

Concrete Mixture—Mixture should be as indicated by Par. 5.

7. Basements in Soils Where Ground-Water Conditions Are Severe—The type shown by Pl. 1, Fig. 14, may be used under these conditions; but the following points should be considered:

"Lifting" Effect of Ground Water—When ground-water pressure is present under and around a basement, the basement may be regarded somewhat as a boat. Concrete is about 2.2 times as heavy as water. Therefore, a ground-water level that is approximately 13" above the bottom of a basement floor will exert a hydrostatic pressure on the underside of the floor that will just about balance the weight of a concrete floor 6" thick. The floors of the types shown by Pl. 1 are held down by the weight of the house and the "suction" (adhesion) of the adjacent soil, but an extreme height of ground water would tend to "float" the basement.

Thickness of Floors—The floors shown by Pl. 1, Fig. 14, should be safe against uplift when the ground-water level is 18" above the under-side of floor, provided that the following requirements are met: (1)

The minimum thickness of floor is 4"; (2) steel reinforcing bars, not less than ¼" diameter, and spaced not less than 12" apart in both directions, are used; and, (3) the piers or columns bearing upon the floor are spaced at intervals not exceeding 8'-0". Where the ground-water level is greater, the floor should be thicker; and larger reinforcing bars, spaced closer together, should be used. In fact, where such extreme conditions exist (even if just temporarily, as during the rainy seasons), the following suggestions should be considered:

Shallow Excavation for Basement—To meet extreme ground-water conditions, it may be well to select a type of house that has a good appearance if set several feet above the ground (and terraced, if necessary), thus allowing the floor of basement to be only several feet below grade. (Bottom of footings must be below frost line, however.)

Special Reinforcing—For extreme ground-water conditions, the advice of a competent engineer, architect, or contractor may be sought, so as to determine the necessary thickness of floor and the amount of steel reinforcing that should be used. See Par. 14, P. 79.

8. Surface Drainage—The ground should be properly graded to carry surface water away from basement walls.

9. Roof Drainage — Discharge from downspouts and gutters should be drained away from foundation walls. See Par. 13, P. 159.

10. Subsoil Drainage—Where the basement walls (or any other foundation walls, for that matter) are built into a side hill, or where there is evidence of underground springs, or where the experience of others in the locality indicates the possibility of trouble from ground water, a subsoil drain, consisting of open-joint drain tile covered with gravel or crushed stone, should be installed around the outer edge of the exterior wall footings. For unusually wet soils, a secondary drainage system should be installed near the inner edge of the footings (Pl. 1). This drainage system should drain into a storm sewer, "dry well", or other approved outlet. Of course, where the ground is low and contains a continuous head of water which is higher than the underside of the basement floor (and drain tile), and there is no place for the water to drain, any drainage system is useless unless a pump or ejector is used. (See Par. 14, P. 159.)

11. Waterproof Joints Between Footing and Basement Floor—For seepage-proof basements, these are essential (see Pl. 1). Hot tar or pitch (asphalt) is recommended.

12. Footings—See Sec. 15, P. 91.

13. Base for Floors—A 5" to 8" bed of well-compacted cinders or gravel is recommended to prevent dampness from coming up through the floor, except in cases where the ground-water level is continuously above the level of the bottom of the basement floor, in which cases this base is useless, and may be omitted. In any case, the ground should be well-compacted before placing the base or floor.

14. Reinforcing Steel—Reinforcing steel is cheap, and its use will pay big dividends by lowering future upkeep costs. It is far better to have the floor and walls too strong rather than too weak. See Pars. 11 to 15, P. 79.

15. Exterior Waterproofing—Exterior waterproofing is advisable for walls constructed of masonry units, even though the soil is well-drained; and is advisable for all types of walls where heavy ground-water pressure exists. See Sec. 19 and Pl. 1.

16. Ventilation — Provide sufficient ventilation, with windows so located as to cause a draft through basement when they are opened. Dampness, due to condensation of warm moist air on the cool masonry surfaces, can then be prevented by keeping the windows open in cool, dry weather and closed in sultry, humid weather.

17. Wall Thickness—See Par. 4, P. 95.

18. Top of Walls (Details)—See Par. 5, P. 95.

WATERPROOFING BASEMENTS AND FOUNDATION WALLS

1. Use of Waterproofing—For locations where the ground is unusually damp during certain seasons of the year, it is advisable to waterproof the basement or foundation walls so as to insure a dry basement or to eliminate dampness from under the house.

2. Making Concrete Watertight—See Par. 17, P. 80.

3. Integral Waterproofing Agents — There are a number of waterproofing agents on the market designed to be mixed with concrete or mortar for the purpose of making such concrete or mortar waterproof. However, most waterproofing substances are only temporary in effectiveness, and some have harmful effects upon the concrete. Finely subdivided, inert fillers (see Ref. R4-3, Sec. 38) are the only type of integral waterproofing agent recommended by this Guide. The best that can be said for even this type of agent is that is tends to reduce the permeability and increase the compressive strength of concrete, for the absorption of the concrete usually remains about the same or becomes greater when such fillers are used.

4. Exterior Waterproofing by Surface Treatment—This treatment gives good results if applied to *exterior* of surfaces to be waterproofed (see Pl. 1, Figs. 5, 9 and 12). The following should be noted, however:

Cement-Plaster Coating—Such a coating is necessary as a preliminary coating on masonry walls that are to be waterproofed, as it seals up all voids and serves as somewhat of a waterproofing itself.

Bitumen Coating—Hot asphalt is commonly used for exterior waterproofing, but it has the disadvantage of becoming brittle, cracked, and ineffective after a few years. There are on the market, however, emulsified asphalts in which fine particles of asphalt are suspended in a mixture of *water*, and which can be applied cold with a brush the same as paint. The manufacturers of this type of asphalt publish data that shows it to be superior to the commonly-used type of asphalt.

5. Waterproofing by Membrane Method — This method consists of waterproofing surfaces by the application of overlapping layers of a prepared waterproofing fabric, and thoroughly coating and bonding every lap with a suitable waterproofing compound, such as emulsified asphalt or hot asphalt. This is an effective means of waterproofing the exterior surfaces of basement walls and floors, but requires experienced and careful workmen to insure a good, water-tight, permanent job. (See Pl. 1, Fig. 14.)

It is recommended that such waterproofing, when required, be done in accordance with Pl. 1, Fig. 14, and the manufacturer's instructions. It is also recommended that the fabric be an approved brand of asphalt saturated wool-and-cotton rag felt, and that the waterproofing compound be an approved brand of emulsified asphalt of the type described in Par. 4. From 3 to 5 layers of fabric and at least two exterior coats of asphalt should be used, depending upon the height of the ground water.

CHIMNEYS AND FIREPLACES

CHIMNEYS

1. Importance of Chimney Location—The location of a chimney in a dwelling affects not only the appearance, floor plan, structural strength, and water-tightness of the dwelling, but the efficiency of the chimney as well.

2. Chimney on End of Dwelling—This type (Pl. 9, Figs. 4 and 5) is an exterior chimney that is built *into* an exterior wall of a dwelling.

Advantages—(1) May tend to improve the appearance of certain types of dwellings. (2) Requires a minimum of space *inside* the dwelling.

Disadvantages—(1) When such a chimney is used with frame construction, the framing is usually cut away as shown by Pl. 9, Figs. 4 and 5, thus weakening the exterior wall considerably. (This is not necessarily true for masonry walls, however, as the chimney would be bonded into the wall.) (2) When such chimneys cut through wood construction, there is danger of leaks and decay at the points of contact between the wood construction and masonry. (3)

The efficiency of such a chimney is lowered, due to the heat losses caused by cold winds. (4) Such chimneys are comparatively costly.

3. Chimneys Passing Through Sloping Roofs—This type (Pl. 9, Fig. 1) is an interior chimney passing through one of the sloping surfaces of a roof.

Advantages—(1) Such a chimney does not weaken the framing of a dwelling. (2) It can readily be made water-tight. (3) It is more efficient than the exterior type of chimney discussed in Par. 2.

Disadvantages—(1) If such a chimney is located any appreciable distance from the roof ridge, and is of proper height (at least 2 feet above high point of roof), it may be top heavy in appearance—and in fact. (2) Such a chimney tends to reduce the available space inside the dwelling. (3) It is apt to be unsightly.

4. Chimneys Passing Through Ridge of Roof—This type (Pl. 9, Fig. 2), is an interior chimney that projects through the ridge of the roof; and this Guide recommends that, where possible, all chimneys be of this type. If only one chimney is required, it should be near the center of the dwelling. Some of the partition space required to house such chimneys can generally be utilized for closets or built-in cupboards, bookcases, etc.

Advantages—(1) This chimney may be used without weakening the framing of a dwelling. (2) It can readily be made water-tight. (3) It is the most efficient type. (4) It is very pleasing in appearance. (5) It is usually the least costly type of chimney to build.

Disadvantages—Such a chimney tends to reduce the available space inside the dwelling.

5. Types of Construction—The construction of the chimney should conform, in general, to that shown by Pl. 8, Fig. 1.

6. Materials—This Guide recommends that all chimneys (except in special cases where all-concrete construction, etc., is used) be constructed of the following materials:

Chimney Walls—Brick construction is recommended throughout. Backing brick should be at least Grade B or C common; and exposed bricks should be

Grade A or B common, or face brick. See Par. 16, P. 85.

Flue Lining—Fire clay flue lining is recommended. A substitute lining of mortar is worthless, as such a lining soon disintegrates, due to the combined effects of wind, flue gases, and the excessive expansion and contraction caused by temperature changes.

Mortar—Cement mortar should be used throughout except for fire bricks of fireplace. Such mortar should contain no pure quartz or other highly siliceous sand or gravel, as such material will not withstand high temperatures.

7. Minimum Wall Thickness — Minimum wall thicknesses (measured from outside of fire clay flue lining) should be 4″ for brick; 4″ for reinforced concrete; 8″ for hollow building units; and 12″ for stone.

8. Special Wall Thicknesses — Outside walls of chimneys, such as those defined by Par. 2, should be at least twice as thick as the minimum thicknesses given above, in order to reduce the heat loss and thus secure an efficient chimney. Also, when any single flue has an effective area exceeding 200 square inches, the walls should be not less than 8″ thick.

9. Height of Chimney—The height of the chimney is governed somewhat by the type of dwelling, size and type of furnace used, etc. Table 1 gives minimum chimney heights for certain types of furnaces. In general, however, the *minimum* height above the grate should be between 30 and 35 feet; and the top of the chimney should extend at least 2 feet above the ridge of peak roofs, and 3 feet above flat roofs. The heights should be indicated on the drawings, and checked carefully.

TABLE 1.—*Sizes of Chimney Flue Linings and Heights of Chimneys Recommended for Flat-grate Furnaces Burning Soft Coal*[1]

Grate Area	Outside Size of Chimney Flue Lining		Height of Chimney Flue Above Grate	Grate Area	Outside Size of Chimney Flue Lining		Height of Chimney Flue Above Grate
	Round (diameter)	Rectangular			Round (diameter)	Rectangular	
Sq. Feet	Inches	Inches	Feet	Sq. Feet	Inches	Inches	Feet
1	9½	8½ by 8½	22	6	17¼	18 by 18	30
2	11¾	8½ by 13	24	7	20½	20 by 20	32
3	13	13 by 13	26	8	20½	20 by 20	35
4	13	13 by 13	30	9	20½	20 by 20	35
5	13	13 by 13	32	10	20½	20 by 20	40

[1]If anthracite is to be burned, the area of the chimney may be reduced by about 25 per cent. *(Reprinted from Reference R3-1, Sec. 38.)*

10. Number of Flues—A separate flue should be provided for each fireplace, heating boiler or furnace, stove, range and room heater, vent for gas stove, etc. When more than one connection is made to a flue, the draft is impaired; and there is danger that fire will be communicated to connecting rooms by way of one of the openings, which may not be in use. Such flues should be indicated on the drawings.

11. Shape of Flue Linings—Round linings are more efficient than square or rectangular linings of the same cross-sectional area. However, it is generally better to use square or rectangular linings, as they fit into the chimney better.

12. Effective Areas of Flue Linings—Such effective (useful) areas vary in accordance with the shape of the lining, and are indicated by the unshaded portions of Pl. 8, Figs. 10 and 11. Tests have proved that the area in corners of square or rectangular linings are dead air spaces, and have little or no effect upon the draft.

13. Size of Flue Lining—Tables 1 and 2 will serve as a general guide. The lining that serves a furnace should have an effective transverse area at least equal to that of the smoke pipe size recommended by the manufacturer. Where the manufacturer recommends the size of the lining, such size should be used. All lining sizes should be indicated on the drawings.

Flue Lining for Fireplace—These should have a minimum effective area of 1/10 the area of the largest opening of fireplace, but in no case should this area be less than 50 sq. ins. Minimum nominal size of lining should be 8½″ x 13″ rectangular outside dimensions, or 8″ round inside dimension.

Flue Linings for Warm-Air Furnaces, Steam or Hot-Water Boilers—These should have a minimum effective area of 70 sq. ins. Minimum nominal size of lining should be 8½″ x 13″ rectangular outside dimensions, or 10″ round inside dimension.

Flue Linings for Stoves, Ranges, and Room Heaters (Burning Coal, Coke, or Wood)—These should have a minimum effective area of 40 sq. ins. Minimum nominal size of lining should be 8½″ x 8½″ rectangular outside dimension, or 8″ round inside dimension.

Flue Lining for Vent Flues—Flue linings for domestic gas appliances such as non-automatic water heaters, stoves, ranges, and other appliances having relatively small gas consumption (excepting gas plates and portable gas heating appliances) should have an effective flue area of not less than 10 sq. ins. Minimum nominal size of lining should be 4½″ x 8½″ rectangular outside dimensions, or 6″ round inside dimension.

14. Separation of Linings—It is better to have all linings separated by at least 4" of masonry, as there will be less danger of leaks between flues.

15. Slope of Flues—Flues should be built as nearly vertical as possible, since each slope decreases their efficiency, forms a lodging place for soot to accumulate, and makes the flues more difficult to clean.

16. Placing Flue Lining—The masonry should not be built hollow and the lining dropped inside, *but the masonry should be built around each section of lining as it is placed.* The linings should be carefully bedded one upon another in mortar, with all joints left smooth on the inside; and all joints and spaces between the masonry and lining should be thoroughly slushed and grouted full as each course of masonry is laid.

17. Corbeled (Offset) Chimneys—Such chimneys should not be supported by hollow walls or walls of hollow units. Solid walls supporting corbeled chimneys should not be less than 12" thick, and the corbeling should not project more than 1" per course and not more than 6" in any case. The total offsets, overhang, or corbel of an independent chimney should not exceed 3/8 of the width of the chimney in the direction of the offset.

18. Filling of Joints—All joints in chimney should be *completely* filled with mortar. All brickwork should be laid with a shoved joint.

19. Thimbles (Sizes) — Thimbles for smokepipes of furnaces, boilers, stoves, etc., should be of the size recommended by the manufacturer of such heating equipment. All other miscellaneous thimbles for vents, etc., should have an area equal to that of the flue lining.

20. Placing Thimbles—The inner end of the thimble should be flush with the inner surface of the lining, but should not project into the flue (Pl. 8, Fig. 8). The top of thimbles should be set not less than 18" below sheet metal ceilings, wood lath, and plaster.

21. Chimney Caps—A reinforced concrete cap on top of the chimney is desirable (Pl. 8, Fig. 1) if such a cap does not affect the appearance of the dwelling adversely. In any case, there should be a sloping, 2", rich (1:1 mix) cement wash at the extreme top, with a 2" projection of the flue linings. The purpose of such cap and wash is to prevent the freezing of water in the exposed end of the chimney, with the resultant disintegration of the chimney; and to prevent water from finding its way down the chimney, with the resultant harm caused by leaks.

22. Smoke Tests—All chimneys should successfully pass a smoke test before they are accepted. As leaks are difficult to repair in the completed chimney, the construction should be carefully inspected as it progresses.

FIREPLACES

23. Fireplace Design (Exterior)—The fireplace design should be shown in detail on the plans. However, when such details are omitted from the plans, or when the design shown does not suit the prospective home owner, a suitable design may be selected from a magazine or other source, such as Ref. R3-6, Sec. 38, and made part of the contract documents. An architect should be consulted in such cases, however, to make sure that the design selected is appropriate, and that it works in properly with the structure in general.

24. Size of Fireplace—As the fireplace is, in most cases, more ornamental than useful, it should be of pleasing proportions. Table 2 and the following paragraphs will serve as a general guide:

Height—The minimum height consistent with tending the fire should be about 30". The maximum height for fireplaces, 6 feet or less in width, should be about 42". The higher the opening, the greater the possibility of a smoky fireplace.

Width—The width should be in proportion, being about the same as the height, for small fireplaces.

Depth—A 12" depth may be sufficient for small fireplaces with properly constructed throats; but an 18" depth is much superior, for it will give a better draft, and there will be less danger of sparks falling out on the floor. The wider the opening, the greater the depth should be, in general.

TABLE 2.—*Fireplace Dimensions*

Width of Opening (Inches)	Approx. Height (Inches)	Depth of Opening (Inches)	Effective Area of Flue Required[1]	RECOMMENDED SIZE OF FLUE LINING	
				Outside Dimensions (Inches)	Effective Area
24	28	17 – 20	67 sq. in.	8½ x 13	70 sq. in.
28	28	17 – 20	78 sq. in.	8½ x 13	70 sq. in.
30	30	17 – 21	90 sq. in.	8½ x 17½	97 sq. in.
34	30	17 – 21	102 sq. in.	13 x 13	100 sq. in.
36	30	21	108 sq. in.	13 x 13	100 sq. in.
40	30	21 – 24	120 sq. in.	[2]13 x 13	100 sq. in.
42	30	21 – 25	126 sq. in.	[2]13 x 13	100 sq. in.
48	32	21 – 26	154 sq. in.	13 x 17½	150 sq. in.

[1]This column shows the theoretically effective area that is required for flue lining, based on 1/10 of the area of the fireplace opening. If height of chimney is 30 feet or more above the grate, the required effective area may be taken as 1/12 of the area of the fire-place opening.

[2]This lining has an effective area of only approximately 1/12 of the area of fireplace opening. If necessary (see note above), a 13 x 17½ rectangular lining, or a 12" inside diameter round lining, may be used.

25. Materials—The following materials are recommended:

Fireplace Lining—The faces of the fireplaces exposed to fire, and the inner hearth of fireplaces, should be lined with fire brick laid in fire clay mortar.

Exterior of Fireplace—It is recommended that all exposed masonry be of a suitable type of brick laid up in cement mortar.

Hearth—Material may be brick, ceramic tile, stone, or concrete. Only a cement mortar should be used.

26. Fireplace Construction Details—It is recommended that the inner construction of the fireplace conform to that shown by Pl. 8, Figs. 1 and 2, except possibly for minor variations due to the type of damper used.

27. Throat Construction—Correct throat construction is essential for an efficient fireplace. The following features are especially important:

Location of Throat—The throat should be located about 8″ above the supporting lintel, as shown by Pl. 8, Fig. 2.

Area of Throat—The length of throat should be equal to the fireplace opening; and the width should be preferably 4″, but not over 5″. The throat area, however, should not be less than that of the flue lining.

Construction Adjoining Throat—The sides of the fireplace should be vertical until throat is passed, and then should be drawn in until the desired flue area is obtained.

28. Wind Shelf and Smoke Chamber — These are absolutely necessary. The purpose of the shelf is shown by a comparison of Fig. 1 and Pl. 8, Fig. 2. The chief purpose of the smoke chamber is to form a space capable of temporarily holding accumulated smoke, whenever a gust of wind momentarily cuts off the draft. This prevents the smoke from being forced out into the room. The smoke chamber also causes the force of down drafts to be less. The following construction features are especially important:

Wind Shelf—This shelf should be formed as shown by Pl. 8, Figs. 1 and 2. Depth of the shelf should not be less than 4″, but may be as much as 12″ or more, depending on depth of fireplace. Length of the shelf should be as great as possible. Height above lintel (where a lintel is used) should be about 8″, as shown.

Smoke Chamber—This includes the space between the tops of the throat and the wind shelf and the lower end of flue lining. A good slope for the walls (Pl. 8, Fig. 2) is 1″ for each 18″ rise. The walls of chamber should be smoothly plastered with cement mortar at least ½″ thick, as this will increase the efficiency of the fireplace.

29. Throat Damper — Every fireplace should be outfitted with a throat damper, as such dampers are necessary for regulating the fire, and for closing off the chimney when desired. It is recommended that the damper be of an approved make, having the following minimum features: (1) Combination throat and damper. (2) Lid hinged at back. (3) Designed to support the masonry over the fireplace opening (Pl. 8, Fig. 1).

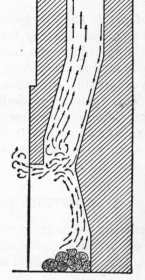

FIG. 1.—*Fireplaces Constructed Like This Without Throat Will Very Likely Smoke*

30. Hearth Construction—It is recommended that the hearth be supported by a concrete slab as shown by Pl. 8, Fig. 5. Such a concrete slab should be at least 4″ thick, reinforced with ⅜″ diam. bars spaced 6″ center to center, in both directions, and securely supported.

CONSTRUCTION ADJACENT TO CHIMNEYS AND FIREPLACES

31. General Construction—This should conform to that shown by Pl. 8 and 9, insofar as these illustrations are applicable to the type of chimney that you have selected.

32. Minimum Clearance for Framing—No combustible beams, joists, or rafters should be placed within 2″ of the outside face of chimneys or masonry inclosing a flue; nor within 4″ of the back of a fireplace. No header beam should be closer than 20″ to the face of any fireplace; and in no case should a framing member be allowed to set in, on, or against a chimney wall.

33. Firestopping—See Pars. 74 to 78, P. 124.

34. Flashing of Chimney—See Pars. 1 to 7, P. 138.

35. Plastering Around Chimney—See Par. 15, P. 148.

WOOD AND ITS PROPERTIES

GENERAL INFORMATION

1. Structure of Wood—Like all other plant matter, wood is composed of cells, or fibers, with an arrangement somewhat similar to that of a honeycomb.

2. Softwoods and Hardwoods—In general, lumber made from cone-bearing trees, such as the pines, spruces, firs, cedars, and hemlocks, is designated as softwood; lumber made from noncone-bearing trees, such as oak, maple, and poplar is designated as hardwood. This manner of designation, though customary, is misleading because some "softwoods", such as Douglas fir and longleaf southern pine, are much harder than some "hardwoods", such as basswood, poplar, etc.

MOISTURE CONTENT

3. Definition—The moisture content of wood is the weight of the water contained in the wood expressed in percentage of the weight of the oven-dry wood.

4. Importance—The moisture content of wood is important from a standpoint of shrinkage, as is pointed out in this Section; and from a standpoint of decay, as pointed out in Sec. 10, P. 71.

5. Correct Moisture Content—The moisture content of wood does not remain constant, but varies as the moisture in the atmosphere increases or decreases. The moisture content should not exceed 12% for framing lumber or exterior millwork; and should not exceed 7% for interior doors, trim, finish floors, and cabinet work.

6. Time Required for Seasoning—If lumber is so placed in the atmosphere as to allow air to circulate around it, the lumber becomes "air-dry" in the course of from one to three months, depending upon the season of the year, type of climate, etc. If this process is hastened or carried beyond the point obtainable by "air-drying" alone, by drying the lumber artificially in a heated oven or kiln, the wood is said to be "kiln dried". Most interior woodwork is kiln dried.

7. Determining Moisture Content — Most up-to-date lumber mills use one of the several types of portable electrical-resistance indicating instruments on the market that have been devised for quickly determining the moisture content of wood. The use of such an instrument is the most practical method of testing lumber, as it is rapid and does not require drilling, sawing, or other disfigurement of the lumber.

SHRINKAGE

8. Importance—A knowledge of lumber shrinkage is very necessary to the person who wishes to build a home that will be free of cracks, leaks, and other ailments resulting from shrinkage.

9. Direction of Shrinkage—As wood becomes seasoned due to the drying out of the moisture in the cell walls, it not only decreases in weight but also decreases in size, or shrinks. It is important to note the directions and amounts of this shrinkage which is as follows:

Shrinkage Lengthwise to Grain—Fortunately, such shrinkage is very little or nothing (Fig. 1).

Shrinkage Parallel to Grain—The greatest shrinkage occurs in this direction, as shown by Fig. 1. The amount of shrinkage from a green to kiln dried condition may be as much as 8%.

Shrinkage at Right Angles to Grain—The shrinkage in this direction is approximately one-half the shrinkage that occurs parallel to grain. See Fig. 1.

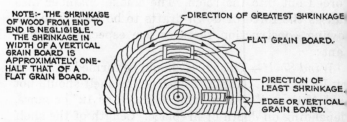

NOTE:- THE SHRINKAGE OF WOOD FROM END TO END IS NEGLIGIBLE. THE SHRINKAGE IN WIDTH OF A VERTICAL GRAIN BOARD IS APPROXIMATELY ONE-HALF THAT OF A FLAT GRAIN BOARD.

DIRECTION OF GREATEST SHRINKAGE

FLAT GRAIN BOARD.

DIRECTION OF LEAST SHRINKAGE.

EDGE OR VERTICAL GRAIN BOARD.

FIG. 1.—*Section Through a Log Showing How Wood Shrinks*

10. How Shrinkage Affects a House—Fig. 2 shows, graphically, how the use of "flatwise" lumber in the framework of a house results in a large amount of settlement. This is one reason why the average home is full of plaster cracks, binding doors, warped floors, etc.

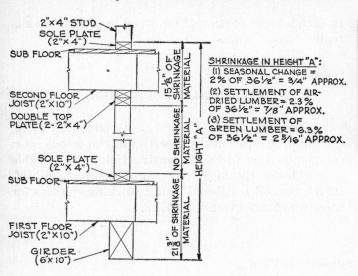

FIG. 2.—*Effect of Shrinkage on Framework of a House (Typical Section Through Platform Frame Type of Construction)*

Labels in figure:
- 2"x4" STUD
- SOLE PLATE (2"x4")
- SUB FLOOR
- SECOND FLOOR JOIST (2"x10")
- DOUBLE TOP PLATE (2-2"x4")
- SOLE PLATE (2"x4")
- SUB FLOOR
- FIRST FLOOR JOIST (2"x10")
- GIRDER (6"x10")
- 1 5/8" OF SHRINKAGE MATERIAL
- NO SHRINKAGE MATERIAL
- HEIGHT "A"
- 2 1/8" OF SHRINKAGE MATERIAL

SHRINKAGE IN HEIGHT "A":
(1) SEASONAL CHANGE = 2% OF 36 1/2" = 3/4" APPROX.
(2) SETTLEMENT OF AIR-DRIED LUMBER = 2.3% OF 36 1/2" = 7/8" APPROX.
(3) SETTLEMENT OF GREEN LUMBER = 6.3% OF 36 1/2" = 2 5/16" APPROX.

DENSITY

11. General—A tree has one "annual ring" for each year of growth. Each ring is composed of a soft, open-grain inner ring known as spring wood and a hard, dense outer ring known as summer wood. See Fig. 3.

12. Effect of Density—Timbers in which summer wood predominates may be one-sixth stronger than those in which spring wood predominates. All structural timbers should have not less than one-third of its cross-sectional area composed of summer wood.

13. Virgin and Second Growth — Virgin growth timber is popularly supposed to be of a slow-growing dense type, due to the lack of sufficient sunlight and moisture in a heavily wooded forest; while second growth timber is supposed to be of a relatively rapid growth, wide annual ring type. So, where strength and toughness are desired, virgin growth is preferred in softwoods, and second growth in hardwoods. However, inasmuch as both virgin and second growth trees mature under such a variety of conditions it often happens that one type may have the characteristics of the other. In fact, it is impossible to examine wood and tell which type of growth it is. It is therefore better to select wood on a basis of density and rate of growth, rather than on the basis of its type of growth.

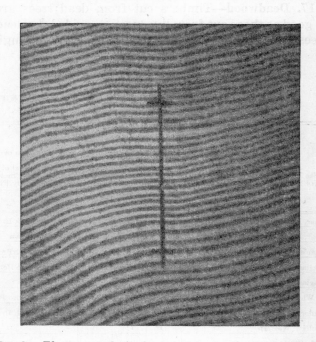

FIG. 3.—*The upper photo shows a 3 by 8 pine joist with five annual rings to the inch and 25 per cent summer wood. It is neither close grained nor dense. The lower photo is part of the end section of a 6 by 8 pine beam. It has six annual rings to the inch and 51 per cent summer wood. It is classified as dense.*

(Reprinted from Reference R11-6, Sect. 38.)

ERRONEOUS BELIEFS

14. Time of Cutting Timber—Contrary to popular belief, the time when timber is cut does not affect its desirable properties, provided that it is properly cared for after it is cut. However, timber cut in late spring, or early summer, is more subject to attacks by insects and decay fungi. Also, timber cut in the summer months may season too rapidly, with resultant checking, if not properly shaded.

15. Relative Strength of Air Dried and Kiln Dried Wood—Wood becomes stronger with the elimination of moisture, and any given piece of wood would be just as strong if properly kiln dried for a certain moisture content, as it would if properly air dried for the same moisture content.

16. Relative Strength of Sapwood and Heartwood—
In mature trees, the heartwood may be the stronger; while in young trees, the sapwood may be the stronger. In any case, strength should be judged on the basis of density.

17. Deadwood—Timbers cut from dead trees are as good as those cut from live trees, provided the dead trees have not been attacked by insects or decay fungi.

In fact, a large portion of the wood in a "live" tree is really "dead" wood.

PHYSICAL PROPERTIES

18. General—Table 1 shows, in condensed form, the important physical properties of the woods most commonly used in house construction. (This Table is based, for the most part, on data given in Ref. R24-1, Sec. 38.) Allowable unit working stresses for these woods are given in Table 2.

TABLE 1.—*Physical Properties of Wood*

SPECIES (See Your Local Lumber Dealers for Species Available Locally.)	Natural Durability[1]	Paint Retention[2]	Workability[3]	COLOR OF HEARTWOOD (The Sapwood of All Species is Light in Color or Practically White Unless Discolored by Fungous or Chemical Stains.)	Weather Checks	Cupping and Pulling Loose From Fastenings	ASSOCIATION UNDER WHICH GRADED[4]
					WEATHERING PROPERTIES OF BOARDS EXPOSED TO WEATHER WITHOUT PROTECTIVE COATING (Edge Grain Wood Weathers Much Better Than Flat Grain Wood.)			
Cedar, Northern White	A	A	A	Light to Dark Brown	Inconspicuous	Slight	S36
Cedar, Western Red	A	A	A	Reddish Brown	"	"	S53
Cypress, Tidewater Red	A	A	B	Light Yellowish Brown to Reddish Brown	"	"	S47
Douglas Fir, Coast	B[5]	D	C	Orange Red to Red; Sometimes Yellow	Conspicuous	Distinct	S53
Douglas Fir, Inland	B[5]	D	B	"	"	"	S54
Fir, White	E	C	B	Nearly White to Pale Reddish Brown	"	"	S54
Hemlock, Eastern	D	C	B	Light Reddish Brown	"	"	S36
Hemlock, Western	D	C	B	"	"	"	S53
Larch, Western	C	D	C	Russet to Reddish Brown	"	"	S54
Pine, Idaho (Western) White	X	B	A	Cream to Light Reddish Brown	"	"	S54
Pine, Longleaf Yellow	B[5]	D	C	Orange to Reddish Brown	"	"	S48
Pine, Northern White	X	B	A	Cream to Light Reddish Brown	"	"	S37
Pine, Norway	X	D	B	Orange to Reddish Brown	"	"	S37
Pine, Ponderosa	X	C	A	"	"	"	S54
Pine, Shortleaf Yellow	B[5]	D	B	"	"	"	S48
Pine, Sugar	X	B	A	Light Creamy Brown	"	"	S54
Redwood, California	A	A	B	Cherry to Deep Reddish Brown	Inconspicuous	Slight	S9
Spruce, Eastern	D	C	B	Light Grayish Brown	Conspicuous	Distinct	S37
Spruce, Sitka	D	C	B	Light Reddish Brown	"	"	S53
Tamarack	C	D	B	Russet Brown	"	"	S36

[1]Ratings apply to **heartwood.** The sapwood of no species is durable when exposed to conditions favoring decay.

A = Heartwood durable even when used under conditions that favor decay.
B = Heartwood of intermediate durability but nearly as durable as "A" group.
C = Heartwood of intermediate durability.
D = Heartwood between intermediate and non-durable group.
E = Heartwood low in durability when used under conditions that favor decay.
X = Insufficient data available to give rating. (However, heartwood of the white pines is rated more durable than heartwood of ponderosa pine.)

[2]Paint retention ratings are as follows:

A = Woods that hold paint longest **and** suffer least when protection against weather becomes inadequate.
B = Woods that hold white-lead paint **as** long as those of group "A" but do not hold mixed-pigment paints quite so long and suffer more than those of group "A" if protection becomes inadequate.

C = Woods that do not hold either white-lead paint or mixed-pigment paints so long as woods of group "A" and suffer more than woods of group "A" if protection becomes inadequate.

D = Woods that do not hold paint coatings so long as woods of group "C".

[3]Ratings apply to working with hand tools, as follows:

A = Easy to work.
B = Medium to work.
C = Difficult to work.

[4]Symbols (S36, S53, etc.) refer to the lumber associations listed in Table 2, P. 181 Valuable "Grade-Use" guides may usually be obtained from these associations upon request.

[5]"B" rating is for "dense" Douglas firs and yellow pines. For "unselected" wood of these species, the rating is "C".

TABLE 2.—*Allowable Unit Stresses for Structural Lumber and Timber (All sizes, dry locations)*

WORKING STRESSES FOR MANUFACTURERS' ASSOCIATION STANDARD COMMERCIAL GRADES

SPECIES OF TIMBER	GRADE	ALLOWABLE UNIT STRESS IN POUNDS PER SQUARE INCH		
		EXTREME FIBER IN BENDING		MODULUS OF ELASTICITY
		Joist and Plank Sizes; 4 Inches and Less in Thickness	Beam and Stringer Sizes; 5 Inches and Thicker	
Douglas Fir, Coast Region	Dense Superstructural	2,000	2,000	1,600,000
	Superstructural and Dense Structural	1,800	1,800	1,600,000
	Structural	1,600	1,600	1,600,000
	Common Structural	1,200	1,400	1,600,000
Douglas Fir, Inland Empire	Dense Superstructural[1]	2,000	2,000	1,600,000
	Dense Structural[1]	1,800	1,800	1,600,000
Larch, Western	No. 1 Common Dimension and Timbers	1,135	1,135	1,500,000
	No. 1 Common Dimension and Timbers	1,135	1,135	1,300,000
Pine, Southern Yellow	Extra Dense Select Structural	2,300	2,300	1,600,000
	Select Structural	2,000	2,000	1,600,000
	Extra Dense Heart	2,000	2,000	1,600,000
	Dense Heart	1,800	1,800	1,600,000
	Structural Square Edge and Sound	1,600	1,600	1,600,000
	Dense No. 1 Common	1,200	1,200	1,600,000
Redwood	Superstructural	2,133	1,707	1,200,000
	Prime Structural	1,707	1,494	1,200,000
	Select Structural	1,280	1,322	1,200,000
	Heart Structural	1,024	1,150	1,200,000

[1]When graded the same as corresponding grade of Coast Region Douglas Fir.

WORKING STRESSES FOR STRUCTURAL LUMBER AND TIMBER GRADED UNDER THE STRUCTURAL GRADE
EXAMPLES OF THE AMERICAN LUMBER STANDARDS

SPECIES OF TIMBER	GRADE	ALLOWABLE UNIT STRESS IN POUNDS PER SQUARE INCH		
		EXTREME FIBER IN BENDING		MODULUS OF ELASTICITY
		Joist and Plank Sizes; 4 Inches and Less in Thickness	Beam and Stringer Sizes; 5 Inches and Thicker	
Cedar, Alaska	Select Structural	1,100	1,100	1,200,000
	Common Structural	880	880	1,200,000
Cedar, Northern and Southern White	Select Structural	750	750	800,000
	Common Structural	600	600	800,000
Cedar, Port Orford	Select Structural	1,100	1,100	1,200,000
	Common Structural	880	880	1,200,000
Cedar, Western Red	Select Structural	900	900	1,000,000
	Common Structural	720	720	1,000,000
Cypress, Southern	Select Structural	1,300	1,300	1,200,000
	Common Structural	1,040	1,040	1,200,000
Douglas Fir, Rocky Mountain Region	Select Structural	1,100	1,100	1,200,000
	Common Structural	880	880	1,200,000
Fir, Balsam	Select Structural	900	900	1,000,000
	Common Structural	720	720	1,000,000
Fir, Golden, Noble, Silver, White (Commercial White)	Select Structural	1,100	1,100	1,100,000
	Common Structural	880	880	1,100,000
Hemlock, Eastern	Select Structural	1,100	1,100	1,100,000
	Common Structural	880	880	1,100,000
Hemlock, West Coast	Select Structural	1,300	1,300	1,400,000
	Common Structural	1,040	1,040	1,400,000
Oak, Commercial White and Red	Select Structural	1,400	1,400	1,500,000
	Common Structural	1,120	1,120	1,500,000
Pine, California, Idaho, and Northern White, Lodgepole, Ponderosa, Sugar	Select Structural	900	900	1,000,000
	Common Structural	720	720	1,000,000
Pine, Norway	Select Structural	1,100	1,100	1,200,000
	Common Structural	880	880	1,000,000
Spruce, Englemann	Select Structural	750	750	800,000
	Common Structural	600	600	800,000
Spruce, Red, White, Sitka	Select Structural	1,100	1,100	1,200,000
	Common Structural	880	880	1,200,000
Tamarack, Eastern	Select Structural	1,200	1,200	1,300,000
	Common Structural	960	960	1,300,000

(Reprinted from Reference R11-6, Sec. 38.)

SUITABILITY OF WOODS FOR USE IN THE FRAME HOUSE

19. General—The following useful data, which is reprinted from Ref. R24-2, Sec. 38, will serve as a *general* guide for the selection of suitable species and grades of wood for the construction of your home, and will serve to supplement the specific recommendations given in Sec. 24, P. 116, and Sec. 25, P. 129. Quoting from Ref. R24-2, Sec. 38:

"Wise selection of lumber for building a house yields high returns in ultimate savings and satisfaction.

"Such selection calls for an understanding of what is required in the various building items. For instance, the actual service conditions for joists call for stiffness, dryness as delivered, ability to stay in place, and minimum tendency to shrink, but it is not uncommon for the builder to select such members largely on the basis of bending strength.

"Detailed information based on actual tests on all of the strength and other physical properties of all the woods available for use in house construction is not at hand through any one source. The accumulated fund of information that is available, however, together with the observations and mature judgment of technical workers and builders affords a sound basis for selection of building lumber items. It is on such a combination of actual test data and practical judgment that the following recommendations are based:"

Flooring (Kitchen; Uncovered)

Usual requirements:
   Resistance to wear, fine texture, ability to withstand washing and wear without discoloring and slivering, minimum warp and shrinkage.

Woods combining usual requirements in a high degree:
   Beech, birch, hard maple. (Fine textured.)

Woods combining usual requirements in a good degree:
   Ash, red and white oak. (Open textured.)
   Soft maple.

Woods combining usual requirements in a fair degree:
   Cypress, Douglas fir, western hemlock, western larch, redwood, southern yellow pine. (Vertical grain preferred.)
   Elm, hackberry, sycamore.

Grades used:
   The flooring grades, Seconds in beech, birch, and hard maple, and Selects in the oaks are used in high-priced houses. In more economical construction Thirds in beech, birch, and hard maple, and No. 1 Common or No. 2 Common in the oaks are used. D (vertical grain) is the lowest grade of softwood that proves thoroughly satisfactory in high-class construction. A grade and B and Better grade (vertical grain) are used most extensively. No 1 and No. 2 are serviceable in low-cost construction but wear unevenly around knots.

Flooring (Living Room and Bedroom)

Usual requirements:
   High resistance to wear, attractive figure or color, minimum warp and shrinkage.

Woods combining usual requirements in a high degree:
   Hard maple, red and white oak. (Most commonly used hardwoods.)

Ash (white), beech, birch, walnut. (Not commonly used.)
Hickory, black locust, pecan. (Not commonly available. Hard to work and nail.)

Woods combining usual requirements in a good degree:
   Cypress, Douglas fir, western hemlock, western larch, redwood, southern yellow pine. (Vertical grain.)
   Cherry, red gum, sycamore (quartered). (Not commonly available. Highly decorative and suitable where wear is light and maintenance good.)

Grades used:
   In beech, birch, and maple flooring the grade of Firsts is ordinarily used for the better class of homes and Seconds and sometimes Thirds in low-cost jobs. In oak the grade of Clear (either plain or quartered) is used in better class work and Selects and sometimes No. 1 Common in low-cost work. Other hardwoods are ordinarily used in the same grades as oak. When softwood flooring is used (without covering) in better class homes grade A or B and Better vertical grain is used. Grade D or C (vertical grain) is used in more economical and low-cost homes.

Flooring (Porch)

Usual requirements:
   Medium to good decay resistance, medium wear resistance, nonsplintering, freedom from warping.

Woods combining usual requirements in a high degree:
   Cypress, Douglas fir (vertical grain), western larch (vertical grain), southern yellow pine (vertical grain), redwood, white oak. (If full drainage is not obtainable only the heartwood of cypress, redwood, and white oak can be given a high rating.)
   Black locust, walnut. (Usually impractical except when cut from home-grown timber.)

Grades used:
   Grades C to A are used in the better types of homes. No. 1 and No. 2 are used in lower cost homes and are serviceable, but wear unevenly around knots, and the maintenance of paint on the knots is difficult. The superior paint-holding qualities and uniform wearing surface of vertical grain makes it preferred in all grades. Hardwoods, if used at all, should be of Select or No. 1 Common quality.

Framing (House)

Usual requirements:
   High stiffness, good bending strength, good nail-holding power, hardness, freedom from pronounced warp. For this use dryness and size are more important factors than inherent properties of the different woods.

Woods combining usual requirements in a high degree:
   Douglas fir, western larch, southern yellow pine. (Extensively used.)
   Ash, beech, birch, maple, oak. (Sometimes used, but more difficult to obtain in straight pieces and harder to nail and saw than preceding group.)
   Cypress, redwood. (Seldom used.)

Woods combining usual requirements in a good degree:
   Eastern hemlock, western hemlock, eastern spruce, Sitka spruce, white fir. (Extensively used.)
   Northern white pine, ponderosa pine, sugar pine, western white pine. (Seldom used because of adaptability to more exacting uses. Low strength may be compensated for by the use of larger members.)
   Chestnut, yellow poplar. (Seldom used.)

Woods combining usual requirements in a fair degree:
Elm, red gum, sycamore, tupelo. (Seldom used.)

Grades used:
No. 1 Dimension is the usual softwood grade for all framing items in both high- and medium-class construction. No. 2 Dimension renders satisfactory service once it is in place, but is not so straight or easily fabricated as No. 1. No. 3 Dimension is serviceable for studs and joists in the more economical and low-cost homes, especially when warped pieces and short lengths resulting from cutting out defects can be used to advantage. When hardwoods are used for framing, sound square edge is used in the better types of construction and for such items as joists, rafters, and sills. Hardwood Common Dimension is used in the more economical type of buildings and for studding in all types.

Lath

Usual requirements:
Low shrinkage, easy nailing, nondiscoloration of plaster.

Woods combining usual requirements in a high degree:
Jack pine, lodgepole pine, northern white pine, sugar pine, ponderosa pine, western white pine, spruce, white fir, yellow poplar.

Woods combining usual requirements in a fair degree:
Cypress, Douglas fir, hemlocks, western larch, southern yellow pine, basswood.

Grades use:
Two grades of lath, No. 1 and No. 2, are available in practically all softwoods and in a number of hardwoods. In high-class and in the standard or medium types of construction No. 1 lath is usually used. No 2 lath meets the less exacting requirements of cottages and lower-cost homes.

Sash (Used in a Dry Location; Low Decay Hazard)

Usual requirements:
Moderate shrinkage, good paint qualities, freedom from warping, ease of working, screw-holding power.

Woods combining usual requirements in a high degree:
Northern white pine, ponderosa pine, sugar pine, western white pine. (Principal woods used for sash.)
Cypress, redwood.

Woods combining usual requirements in a good degree:
Douglas fir, western larch, southern yellow pine. (Vertical grain. Use limited by milling and finishing characteristics.)

Sash (Used in a Moist Location; High Decay Hazard)

Usual requirements:
High decay resistance. Moderate shrinkage, good paint qualities, freedom from warping, ease of working, screw-holding power.

Woods combining usual requirements in a high degree:
Northern white pine, ponderosa pine, sugar pine, western white pine. (Principal woods used for sash. Require good preservative treatment.)
Cypress, cedars, redwood, chestnut. (Heartwood only or sapwood when treated.)

Woods combining usual requirements in a good degree:
Douglas fir, western larch, southern yellow pine. (Heartwood only.)
White oak. (Harder to work and higher shrinkage than the softwoods.)

Grades used:
Grades of lumber used for sash are primarily of interest to manufacturers rather than users.

Sheathing (Roof)

Usual requirements:
High stiffness, good nail holding, small tendency to warp, ease of working.

Woods combining usual requirements in a high degree:
Douglas fir, western larch, southern yellow pine. (Commonly used.)
Cypress. (Not commonly used because of adaptability to more exacting uses.)
Ash, beech, birch, chestnut, elm, hackberry, maple, oak, tupelo. (Seldom used because not readily available and hard to work.)

Woods combining usual requirements in a good degree:
Hemlocks, ponderosa pine, spruces, white fir. (Commonly used.)
Northern white pine, sugar pine, western white pine, redwood, yellow poplar. (Seldom used because of adaptability to more exacting uses.)

Grades used:
No. 2 boards are used extensively in higher type homes. In more economical construction both No. 2 and No. 3 are used. No. 3 is serviceable but not so tight as No. 2. No. 4 and No. 5 are available in some species but entail waste in cutting. When hardwoods are used No. 2 Common is adapted to the better class houses and No. 3 Common to the more economical.

Sheathing (Side Walls)

Usual requirements:
Easy working, easy nailing, moderate shrinkage. All woods can be used for sheathing with satisfactory results although some woods are less time-consuming to work than are others.

Woods combining usual requirements in a high degree:
Cedar, cypress, hemlocks, northern white pine, ponderosa pine, sugar pine, western white pine, redwood, spruce, white fir, basswood, chestnut, yellow poplar.

Woods combining usual requirements in a good degree:
Douglas fir, western larch, southern yellow pine, cottonwood.

Grades used:
No. 3 grade of softwoods makes a serviceable sheathing when covered with good building paper. No. 1 and No. 2 make a tighter coverage, but do not warrant omitting use of building paper. No. 4 and No. 5 are used in low-cost homes, but are not generally available. They both entail some waste in cutting. When a hardwood is used for sheathing, No. 2 Common is adapted to the better type homes, and No. 3 Common to the more economical.

Shelving (With Natural or High-Class Paint Finish)

Usual requirements:
Stiffness, good finishing qualities, freedom from pitch and warp.

Woods combining usual requirements in a high degree:
Ash, birch, maple, oak, walnut. (Suitable for natural finishes used principally to match interior trim.)
Cypress, redwood, yellow poplar. (Suitable for high-class paint finishes, but use limited.)

Northern white pine, ponderosa pine, sugar pine, western white pine. (Principal woods used for high-class paint finishes.)

Woods combining usual requirements in a good degree:

Douglas fir, hemlocks, western larch, southern yellow pine, spruces, white fir, basswood, chestnut. (May be used with either natural or paint finishes.)

Shelving (with Unfinished or Plain Paint Coating)

Usual requirements:

Stiffness, ease of working, freedom from pitch and warp.

Woods combining usual requirements in a good degree:

Northern white pine, ponderosa pine, sugar pine, western white pine. (Principal woods used.)

Cypress, hemlocks, redwood, spruces, white fir, basswood, chestnut, yellow poplar.

Douglas fir, western larch, southern yellow pine. (Softwoods with high stiffness.)

Birch, maple, oak. (Seldom used; difficult to work.)

Grades used:

The grade best adapted to use depends on the character of the shelving as well as on type of construction. C or a better grade is used for shelves that are to receive a high-class paint or enamel finish. D grade is serviceable, but may entail some waste. No. 1 and No. 2 are used for shelving that is unpainted or receives only a rough-paint finish. No. 3 is serviceable, especially when cut into short lengths, but may entail some waste. When hardwoods are used for shelving in closets or storerooms No. 1 or No. 2 Common is used. These two grades are suitable for higher class shelving where short-length or narrow, clear cutting can be used to advantage.

Shingles (Side Walls and Roof)

Usual requirements:

High decay resistance, small tendency to curl or check, freedom from splitting in nailing.

Woods combining usual requirements in a high degree:

Cedars, cypress, redwood. (Principal shingle woods; heartwood only, edge grain.)

Northern white pine, ponderosa pine, sugar pine, western white pine. (Hand-made shingles or shakes from locally grown timber; require good preservative treatment.)

Chestnut, white oak. (Hand-made shingles or shakes from locally grown timber; require care in nailing.)

Grades used:

In western red cedar, cypress, and redwood No. 1 shingles (all heart, edge grain clear stock) should be used for the longest life and greatest ultimate economy in dwelling roofs. Other all-heart but not edge-grain grades, such as No. 2 in redwood and western red cedar and Bests in cypress, are frequently used to reduce the first cost. Other grades permitting sapwood and flat grain are available and are used where low initial cost is the determining factor.

Siding

Usual requirements:

Good painting characteristics, easy working qualities, freedom from warp.

Woods combining usual requirements in a high degree:

Cedars, cypress, northern white pine, sugar pine, western white pine, redwood.

Woods combining usual requirements in a good degree:

Western hemlock, ponderosa pine, spruce, yellow poplar.

Woods combining usual requirements in a fair degree:

Douglas fir, western larch, southern yellow pine.

Grades used:

Redwood and cypress are available in special siding grades of Clear Heart, and western red and Port Orford cedar in a siding grade of Clear. In other softwoods the B and Better siding is used in the highest class of construction. Siding in more economical types of construction is usually of C or D grade, but No. 1 and No. 2 are avaliable in a number of species.

Stepping (Outdoor Use)

Usual requirements:

High decay resistance, nonsplintering, good bending strength and wear resistance, freedom from warping.

Woods combining usual requirements in a high degree:

Cypress, white oak (especially when quartersawn). (Heartwood only.)

Black locust, walnut. (Usually impractical except when cut from home-grown timber.)

Woods combining usual requirements in a good degree:

Douglas fir, western larch, redwood, southern yellow pine. (Vertical-grain heartwood only.)

Woods combining usual requirements in a fair degree:

Cedar, Douglas fir, western larch, southern yellow pine. (Flat grain.)

Grades used:

C or a higher grade of softwoods and Firsts and Seconds in hardwoods are used in high-class construction. In the less costly construction, No. 1 Common in hardwoods and as low as No. 2 grade in softwoods are used. No. 1 and No. 2 grades in softwoods are serviceable but wear unevenly around knots. Dense No. 1 southern pine is sometimes used in better type homes.

Subfloors (House)

Usual requirements:

Requirements are not exacting, but high stiffness, medium shrinkage and warp, and ease of working are desired.

Woods combining usual requirements in a high degree:

Douglas fir, western larch, southern yellow pine. (Commonly used.)

Cypress, redwood, ash, yellow poplar. (Seldom used because of adaptability to more exacting uses.)

Woods combining usual requirements in a good degree:

Hemlocks, ponderosa pine, spruces, white fir. (Commonly used.)

Northern white pine, sugar pine, western white pine. (Seldom used because of adaptability to more exacting uses.)

Beech, birch, chestnut, elm, hackberry, maple, oak, tupelo. (Seldom used. Not readily available and hard to work.)

Grades used:

No. 2 boards are used extensively in higher type homes. In more economical construction both No. 2 and No. 3 are used. No. 3 is serviceable, but not so tight as No. 2. No. 4 and No. 5 are available in some species, but entail waste in cutting. When hardwoods are used, No. 2 Common is adapted to the better class houses and No. 3 Common to the more economical.

Trim (Exterior)

Usual requirements:

Medium decay resistance, good painting and weathering characteristics, easy-working qualities, maximum freedom from warp.

Woods combining usual requirements in a high degree:

Cedars, cypress, redwood. (Heartwood only. Adapted to blinds, rails, and balcony and porch trim, where decay hazard is high.)

Northern white pine, sugar pine, western white pine, yellow poplar. (Heartwood only. Adapted to ordinary trim where decay hazard is moderate or low.)

Woods for special architectural treatments:

Chestnut, white oak. (Heartwood only. Used with natural finish.)

Woods combining usual requirements in a good degree:

Hemlocks, ponderosa pine, spruces, white fir. (When drainage is good.)

Douglas fir, western larch, southern yellow pine. (Special priming treatment advisable to improve paint-holding qualities.)

Grades used:

A, B, or B and Better finish is used in the best construction, C and D finish in more economical construction, and No. 1 or No. 2 boards where appearance is not important.

Trim (Interior; with Natural Finish)

Usual requirements:

Pleasing figure, hardness, freedom from warp.

Woods combining usual requirements in a high degree:

Ash, birch, cherry, chestnut, oak, sycamore (quartered), walnut.

Woods adaptable to special selection and architectural treatment:

Pecky cypress, etched or special-grain cypress, Douglas fir, western larch, southern yellow pine, curly or bird's eye maple.

Knotty cedars, ponderosa pine, spruces, sugar pine, white pine. (Lack hardness of the preceding group.)

Woods combining usual requirements in a good degree:

Cypress, Douglas fir, western hemlock, western larch, southern yellow pine, redwood, beech, maple, red gum. (With conventional treatment.)

Grades used:

High-class hardwood interior trim is usually of A grade. The softwood grade A or B and Better is commonly used in high-class construction. In the more economical types of construction C grade is serviceable. D grade requires special selection or some cutting to obtain clear material. Special grades of knotty pine, pecky cypress, and sound wormy oak and chestnut are available to meet special architectural requirements in some types of high-class construction.

Trim (Interior; with Paint Finish)

Usual requirements:

Fine and uniform texture, hardness, absence of discoloring pitch, freedom from warp and shrinkage.

Woods combining usual requirements in a high degree:

Birch, cherry, walnut, yellow poplar.

Northern white pine, ponderosa pine, sugar pine, western white pine. (Where liability to marring is negligible and special priming is used.)

Woods combining usual requirements in a good degree:

Hemlocks, redwood, spruce, white fir.

Basswood, beech, red gum, maple, tupelo.

Cypress, Douglas fir, western larch, southern yellow pine, ash, chestnut, oak. (Used satisfactorily where requirements for smoothness of finish are not exacting.)

Grades used:

C is the lowest softwood grade commonly used for high-class paint and enamel finish. D can be used but requires some selection or cutting. No. 1 is used for ordinary or rough-paint finishes. In cheaper and more economical homes No. 2 may be used for ordinary or rough-paint finishes. Smooth-paint finishes are difficult to obtain and maintain over knots in No. 1, No. 2, and No. 3 grades. The A trim grade in the hardwoods is used for exacting requirements of high-class paint and enamel finish in high-cost homes. The standard grade of Firsts and Seconds is also used but requires some selection or cutting. No. 2 Common hardwoods are used for interior trim in the low-cost home, but in this class of home softwoods are generally used for the interior trim that is to be painted.

GRADING OF LUMBER

GENERAL INFORMATION

1. Purposes of Grading Lumber—The purpose of grading is to classify lumber in accordance with certain established and accepted standards, so that the consumer will be assured of a standard product.

2. Accuracy of Grading — Lumber is graded by visual inspection, only; therefore, the judgment of the grader plays an important role. It is estimated, however, that the results of any group of careful and competent graders would coincide, within 5%.

3. Surfaces Graded—With the exception of "dimension" material, the grade of yard lumber (when rough or surfaced on two sides) is determined from the better, or "face", side of the piece. When surfaced on one side only, however, lumber is graded from that side.

4. Defects and Blemishes — Defects or blemishes which are not described in the standard grading rules are considered according to a comparison with known defects, and are graded on a basis of the damaging effect upon the piece of lumber being graded.

5. Edge and Flat Grain—When the angle between the surface of the lumber and the rings (grain) is 45° or more, the material is considered "edge" grain. If the angle is less than 45° at any point, the material is known as "flat" (slash) grain (Fig. 1, P. 104).

CLASSIFICATION OF LUMBER

6. General—Lumber is classified according to its principal uses, which are: Yard lumber, structural timber, and factory or shop lumber. Practically all the lumber used in house construction is yard lumber.

7. Yard Lumber—Yard lumber is less than 5″ in thickness and is intended to be used for general building purposes. Unlike factory or shop lumber, it is graded upon the use of the entire piece. The classification of yard lumber by dimensions is as follows:

Strips—Strips are less than 2″ thick, and not 8″ wide.

Boards—Boards are less than 2″ thick, and 8″ or more in width.

Dimension—This consists of all yard lumber with the exception of boards, strips, and timbers. Yard lumber which is between 2″ and 5″ thick, and of any width, comes under the classification of dimension:

(a) Planks are yard lumber of 2″ and less than 4″ in thickness, and 8″ or over in width.

(b) Scantlings are yard lumber of 2″ and under 5″ in thickness, and less than 8″ wide.

(c) Heavy joists are yard lumber 4″ and less than 6″ in thickness, and 8″ or over in width.

8. Key to Grade Classification—Table 2 will serve as a key to the American Lumber Standards.

TABLE 1.—*Standard Dimension Lumber Sizes*[1]

Nominal Size in Inches	American Standard Dressed Size in Inches	Nominal Size in Inches	American Standard Dressed Size in Inches
2 by 4	1⅝ by 3⅝	3 by 6	2⅝ by 5⅝
2 by 6	1⅝ by 5⅝	3 by 8	2⅝ by 7½
2 by 8	1⅝ by 7½	3 by 10	2⅝ by 9½
2 by 10	1⅝ by 9½	3 by 12	2⅝ by 11½
2 by 12	1⅝ by 11½	3 by 14	2⅝ by 13½
2 by 14	1⅝ by 13½		

[1]Dimension lumber is used for joists, studs, rafters, plates, and girders.

TABLE 2.—*Basic Grade Classification for Yard Lumber*

Total products of a typical log arranged in series according to quality as determined by appearance.	Select—Lumber of good appearance and finishing qualities.	Suitable for natural finishes.	Grade A—Practically free from defects. Grade B—Allows a few small defects or blemishes.
		Suitable for paint finishes.	Grade C—Allows a limited number of small defects or blemishes which can be covered with paint. Grade D—Allows any number of defects or blemishes which do not detract from a finish appearance, especially when painted.
	Common—Lumber containing defects or blemishes which detract from a finish appearance but which is suitable for general utility and construction purposes.	Lumber suitable for use without waste.	No. 1 Common—Sound and tight knotted stock. Size of defects and blemishes limited. May be considered watertight lumber. No. 2 Common—Allows large and coarse defects. May be considered grain-tight lumber.
		Lumber permitting waste.	No. 3 Common—Allows larger and coarser defects than No. 2 and occasional knot holes. No. 4 Common—Low-quality lumber admitting the coarsest defects such as decay and holes. No. 5 Common—Must hold together under ordinary handling.

GRADE MARKING

9. Definition—Grade marking consists of stamping each piece of lumber at the mill where it is graded, with certain standard symbols which indicate the species and grade of the lumber. Also, more often than not, the name of the manufacturer and association under which it is graded is stamped on the lumber.

10. Cost of Grade Marking — According to Ref. R24-9, Sec. 38, the cost of grade marking lumber is negligible, varying from 1½ to 3 cents per thousand feet.

11. Advantages to Consumer—The advantages of grade marking is all-important to the consumer, as it is his assurance that he is getting what he has specified and contracted to pay for. Therefore, make sure that the mill furnishing lumber for your home grade marks each piece in accordance with standard practice. As pointed out in Par. 10, the extra cost to the mill is negligible.

12. Selection of Grade—See Par. 3, P. 116.

13. Grading Rules—Grading rules and "Grade-Use Guides" are issued by S9, S22, S30, S32, S36, S37, S38, S42, S47, S48, S53, and S54 listed in Table 2 of Sec. 38.

HOUSE FRAMING METHODS

GENERAL DISCUSSION

1. Types of House Framing—There are three recognized types of house framing in use to-day. These are: (1) The platform frame (Fig. 1). (2) The modern braced frame (Fig. 2). (3) The modern balloon frame (Pls. 10 and 11). Each type of frame has good and bad features which will be discussed.

2. Methods Usually Followed—Due to a lack of popular knowledge on the subject, most home builders fail to furnish the contractor with adequate detail framing drawings. This often results in the house being framed in accordance with the frail and undesirable methods long established as "standard" for the community by the lower grade of contractors, with whom the better type of contractor must compete.

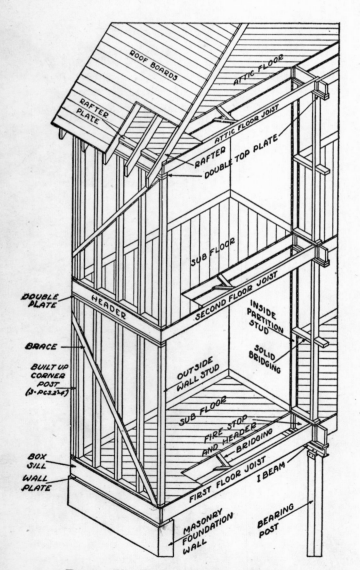

FIG. 1.—*The Platform Frame Construction*

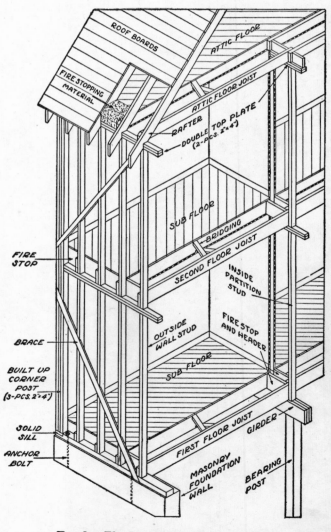

FIG. 2.—*The Braced Frame Construction*

Such framing usually consists of a conglomeration of several types of framing, with many of the bad features of each type retained, and many of the good features omitted.

3. Results of Faulty Framing—The harmful results of faulty framing are too numerous to list. For a few results, see Par. 1, P. 65.

4. Features Desired—The most important features desired in a house frame are: (1) Strength and rigidity. (2) Ample fire stopping. (3) Equalized shrinkage. (4) Moderate cost.

THE PLATFORM FRAME

5. Advantages—The platform frame, if constructed in the *approved* manner shown by Fig. 1, will have an uniform or equalized shrinkage at each floor, and also moderate fire stopping qualities.

6. Disadvantages—The chief disadvantages are as follows:

Excessive Total Shrinkage—The total shrinkage of the framework, in height, may be several inches. See Fig. 2, P. 105.

Unsuited for Brick Veneer or Stucco Construction—If such frames are used inside of a veneering of brick or stucco, there is sure to be trouble at windows, doors, wall ties, etc., due to the excessive shrinkage of the wooden frame.

Sheathing Must be Horizontal—Diagonal sheathing (which is much stronger than horizontal sheathing) cannot be used on account of the harmful effect of the excessive shrinkage on the nailing, wall ties, etc.

Cutting for Pipes, Etc.—In order to pass pipes, etc., up the outside walls, it is necessary to cut away the second floor members, and thus weaken the framework considerably.

Weak—On account of the studs being in two pieces throughout the framework, the platform frame is weaker than the other two types.

Cost—The cost of this frame is greater than that of balloon framing.

THE MODERN BRACED FRAME

7. Advantages—The modern braced frame, if constructed in the so-called "approved" manner shown by Fig. 2, will fulfill nearly all of the requirements outlined in Par. 4, *provided* that a steel girder is substituted for the wooden girder shown (to prevent the center of the house from settling), and *provided* that fire stopping is used as shown by Pl. 10.

8. Disadvantages—The chief disadvantages are:

Somewhat Weak — Although continuous corner posts and diagonal sheathing make this framing far stronger and more rigid than the platform type, it is still weaker than the balloon type framing on account of the outside wall studs being in two pieces.

Cutting for Pipes, Etc.—Same as for the Platform Frame.

Cost—This frame costs more to erect than does the balloon or platform frames.

THE MODERN BALLOON FRAME

9. Advantages—The modern balloon frame, if constructed as shown by Pls. 10 or 11, meets every requirement outlined in Par. 4.

10. Disadvantages—The floor plan of the house (arrangement of rooms) must be such as to allow the center bearing partition to be continuous from the steel supporting girder to the bottom of the uppermost joists (Pls. 10 or 11).

SELECTING TYPE OF FRAME

11. Type Recommended—This Guide recommends the use of the minimum-shrinkage type modern balloon frame, as shown by Pl. 10, for houses with brick veneer exteriors. For all other types of frame houses where the frame and exterior side walls may safely move up and down in relation to the foundation (due to variation of moisture content of wood), the type of modern balloon frame shown by Pl. 11 is recommended, as it is somewhat more economical to construct. For houses with exterior walls of masonry, the type of construction shown by Pl. 7, Figs. 1 to 3, is recommended.

It should be noted, however, that if the above recommended types of framing are used, the house selected must be so designed that the center bearing partition may be constructed as shown by Pls. 7, 10, or 11. If the recommended types of framing are not adaptable for framing the house you have selected, the type of framing used should at least be designed and constructed in such a manner as to provide equalized shrinkage to the greatest extent practicable.

HOUSE FRAMING DETAILS

GENERAL RECOMMENDATIONS

1. Detail Construction—The completed framework of a house can be no better than the quality of its component parts known as framing "details". It is recommended, therefore, that each detail be constructed in a workmanlike manner from good, sound material by first-class workmen.

2. Materials—Suitable materials are listed under Par. 19, P. 108. Consult with your architect or a reputable local lumber mill to ascertain what species are available locally, and at what comparative prices. Ref. R24-5, Sec. 38, will also be helpful when selecting suitable materials.

3. Grades—A suitable grade of material is indicated by this Guide for most items (see the following Pars. and Sec. 25, P. 129). However, after selecting the species of wood, it is well to refer to the "Lumber Grade-Use Guide" issued by the association having jurisdiction over the wood selected (Par. 13, P. 113). Such bulletins contain much valuable information, including photographs of various grades of the particular species covered by the bulletin. These bulletins should be available for inspection at a better-class mill; also, the mill can furnish the home builder with samples and comparative prices of various grades.

SILLS

4. Definition—Sills are timbers that rest upon the foundation wall and form a support, or bearing surface, for the superstructure of the building (see Pls. 10 and 11). Sills are usually omitted for the exterior walls of masonry houses (Pl. 7, Figs. 1 and 2).

5. Size—Use 2″ x 6″ sills under 2″ x 4″ studs, and 2″ x 8″ sills under 2″ x 6″ studs, for type of construction shown by Pls. 10 or 11. For use over piers, as is customary in warm climates, sill should be calculated as a girder (Par. 22); and should in no case be less than a 6″ x 8″ member, used on edge.

6. Material (General)—As it would be difficult and expensive (if not impossible) to replace a decayed or termite infested sill, the material for sills should be chosen for permanency.

7. Material (Normal Conditions)—A suitable wood, such as southern yellow pine (dense), Douglas fir (dense), redwood, cypress, etc., may be selected from Table 1, P. 106.

8. Grade (Normal Conditions)—Sills supported by continuous foundation walls may be No. 1 common, dense heart grade. Sills supported by piers may be of a dense structural heart grade.

9. Material (Abnormal Conditions) — All sills exposed to dampness and decay (such as sills of wooden porches) should be made from untreated wood of a naturally durable species, or from treated wood of a less durable species.

10. Grade (Abnormal Conditions)—Grade should be the same as for "Normal Conditions" (Par. 8) except that, for treated wood, the wood should *not* be dense *heart*, as the preservative will penetrate sapwood to a much greater depth.

11. Painting Bottom of Sill—This is recommended for untreated sills, to prevent dampness from entering the wood, insofar as possible. Hot pitch, aluminum paint, or white lead and linseed oil are suitable.

12. Grouting—It is essential that the sill has a *full, uniform* bearing on the foundation to prevent settlement. This is best accomplished by the use of cement mortar or "grout".

13. Anchor Bolts—All authorities recommend the use of anchor bolts. See Pls. 10 or 11.

GIRDERS

14. Definition—A girder, as used in house construction, is a large beam used at the first story line to support the inner ends of the floor joists. See Pls. 7, 10, 11 and 13.

15. Where Needed—Where the width of the building is greater than 14 feet, and it is not desirable to use an interior foundation wall (Pls. 10 or 11, Fig. 3), a girder should be used for furnishing additional support near the center, thus making the use of excessively large joists unnecessary. See Pl. 13, Figs. 4 to 6.

16. Girders for House With Full Basement — For such houses, a girder supported on columns is recommended, so as to eliminate all interior foundation walls that are not expressly desired. See Pl. 7, Fig. 3; Pls. 10 and 11; and Pl. 13, Figs. 4 to 6.

17. Girder for House With Half Basement or No Basement—For such houses, the girder may be supported on masonry piers as indicated by Pls. 10 and 11, Item 26; or the girder may be eliminated, and the type of construction shown by Pls. 10 and 11, Fig. 3, may be used. The latter type, although somewhat more expensive, is more substantial.

18. Types of Girders — There are two principal types. These are: Wood girders and steel girders.

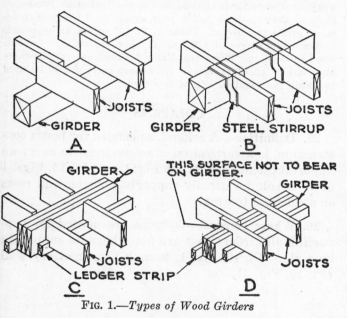

FIG. 1.—*Types of Wood Girders*

19. Wood Girders—Wood girders are not recommended, on account of their resultant harmful shrinkage. However, if used, the wood should be exceptionally well seasoned so as to minimize shrinkage. To insure proper seasoning and to guard against hidden defects, the girder should be built-up of several pieces. The recommendations of Pars. 6 to 10 should be reviewed when making selection, as such recommendations are applicable to girders, as well as to sills. Wood girders may be constructed in several ways as follows:

Joists over top of Girder—See Fig. 1, A. This girder will shrink and cause the center portion of house to settle.

Joists in Stirrups—See Fig. 1, B. Such construction allows for more headroom, but this girder will

also shrink and cause the center portion of house to settle.

Joists over Ledger Strips—See Fig. 1, C. This construction also allows for more headroom, but the joists have insufficient bearing areas due to thinness of ledger strips. It is difficult to notch the joists as shown and secure a good bearing at all points, and the joists and girder are very likely to develop cracks.

Joists Notched over Girder—See Fig. 1, D. This construction has the combined disadvantages of shrinkage and weakness.

20. Steel Girders — Where a girder is required (Par. 15), a steel I-beam is recommended, inasmuch as steel girders have the advantage of strength combined with minimum shrinkage.

21. Type of Construction—It is recommended that the girder always be placed *under* the joists (Pl. 13, Figs. 5 and 6), as this is the safest and most substantial method.

22. Determining Girder Size—The total *uniformly distributed* load imposed upon the girder *between supports* must first be determined. The proper girder size can then be selected from the Tables 1 to 5, depending upon the material used. In order to save headroom, the depth of the girder should preferably not exceed 10″, with 12″ being the maximum. Therefore, to conserve on depth of beam, it may be necessary to use a heavier (or wider) beam and space supporting columns, or piers, closer together.

(a) DETERMINING LOADS ON GIRDERS—The loads on the average, simple girder may be determined as outlined below. (For more complex conditions, see Ref. R11-6, Sec. 38, which discusses various types of girders in detail.)

First Step—Using Fig. 3, P. 92, as a guide, determine for each floor the *length of joist spans* that are to be supported by the girder. For the first floor it is equal to the sum of A/2 + B/2, or in other words, to one-half the total distance from center line of girder measured both ways to the next girder, basement bearing partition, or foundation wall, except when joists are *continuous* (not broken and lapped) over this girder, and broken over nearest support on each side, in which case, it is equal to ⅝ this total distance, (see Fig. 2). Use the same method for second and third floors, also for the roof when part of the roof's weight is to be supported by the girder through a bearing partition, struts, etc.

Second Step—Multiply the load per square foot, as indicated by Fig. 3, P. 92, for each of these floors and roof by the various spans, including 20 lbs. per square foot of floor area for first and second story partitions.

Third Step—Decide upon the length of girder span (distance between columns). Relatively close spacing of the columns will result in three advantages: (1) Smaller girder. (2) Smaller columns. (3) Less load on column footings.

A good average span is about 8 feet (Par. 31).

Fourth Step—Multiply the load per linear foot on girder by the span of girder in feet to obtain the total uniformly distributed load imposed upon the girder between supports.

(b) EXAMPLE OF SELECTING GIRDER SIZE—Referring to Fig. 3, P. 92, assume that the length of joist spans (A/2 + B/2) supported by the girder is 12 feet for all floors and zero feet for the dimension "H" of the roof (roof bracing omitted). Using these dimensions and data given by Fig. 3, P. 92, a typical example is as follows:

		lbs.
First floor plus partitions..........	70 lbs. per sq. ft. x 12 ft.=	840
Second floor plus partitions........	80 lbs. per sq. ft. x 12 ft.=	960
Attic floor, not floored................	30 lbs. per sq. ft. x 12 ft.=	360
Total load per linear foot of girder length.............=		2160

Now, assuming a girder span of 8 feet between columns or supports, the uniformly distributed load upon the girder between supports would be 2160 lbs. x 8 = 17,280 lbs.

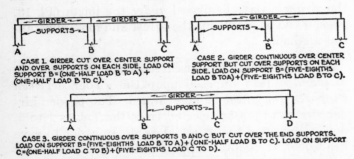

FIG. 2.—*Distribution of Loads on Columns*

23. Selecting Steel Girder Size — Having determined the uniformly distributed load on the girder (Par. 22), the size of the girder, if made from a steel I-beam, may be selected from Table 1. The lightest weight for a given depth is the strongest I-beam for the amount of material used.

24. Selecting Wood Girder Size—This procedure is divided into the following two steps, after the uniformly distributed load on the girder has been determined (Par. 22):

First Step—Select the species and grade of wood to be used, and ascertain from Table 2, P. 107, the allowable stress for the wood selected.

Second Step—Refer to Tables 2 to 5, and select the girder from the table that is based on the same (or next smaller) working stress as that allowed for the wood selected. Example: Suppose that southern yellow pine, dense No. 1 common structural grade is selected. Table 2, P. 107, gives an allowable unit working stress of 1,200 pounds per square inch for this wood in bending. Therefore, Table 4, based on an "allowable fiber stress" of 1,200 pounds per square inch, should be used to obtain the required size of this girder.

COLUMNS

25. Definition—A column, as defined for house construction, is a vertical member designed to carry an important load. See Pl. 10, Fig. 1, and Pl. 13, Figs. 1 to 3. A column usually supports a girder and rests on a concrete footing.

26. Where Needed—Columns are needed for supporting all girders that are not otherwise supported by a pier (Pl. 10, Fig. 1, Item 26), or masonry wall (Pl. 10, Fig. 3).

TABLE 1.—*Steel I-beam Girders—Safe loads in thousands of pounds uniformly distributed*

[Standard I-beams. Allowable fiber stress 18,000 pounds]

Span in Feet	4 Inches Deep by—				5 Inches Deep by—			6 Inches Deep by—			7 Inches Deep by—			8 Inches Deep by—				9 Inches Deep by—			
	7.7	8.5	9.5	10.5	10.0	12.25	14.75	12.5	14.75	17.25	15.3	17.5	20.0	18.4	20.5	23.0	25.5	21.8	25.0	30.0	35.0
4.........	9.0	9.5	10.1	10.7	14.5	16.2	18.0	21.8	23.8	26.0	31.0	33.4	36.0	42.7	45.2	48.2	51.1	56.6	60.9	67.6	74.2
5.........	7.2	7.6	8.0	8.5	11.6	13.0	14.4	17.4	19.0	20.8	24.8	26.7	28.7	34.1	36.1	38.5	40.9	45.3	48.7	54.1	59.4
6.........	6.0	6.3	6.7	7.1	9.7	10.8	12.0	14.5	15.9	17.3	20.7	22.2	24.0	28.5	30.1	32.1	34.1	37.7	40.6	45.1	49.5
7.........	5.1	5.4	5.7	6.1	8.3	9.3	10.3	12.5	13.6	14.9	17.7	19.1	20.5	24.4	25.8	27.5	29.2	32.3	34.8	38.6	42.4
8.........	4.5	4.7	5.0	5.3	7.3	8.1	9.0	10.9	11.9	13.0	15.5	16.7	18.0	21.3	22.6	24.1	25.5	28.3	30.5	33.8	37.1
9.........	4.0	4.2	4.5	4.7	6.5	7.2	8.0	9.7	10.6	11.6	13.8	14.8	16.0	19.0	20.1	21.4	22.7	25.2	27.1	30.0	33.0
10.........	3.6	3.8	4.0	4.3	5.8	6.5	7.2	8.7	9.5	10.4	12.4	13.3	14.4	17.1	18.1	19.3	20.4	22.6	24.4	27.0	29.7
11.........					5.3	5.9	6.5	7.9	8.7	9.5	11.3	12.1	13.1	15.5	16.4	17.5	18.6	20.6	22.2	24.6	27.0
12.........								7.3	7.9	8.7	10.3	11.1	12.0	14.2	15.1	16.1	17.0	18.9	20.3	22.5	24.7

NOTE.—If the reading in the table above is 12.4, the safe load is 12,400 pounds.

Example: If the total load on the girder is 13,500 pounds uniformly distributed and the span or distance between basement piers is 9 feet, then a 7-inch by 15.3-pound I-beam is the proper size to use, for by the table it will carry 13,800 pounds (13.8 in the table). This figure will be found on the line of 9-foot span and in the 15.3-pound column of the 7-inch beam.

These figures are taken from A. I. S. C. Manual.

(*Reprinted from Reference R11-6, Sec. 38*)

SOLID WOOD GIRDERS[1]

(Allowable Uniformly Distributed Loads for Solid Wood Girders and Beams in Pounds Computed for Actual Dressed Sizes)

TABLE 2.—*Allowable fiber stress 1,600 pounds per square inch; modulus of elasticity, E—1,600,000*

Solid Dressed Sizes	Span in Feet					
	4, 5, 6,	7	8	9	10	11
3 by 6	2,435					
4 by 6	3,366					
6 by 6	4,885					
2 by 8	2,145	2,145	2,016			
3 by 8	3,460	3,460	3,233			
4 by 8	4,770	4,770	4,470			
6 by 8	7,260	7,260	6,783			
8 by 8	9,880	9,880	9,247			
2 by 10	2,700	2,700	2,700	2,700	2,564	
3 by 10	4,370	4,370	4,370	4,370	4,139	
4 by 10	6,035	6,035	6,035	6,035	5,719	
6 by 10	9,160	9,160	9,160	9,160	8,680	
8 by 10	12,500	12,500	12,500	12,500	11,835	
10 by 10	15,805	15,805	15,805	15,805	14,992	
2 by 12	3,265	3,265	3,265	3,265	3,265	3,265
3 by 12	5,260	5,260	5,260	5,260	5,260	5,260
4 by 12	7,270	7,270	7,270	7,270	7,270	7,270
6 by 12	11,050	11,050	11,050	11,050	11,050	11,050
8 by 12	15,050	15,050	15,050	15,050	15,050	15,050
10 by 12	19,080	19,080	19,080	19,080	19,080	19,080
12 by 12	23,130	23,130	23,130	23,130	23,130	23,130
2 by 14	4,115	4,115	4,115	4,115	4,115	4,115
3 by 14	6,165	6,165	6,165	6,165	6,165	6,165
4 by 14	8,510	8,510	8,510	8,510	8,510	8,510
6 by 14	12,930	12,930	12,930	12,930	12,930	12,930
8 by 14	17,630	17,630	17,630	17,630	17,630	17,630
10 by 14	22,335	22,335	22,335	22,335	22,335	22,335
12 by 14	27,040	27,040	27,040	27,040	27,040	27,040
14 by 14	31,760	31,760	31,760	31,760	31,760	31,760

TABLE 4.—*Allowable fiber stress 1,200 pounds per square inch*

Solid Dressed Sizes	Span in Feet					
	4, 5, 6,	7	8	9	10	11
2 by 6	1,127	961	837			
3 by 6	1,820	1,552	1,351			
4 by 6	2,514	2,144	1,866			
6 by 6	3,650	3,111	2,708			
2 by 8	1,605	1,605	1,503	1,331	1,191	1,075
3 by 8	2,580	2,580	2,414	2,135	1,911	1,726
4 by 8	3,570	3,570	3,340	2,953	2,643	2,388
6 by 8	5,420	5,420	5,064	4,481	4,011	3,625
8 by 8	7,390	7,390	6,905	6,110	5,464	4,941
2 by 10	2,020	2,020	2,020	2,020	1,912	1,730
3 by 10	3,255	3,255	3,255	3,255	3,088	2,792
4 by 10	4,500	4,500	4,500	4,500	4,267	3,864
6 by 10	6,830	6,830	6,830	6,830	6,473	5,860
8 by 10	9,320	9,320	9,320	9,320	8,827	7,980
10 by 10	11,795	11,795	11,795	11,795	11,181	10,110
2 by 12	2,435	2,435	2,435	2,435	2,435	2,435
3 by 12	3,920	3,920	3,920	3,920	3,920	3,920
4 by 12	5,430	5,430	5,430	5,430	5,430	5,430
6 by 12	8,250	8,250	8,250	8,250	8,250	8,250
8 by 12	11,240	11,240	11,240	11,240	11,240	11,240
10 by 12	14,250	14,250	14,250	14,250	14,250	14,250
12 by 12	17,240	17,240	17,240	17,240	17,240	17,240
2 by 14	3,065	3,065	3,065	3,065	3,065	3,065
3 by 14	4,600	4,600	4,600	4,600	4,600	4,600
4 by 14	6,340	6,340	6,340	6,340	6,340	6,340
6 by 14	9,630	9,630	9,630	9,630	9,630	9,630
8 by 14	13,140	13,140	13,140	13,140	13,140	13,140
10 by 14	16,640	16,640	16,640	16,640	16,640	16,640
12 by 14	20,140	20,140	20,140	20,140	20,140	20,140
14 by 14	23,640	23,640	23,640	23,640	23,640	23,640

TABLE 3.—*Allowable fiber stress 1,400 pounds per square inch*

Solid Dressed Sizes	Span in Feet					
	4, 5, 6,	7	8	9	10	11
2 by 6	1,318	1,124				
3 by 6	2,127	1,816				
4 by 6	2,938	2,507				
6 by 6	4,263	3,638				
2 by 8	1,865	1,865	1,760	1,558		
3 by 8	3,020	3,020	2,824	2,500		
4 by 8	4,165	4,165	3,904	3,456		
6 by 8	6,330	6,330	5,924	5,244		
8 by 8	8,630	8,630	8,078	7,151		
2 by 10	2,360	2,360	2,360	2,360	2,237	2,026
3 by 10	3,810	3,810	3,810	3,810	3,612	3,271
4 by 10	5,265	5,265	5,265	5,265	4,992	4,520
6 by 10	7,990	7,990	7,990	7,990	7,576	6,860
8 by 10	10,920	10,920	10,920	10,920	10,330	9,352
10 by 10	13,825	13,825	13,825	13,825	13,085	11,849
2 by 12	2,845	2,845	2,845	2,845	2,845	2,845
3 by 12	4,590	4,590	4,590	4,590	4,590	4,590
4 by 12	6,350	6,350	6,350	6,350	6,350	6,350
6 by 12	9,640	9,640	9,640	9,640	9,640	9,640
8 by 12	13,160	13,160	13,160	13,160	13,160	13,160
10 by 12	16,670	16,670	16,670	16,670	16,670	16,670
12 by 12	20,170	20,170	20,170	20,170	20,170	20,170
2 by 14	3,595	3,595	3,595	3,595	3,595	3,595
3 by 14	5,365	5,365	5,365	5,365	5,365	5,365
4 by 14	7,420	7,420	7,420	7,420	7,420	7,420
6 by 14	11,290	11,290	11,290	11,290	11,290	11,290
8 by 14	15,360	15,360	15,360	15,360	15,360	15,360
10 by 14	19,465	19,465	19,465	19,465	19,465	19,465
12 by 14	23,590	23,590	23,590	23,590	23,590	23,590
14 by 14	27,690	27,690	27,690	27,690	27,690	27,690

TABLE 5.—*Allowable fiber stress 900 pounds per square inch*

Solid Dressed Sizes	Span in Feet					
	4, 5, 6,	7	8	9	10	11
2 by 6	842	717	623	548	489	439
3 by 6	1,359	1,159	1,005	884	788	708
4 by 6	1,877	1,600	1,390	1,223	1,089	980
6 by 6	2,723	2,319	2,013	1,773	1,579	1,430
2 by 8	1,195	1,195	1,123	991	885	796
3 by 8	1,928	1,928	1,801	1,589	1,419	1,278
4 by 8	2,666	2,666	2,488	2,198	1,963	1,770
6 by 8	4,045	4,045	3,781	3,335	2,980	2,687
8 by 8	5,515	5,515	5,148	4,547	4,062	3,663
2 by 10	1,504	1,504	1,504	1,504	1,423	1,286
3 by 10	2,428	2,428	2,428	2,428	2,296	2,074
4 by 10	3,357	3,357	3,357	3,357	3,174	2,864
6 by 10	5,095	5,095	5,095	5,095	4,818	4,352
8 by 10	6,947	6,947	6,947	6,947	6,570	5,933
10 by 10	8,800	8,800	8,800	8,800	8,523	7,518
2 by 12	1,812	1,812	1,812	1,812	1,812	1,812
3 by 12	2,918	2,918	2,918	2,918	2,918	2,918
4 by 12	4,038	4,038	4,038	4,038	4,038	4,038
6 by 12	6,130	6,130	6,130	6,130	6,130	6,130
8 by 12	8,360	8,360	8,360	8,360	8,360	8,360
10 by 12	10,595	10,595	10,595	10,595	10,595	10,595
12 by 12	12,822	12,822	12,822	12,822	12,822	12,822
2 by 14	2,278	2,278	2,278	2,278	2,278	2,278
3 by 14	3,409	3,409	3,409	3,409	3,409	3,409
4 by 14	4,717	4,717	4,717	4,717	4,717	4,717
6 by 14	7,157	7,157	7,157	7,157	7,157	7,157
8 by 14	9,751	9,751	9,751	9,751	9,751	9,751
10 by 14	12,365	12,365	12,365	12,365	12,365	12,365
12 by 14	14,965	14,965	14,965	14,965	14,965	14,965
14 by 14	17,567	17,567	17,567	17,567	17,567	17,567

[1]Built-up girders are computed as follows:

Multiply above figures by 0.897 when 4-inch girder is made up of two 2-inch pieces.
.887 when 6-inch girder is made up of three 2-inch pieces.
.867 when 8-inch girder is made up of four 2-inch pieces.
.856 when 10-inch girder is made up of five 2-inch pieces.

(Built-up girders of dressed lumber will carry somewhat smaller loads than solid girders, that is, two 2-inch dressed planks will equal only 3¼, whereas dressed 4-inch lumber will equal 3⅝. It is, therefore, necessary to multiply by the above figures in order to compute the loads for built-up girders.)

(Reprinted from Reference R11-6, Sec. 38)

27. Types of Columns — Several types are shown by Pl. 13, Figs. 1 to 3. The type shown by Pl. 13, Fig. 1, is recommended.

28. Steel Columns — Steel columns are recommended, as they have the advantage of being fireproof, shrink-proof, and less subject to deterioration (if properly painted). Steel pipe columns are preferable from a standpoint of appearance, lack of projecting sharp edges, and low cost.

29. Wood Columns—Wood columns, if used, should not be less than 6″ x 6″ in size; and should be of type of construction shown by Pl. 13, Fig. 3.

30. Masonry Columns (Piers)—See Sec. 16, P. 94.

31. Spacing—A spacing of about 8 feet is recommended. This spacing may vary but should not exceed 10 feet. A spacing of less than 8 feet will make it possible to use a smaller girder, lighter columns, and smaller footings.

32. Determining Column Size — The column size may readily be determined as follows:

First Step—Decide upon column spacing (Par. 31).

Second Step—Determine load on column as follows: Determine the length of girder span that is supported by column. (This is equal to one-half of the girder span on each side of the center of column, except when girder is continuous over this column, and broken over the column or bearing wall on each side, in which case, it is equal to ⅝ of the girder span on each side of the center of column. For example, refer to Fig. 2.) Multiply the *length* of this span, in feet, by the load *per linear foot* on girder (Par. 22, "First Step" and "Second Step"), and the product thus obtained will be the total load on the column.

Third Step—Decide upon the material for column.

Fourth Step—Ascertain height of column. (Refer to your house plans.)

Fifth Step—Knowing the load, material, and height of columns, the proper size may be selected from Tables 6 to 11.

TABLE 6.—*Steel Pipe Columns—Standard Pipe*

(Safe Loads in Thousands of Pounds)

Nominal size, inches.....	5	4½	4	3½	3	2½	2
External diameter, inches.	5.563	5.000	4.500	4.000	3.500	2.875	2.375
Thickness, inches........	.258	.247	.237	.226	.216	.203	.154
Effective length:							
5 feet...............	55.9	48.0	41.2	34.8	29.0	21.6	12.2
6 feet...............	55.9	48.0	41.2	34.8	28.6	19.4	10.6
7 feet...............	55.9	48.0	41.2	34.1	26.3	17.3	9.0
8 feet...............	55.9	48.0	40.1	31.7	24.0	15.1	7.4
9 feet...............	55.9	46.4	37.6	29.3	21.7	12.9	6.6
10 feet..............	54.2	43.8	35.1	26.9	19.4	11.4	5.8
Area in square inches....	4.30	3.69	3.17	2.68	2.23	1.70	1.08
Weight per pound per foot.	14.62	12.54	10.79	9.11	7.58	5.79	3.65

Allowable fiber stress per square inch, 13,000 pounds for lengths of 60 radii or under, reduced for length over 60 radii.

TABLE 7.—*Steel I-beam Columns—American Standard Sections*
(Safe Loads in Thousands of Pounds)

Depth in inches.................	8	7	6	5	4	3
Weight per pound per foot.......	18.4	15.3	12.5	10.0	7.7	5.7
Effective length:						
3 feet................	80.1	66.5	54.2	43.1	33.0	23.5
4 feet................	80.1	65.9	52.1	39.7	29.1	20.3
5 feet................	74.9	60.0	46.9	35.1	25.3	17.2
6 feet................	68.3	54.1	41.8	30.7	21.8	14.6
7 feet................	61.8	48.5	37.0	26.8	18.7	12.3
8 feet................	55.7	43.3	32.7	23.4	16.1	10.5
9 feet................	50.1	38.6	28.9	20.4	13.9	.....
10 feet................	45.0	34.5	25.5	17.9	.....	.....
Area in square inches...........	5.34	4.43	3.61	2.87	2.21	1.64

Safe loads in accordance with A. I. S. C. column formula, maximum 15,000 pounds for lengths of 60 radii and under.

WOOD COLUMNS

(Maximum Allowance Loads in Pounds)

TABLE 8.—*For Douglas fir, southern pine, and North Carolina pine, No. 1 common grade*

Nominal size, inches........	4 by 6	6 by 6	6 by 8	8 by 8
Actual size, inches.........	3⅝ by 5⅝	5½ by 5½	5½ by 7½	7½ by 7½
Area in square inches.......	20.39	30.25	41.25	56.25
Height of column:				
4 feet...............	19,850	30,250	41,250	56,250
5 feet...............	19,200	30,050	41,000	56,250
6 feet...............	17,950	29,500	40,260	56,250
6 feet 6 inches............	16,850	29,300	39,950	56,000
7 feet...............	15,550	29,000	39,600	55,650
7 feet 6 inches............	14,400	28,800	39,000	55,300
8 feet...............	12,950	28,150	38,300	55,000
9 feet...............	10,100	26,850	36,600	54,340
10 feet...............	....	24,670	33,600	53,400

TABLE 9.—*For red cypress and redwood, No. 1 common grade*

Nominal size, inches........	4 by 6	6 by 6	6 by 8	8 by 8
Actual size, inches.........	3⅝ by 5⅝	5½ by 5½	5½ by 7½	7½ by 7½
Area in square inches.......	20.39	30.25	41.25	56.25
Height of column:				
4 feet...............	17,410	26,620	36,300	49,500
5 feet...............	16,480	26,440	36,050	49,500
6 feet...............	14,800	25,860	35,270	49,500
6 feet 6 inches............	13,580	25,500	34,770	49,330
7 feet...............	12,210	25,050	34,150	49,050
7 feet 6 inches............	10,930	24,500	33,410	48,660
8 feet...............	9,620	23,960	32,620	48,260
9 feet...............	7,560	22,260	30,360	47,250
10 feet...............	....	19,810	27,020	45,960

TABLE 10—*For tamarack and west coast hemlock, No. 1 common grade*

Nominal size, inches........	4 by 6	6 by 6	6 by 8	8 by 8
Actual size, inches.........	3⅝ by 5⅝	5½ by 5½	5½ by 7½	7½ by 7½
Area in square inches.......	20.39	30.25	41.25	56.25
Height of column:				
4 feet...............	14,500	21,780	29,700	40,500
5 feet...............	14,110	21,720	29,620	40,500
6 feet...............	13,480	21,510	29,330	40,500
6 feet 6 inches............	13,070	21,360	29,130	40,440
7 feet...............	12,480	21,170	28,870	40,330
7 feet 6 inches............	11,790	20,960	28,590	40,220
8 feet...............	10,870	20,750	28,300	40,050
9 feet...............	8,810	20,120	27,430	39,660
10 feet...............	....	19,240	26,230	39,150

TABLE 11.—*For eastern hemlock, western red cedar, white fir, the white pines, and spruces (red, white, and Sitka), No. 1 common grade*

Nominal size, inches.......	4 by 6 3⅝ by 5⅝ 20.39	6 by 6 5½ by 5½ 30.25	6 by 8 5½ by 7½ 41.25	8 by 8 7½ by 7½ 56.25
Actual size, inches..........				
Area in square inches.......				
Height of column:				
4 feet.....................	11,300	16,940	23,100	31,500
5 feet.....................	11,000	16,900	23,060	31,500
6 feet.....................	10,300	16,700	22,850	31,500
6 feet 6 inches.............	9,800	16,600	22,700	31,400
7 feet.....................	9,270	16,400	22,400	31,300
7 feet 6 inches.............	8,720	16,200	22,100	31,100
8 feet.....................	7,930	15,950	21,800	31,000
9 feet.....................	6,300	15,350	20,950	30,640
10 feet....................		14,400	19,600	30,240

(Reprinted from Reference R11-6, Sec. 38)

JOISTS

33. Definition—Joists are the members that carry the floors and ceiling between supports. See Pls. 7 to 15.

34. Rigidity Necessary—Joists must be of such size that they will carry the required load in safety. Joists supporting plastered ceilings must also be sufficiently stiff so that they will not deflect (bend), under load, an amount exceeding 1/360 of the joist span. A greater deflection will result in plaster cracks.

35. Material and Grade — For normal conditions, any species of framing lumber listed in Par. 19, P. 108, may be used. However, southern yellow pine or Douglas fir are the species most commonly used. The grade should preferably be No. 1 common. For joists exposed to decay, such as porch joists, the wood should be impregnated with a wood preservative.

36. Spacing—Spacing should be 16″ (center to center) for all floors except those supporting tile or concrete floors. For the latter floors, the joist spacing should be 12″.

37. Double Joists, Trimmers, Etc.—For special loads or conditions, joists, trimmers, headers, etc., should be arranged as shown by Pls. 8, 9, and 14, so as to insure ample strength.

38. Determining Joist Size — The proper sizes of joists are readily determined as follows:

First Step—Determine the maximum joist span for each floor. (Refer to your house plans.)

Second Step—Ascertain from your local Building Code the amount of live load to be provided for. (Usually this will be 40 pounds per square foot for all floors used for living purposes; and 20 pounds per square foot for attic floors, used for

light storage.) Do not make any allowance for the weight of the sub floor or finish floor, or of the joist itself, as these "dead loads" have been included in computing the tables to which you will be referred. For plastered ceilings, the weight of plaster has also been included.

Third Step—Select species and grade of wood to be used, and ascertain from Table 2, P. 107, the allowable working stress for the wood selected.

Fourth Step—Refer to Tables 12 to 19, and select the table that is based on the same (or next smaller) working stress as that allowed for the wood selected. (Note that Tables 12 to 15 are for plastered ceilings, and Tables 16 to 19 are for ceilings without plaster.)

Fifth Step—In the left-hand column of the table select the proper "live load" and, reading towards the right, select the proper joist spacing. Follow along this line from left to right until a span is found which is equal to or greater than the required span. At the top of the column in which the span is found will be seen the proper nominal size for joist.

39. Example of Selecting Joist Size—Assume that the live load for a house floor is 40 pounds per square foot; the joist span is 14 feet; the joist spacing is 16″ o.c.; and the ceiling is plastered. If No. 1 common grade southern yellow pine is selected, Table 12 should be used. By starting at 40 pounds in the left-hand column and following to the right (using 16″ spacing), it will be found that a 14 foot span is not listed in the table; so the next longer span, which is 15′-3″, must be used. Therefore, the joist size will be 2″ x 10″ (nominal size).

MAXIMUM SPANS FOR JOISTS
(UNIFORMLY LOADED)

(All Sizes Given in Tables are American Standard Dressed Sizes)

TABLE 12.—*Fiber stress, 1,200 pounds per square inch; modulus of elasticity, 1,600,000*

[Plastered ceiling below (deflection not over 1/360 of span)]

LIVE LOAD—POUNDS PER SQUARE FOOT	SPACING	2 INCHES WIDE BY DEPTH OF—				
		6	8	10	12	14
10...............	12	12- 9	16- 9	21- 1	24- 0	......
	16	11- 8	15- 4	19- 4	23- 4	24- 0
	24	10- 3	14- 6	17- 3	20- 7	24- 0
20...............	12	11- 6	15- 3	19- 2	23- 0	24- 0
	16	10- 5	13-11	17- 6	21- 1	24- 0
	24	9- 2	12- 3	15- 6	18- 7	21- 9
30...............	12	10- 8	14- 0	17- 9	21- 4	24- 9
	16	9- 9	12-11	16- 3	19- 6	22- 9
	24	8- 6	11- 4	14- 4	17- 3	20- 2
40...............	12	10- 0	13- 3	16- 8	20- 0	23- 5
	16	9- 1	12- 1	15- 3	18- 5	21- 5
	24	7-10	10- 4	13- 1	15- 9	18- 5
50...............	12	9- 6	12- 7	15-10	19- 1	22- 4
	16	8- 7	11- 6	14- 7	17- 6	20- 5
	24	7- 3	9- 6	12- 1	14- 7	17- 0
60...............	12	9- 0	12- 0	15- 2	18- 3	21- 4
	16	8- 1	10-10	13- 8	16- 6	19- 3
	24	6- 8	8-11	11- 3	13- 7	15-11

TABLE 13.—*Fiber stress, 1040 pounds per square inch; modulus of elasticity, 1,400,000*

[Plastered ceiling below (deflection not over 1/360 of span)]

LIVE LOAD—POUNDS PER SQUARE FOOT	SPACING	2 INCHES WIDE BY DEPTH OF—				
		6	8	10	12	14
10	12	12- 2	16- 1	20- 2	24- 0	......
	16	11- 2	14- 9	18- 6	22- 4	24- 0
	24	9-10	13- 1	16- 6	19- 9	23- 1
20	12	11- 0	14- 7	18- 5	21-11	24- 0
	16	10- 1	13- 4	16- 9	20- 2	23- 6
	24	8-10	11- 9	14-10	18- 0	20-10
30	12	10- 2	13- 6	17- 0	20- 5	23- 9
	16	9- 3	12- 4	15- 6	18- 8	21- 9
	24	8- 0	10- 7	13- 6	16- 2	18-10
40	12	9- 6	12- 8	16- 0	19- 3	22- 6
	16	8- 8	11- 7	14- 7	17- 7	20- 6
	24	7- 3	9- 7	12- 2	14- 8	17- 1
50	12	9- 0	12- 0	15- 2	18- 3	21- 4
	16	8- 3	11- 0	13-10	16- 9	19- 6
	24	6- 8	8-11	11- 2	13- 7	15-10
60	12	8- 8	11- 6	14- 6	17- 6	20- 5
	16	7- 7	10- 1	12- 9	15- 4	17-10
	24	6- 2	8- 3	10- 5	12- 7	14-10

TABLE 14.—*Fiber stress, 900 pounds per square inch; modulus of elasticity, 1,200,000*

[Plastered ceiling below (deflection not over 1/360 of span)]

LIVE LOAD—POUNDS PER SQUARE FOOT	SPACING	2 INCHES WIDE BY DEPTH OF—				
		6	8	10	12	14
10	12	11- 7	15- 2	19- 1	23- 0	24- 0
	16	10- 7	13-10	17- 6	21- 2	24- 0
	24	9- 3	13- 2	15- 8	18- 9	21- 9
20	12	10- 5	13-10	17- 5	20-10	24- 0
	16	9- 7	12- 8	16- 0	19- 2	22- 4
	24	8- 4	11- 1	14- 0	16-10	19- 8
30	12	9- 9	12-10	16- 1	19- 5	22- 7
	16	8-11	11- 9	14-10	17-10	20- 9
	24	7- 4	9-10	12- 4	14-10	17- 4
40	12	9- 1	12- 0	15- 2	18- 3	21- 2
	16	8- 3	11- 0	13-10	16- 9	19- 6
	24	6- 8	8-10	11- 2	13- 6	15- 9
50	12	8- 7	11- 5	14- 5	17- 5	20- 3
	16	7- 8	10- 1	12- 8	15- 3	17-10
	24	6- 2	8- 1	10- 3	12- 5	14- 6
60	12	8- 0	10- 8	13- 5	16- 1	18-10
	16	7- 0	9- 3	11- 8	14- 0	16- 5
	24	5- 8	7- 7	9- 7	11- 7	13- 7

TABLE 15.—*Fiber stress, 720 pounds per square inch; modulus of elasticity, 1,000,000*

[Plastered ceiling below (deflection not over 1/360 of span)]

LIVE LOAD—POUNDS PER SQUARE FOOT	SPACING	2 INCHES WIDE BY DEPTH OF—				
		6	8	10	12	14
10	12	10-11	14- 4	18- 1	21- 6	24- 0
	16	10- 0	13- 2	16- 7	20- 0	23- 4
	24	8- 9	12- 5	14- 9	17- 8	20- 7
20	12	9-10	13- 1	16- 4	19- 7	22- 9
	16	9- 0	11-10	15- 0	18- 0	21- 1
	24	7- 6	10- 0	12- 6	15- 1	17- 6
30	12	9- 1	12- 0	15- 2	18- 3	21- 3
	16	8- 1	10- 9	13- 5	16- 2	18- 9
	24	6- 8	8-10	11- 2	13- 5	15- 8
40	12	8- 6	11- 2	14- 1	16-11	19- 7
	16	7- 3	9- 9	12- 4	14- 9	17- 2
	24	6- 0	7-11	10- 2	12- 3	14- 3
50	12	7-10	10- 4	13- 1	15- 8	18- 2
	16	6-10	9- 0	11- 4	13- 8	15-11
	24	5- 7	7- 4	9- 4	11- 3	13- 1
60	12	7- 2	9- 7	12- 2	14- 7	17- 1
	16	6- 4	8- 5	10- 7	12- 9	14-10
	24	5- 2	6-10	8- 8	10- 6	12- 4

(Reprinted from Reference R11-6, Sec. 38)

TABLE 16.—*Extreme fiber stress in bending 1,200 pounds per square inch*

[No plastered ceiling below]

LIVE LOAD—POUNDS PER SQUARE FOOT	SPACING	2 INCHES WIDE BY DEPTH OF—				
		6	8	10	12	14
30	12	13- 5	17- 8	22- 2	24- 0	......
	16	11- 9	15- 6	19- 5	23- 3	24- 0
	24	9- 8	12-10	16- 2	19- 5	22- 6
40	12	12- 0	15-11	19-11	23-11	24- 0
	16	10- 6	13-11	17- 4	20-11	24- 0
	24	8- 7	11- 5	14- 5	17- 5	20- 3
50	12	10-11	14- 5	18- 2	21-11	24- 0
	16	9- 6	12- 7	15-10	19- 1	22- 3
	24	7-10	10- 4	13- 1	15- 9	18- 5
60	12	10- 0	13- 4	16-10	20- 2	23- 6
	16	8- 9	11- 8	14- 8	17- 8	20- 7
	24	7- 3	9- 6	12- 1	14- 7	17- 0

TABLE 17.—*Extreme fiber stress in bending 1,040 pounds per square inch*

[No plastered ceiling below]

LIVE LOAD—POUNDS PER SQUARE FOOT	SPACING	2 INCHES WIDE BY DEPTH OF—				
		6	8	10	12	14
30	12	12- 6	16- 6	20- 7	24- 0	......
	16	10-10	14- 9	18- 1	21- 9	24- 0
	24	9- 0	11-11	15- 0	18- 1	21- 0
40	12	11- 2	14-10	18- 7	22- 4	24- 0
	16	9- 8	13- 0	16- 2	19- 7	22- 9
	24	8- 0	10- 7	13- 6	16- 2	18-10
50	12	10- 1	13- 5	16-11	20- 4	23- 8
	16	8-10	11- 8	14- 9	17- 9	20- 8
	24	7- 3	9- 7	12- 2	14- 8	17- 1
60	12	9- 5	12- 5	15- 8	18- 9	21-10
	16	8- 1	10-10	13- 7	16- 6	19- 1
	24	6- 8	8-11	11- 2	13- 7	15-10

TABLE 18.—*Extreme fiber stress in bending 900 pounds per square inch*

[No plastered ceiling below]

LIVE LOAD—POUNDS PER SQUARE FOOT	SPACING	2 INCHES WIDE BY DEPTH OF—				
		6	8	10	12	14
30	12	11- 7	15- 4	19- 2	22-11	24- 0
	16	10- 2	13- 5	16-10	20- 1	23- 5
	24	8- 4	11- 1	14- 0	16-10	19- 6
40	12	10- 4	13- 9	17- 3	20- 8	24- 0
	16	9- 1	12- 0	15- 1	18- 1	21- 0
	24	7- 5	9-11	12- 6	15- 0	17- 6
50	12	9- 6	12- 6	15- 9	18-11	21-11
	16	8- 3	10-11	13- 9	16- 6	19- 2
	24	6- 9	8-11	11- 4	13- 8	15-11
60	12	8- 9	11- 7	14- 7	17- 6	20- 4
	16	7- 8	10- 1	12- 8	15- 3	17-10
	24	6- 3	8- 3	10- 5	12- 7	14- 8

TABLE 19.—*Extreme fiber stress in bending 720 pounds per square inch*

[No plastered ceiling below]

LIVE LOAD—POUNDS PER SQUARE FOOT	SPACING	2 INCHES WIDE BY DEPTH OF—				
		6	8	10	12	14
30	12	10- 5	13- 8	17- 2	20- 6	23- 9
	16	9- 1	12- 0	15- 1	17-11	21- 0
	24	7- 6	10- 0	12- 6	15- 1	17- 6
40	12	9- 3	12- 4	15- 6	18- 6	21- 5
	16	8- 1	10- 9	13- 6	16- 2	18- 9
	24	6- 8	8-10	11- 2	13- 5	15- 8
50	12	8- 6	11- 2	14- 1	16-11	19- 8
	16	7- 4	9- 9	12- 4	14- 9	17- 3
	24	6- 0	8- 0	10- 2	12- 3	14- 3
60	12	7-10	10- 4	13- 0	15- 8	18- 2
	16	6-10	9- 0	11- 4	13- 7	15-11
	24	5- 7	7- 4	9- 4	11- 3	13- 1

BRIDGING

40. Definition—Cross bridging is shown by Pl. 13, Fig. 14; and solid bridging is shown by Pl. 12, Fig.

41. Function—Cross bridging not only prevents the joists from "rolling over" but also, by serving as diagonal struts, distributes the load imposed on one joist to several joists on either side.

42. Spacing—One row of cross bridging should be provided for all joists having a span of from 6'-0" to 15'-0"; and 2 rows for all joists having a span of from 15'-0" to 20'-0".

43. Material and Grade—A No. 2 common grade of practically any softwood species is suitable.

44. Size—1" x 3" is sufficient. Rough (not dressed) material is preferable, as it is cheaper and slightly stronger.

CORNER POSTS (EXTERIOR WALLS)

45. Definition—Corner posts are the corner studs which occur at the intersection of two exterior walls at right angles to each other. See Pls. 10 and 11, Figs. 5 and 6.

46. Type of Construction—The type shown by Pls. 10 and 11, Fig. 6, is recommended as being the most rigged and durable. However, for the average house, the type shown by Pls. 10 and 11, Fig. 5, should prove entirely satisfactory.

47. Material—The same species as for studs is suitable (Par. 52).

48. Grade—Considering the importance of corner posts, and the greater possibility of their being subjected to dampness from leaks than the other studs, it is recommended that a No. 1 common, dense heart grade be used.

49. Size—2" x 4" studs should be used for a three-piece post. One 2" x 4" and one 4" x 6" stud should be used for a two-piece post.

STUDS (WALLS AND PARTITIONS)

50. Definition—Studs are the closely spaced, vertical members of partitions and outside walls that support the weight of the upper floors, and provide a framework for the interior and exterior finishes. (See Pls. 10 and 11.)

51. Spacing—16" spacing (center to center) is recommended.

52. Material—The same species as is ordinarily used for joists, rafters, and other framing is suitable. Par. 19, P. 108.

53. Grade—No. 1 common is recommended for two-story houses; No. 2 common may be used for bungalows.

54. Size—2" x 4" studs are suitable for the average house.

SOLE AND TOP PLATES (WALLS AND PARTITIONS)

55. Sole Plate (Definition)—A sole plate is a horizontal member at the bottom of a frame wall or partition, which serves as a support and attachment for studs. See Pl. 14, Fig. 2.

56. Top Plate (Definition)—A top plate is a horizontal member at the top of a partition or frame wall, that serves as a cap for studs and as a support for joists, rafters, or other studs. See Pl. 14, Figs. 1 and 3.

57. Material and Size—Same as for studs (Pars. 52 and 54).

58. Grade—Preferably No. 1 common; otherwise, No. 2 common.

OPENINGS (WALLS AND PARTITIONS)

59. Definition—Openings in walls and partitions, for purposes of this discussion, are those openings necessary for the installation of windows, doors, etc. See Pl. 13, Figs. 7 to 13.

60. Opening in Bearing Walls—Such openings (Pl. 13, Figs. 7 to 12) must be sufficiently strong overhead to carry the weight of the wall above, and any bearing loads imposed by the joists or rafters.

61. Openings in Non-Bearing Walls—Such openings (Pl. 13, Fig. 13) must be sufficiently strong overhead to carry the weight of the wall above.

62. Headers at Openings—By using headers of sufficient size, and omitting trusses (Pl. 13, Fig. 13), the loads imposed overhead of openings could be carried *safely*, but an appreciable amount of shrinkage might result (see Fig. 2, P. 105). When trusses are omitted, headers of the following sizes should be used:

2" x 4" headers for spans up to 3 feet.
2" x 6" headers for spans 3 feet to 5 feet.
2" x 8" headers for spans 5 feet to 7 feet.
2" x 10" headers for spans over 7 feet.

63. Trusses at Openings—Types of trusses for various size openings are shown by Pl. 13, Figs. 7 to 12. As, theoretically, the only stresses placed on a truss are tension and compression (Pl. 13, Figs. 7 to 12), the top member (in compression) and the bottom member (in tension) may be made relatively small for supporting a large load. The use of such relatively small members reduce shrinkage with its resultant plaster cracks, etc.

64. Material, Grade, and Size—Same as for studs. (Pars. 52 to 54), except as noted otherwise by Pl. 13.

RIBBAND (EXTERIOR WALLS)

65. Definition—A ribband (or ribbon) is a horizontal strip of wood notched into the studs in "balloon" frame construction, to tie the studs together and form a support for the second floor joists (Pls. 10 and 11). Ribbands are not required for one-story houses.

66. Material—Any species recommended for joists, studs, or other framing may be used; but the denser, harder woods of these species, such as longleaf southern yellow pine, are preferable.

67. Grade—No. 1 common, selected for straightness and freedom from structural defects, is recommended.

68. Size—1" x 4" (nominal) size is sufficiently large for the average house.

BRACING (EXTERIOR WALLS)

69. Let-In Bracing—This type is shown by Pls. 10 and 11, Fig. 1. A test panel sheathed horizontally, but with 1" x 4" bracing strips let into the stud faces diagonally under the sheathing, showed an increase of from 2½ to 4 times in stiffness and from 3½ to 4 times in strength over the panel sheathed horizontally only.

70. Cut-In Bracing and "Herringbone" Bracing—These types are shown by Pls. 10 and 11, Item 10, and have very little value as bracing.

71. When Necessary—Bracing should always be used when the house is likely to be subjected to high winds or when, for one reason or another, the sheathing is omitted, or applied horizontally. Even diagonally sheathed houses will be much stiffer and stronger if bracing is used.

72. Type Recommended—Bracing, when used, should be of the diagonal, let-in type. See Pls. 10 and 11, Fig. 1.

73. Material, Grade, and Size—Same as for ribband, Pars. 66 to 68.

FIRE STOPPING

74. Definition—Fire stops are obstructions provided in the hollow floors, walls, and similar air passages of a house in such a manner as to prevent the passage of flames up or across a building. See Pls. 10 and 11, Items 7, 10, 12, 15, 24, and 32.

75. House Without Fire Stopping—Without fire stopping (Fig. 3) the average house, due to the unrestricted passages through its walls and floors, is a veritable honeycomb of natural "flues" through which a fire may race, and quickly consume the structure. As will be seen from Fig. 3, the control of such a fire is beyond all probability.

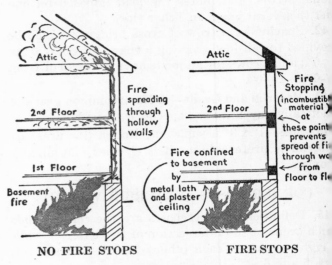

NO FIRE STOPS   FIRE STOPS

Fig. 3.—*How Fires in the Home Spread*
(*Courtesy National Fire Protection Association*)

76. Houses With Fire Stopping—A fire in such houses (Fig. 3) cannot make rapid headway due to lack of exit "flues," and subsequent lack of necessary air for combustion. Such fires can be controlled and extinguished with a minimum loss of life and property.

77. Filling of Fire Stop Boxes—For maximum efficiency, fire stop boxes (except those at sills of houses without basements) should be filled with a suitable material, selected to comply with the three following requirements: (1) It should be incombustible. (2) It should not absorb and hold moisture (and thus cause rot). (3) When used for such boxes as those shown by Pl. 10, Figs. 2 and 3, and Pl. 11, Figs. 2, and 5, it should be flexible enough to become slightly re-arranged if the timbers shrink and the flooring compresses it. (*Solid* concrete, masonry, etc., would cause the floor to bulge, and should not be used in such boxes.)

78. Type of Filling Material Recommended—Loose boiler cinders are rated as one of the best all-around fire stopping materials. Crushed concrete, brick, tile, etc., may also be used. For *dry* locations, mineral wool, of a type having a high melting point, is suitable, especially around chimneys and fireplaces.

ROOF FRAMING

79. Types of Roofs—The principal types are shown by Pl. 12, Figs. 1 to 4.

80. Function of Rafters—Rafters serve the same purpose for the roof as joists do for floors, by providing a support for the roof sheathing and shingles.

81. Definition of Rafter Span—The rafter span is the *horizontal* distance between supports, and is *not* the length along the rafter. The span may be between wall plate and ridge (Fig. 4), or from wall to wall (Fig. 5); or, where collar beams are used on every rafter, it may be from wall to collar beam connection, or from collar beam connection to ridge, whichever is greatest (Fig. 6).

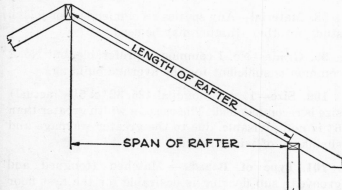

Fig. 4.—*Illustrating Rafter Span Between Wall Plate and Ridge*

Fig. 5—*Span of Rafter When Measured from Wall to Wall*

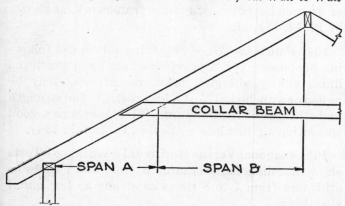

Fig. 6.—*Showing How the Span is Determined Where a Collar Beam is Used on Every Rafter. The Span is "B" Because It Is the Larger of the Two Spans.*

82. Thrust of Rafters—Rafters exert an outward thrust which tends to spread the upper portion of the building apart. This outward thrust is less for steep roofs than for roofs with slight pitch. Such thrust should be resisted by the attic joists, or other suitable ties. See Pl. 12, Figs. 1 to 6.

83. Collar Beams (Function)—These are shown by Figs. 6 and 7, and Pl. 12, Figs. 1 and 2. Collar beams, when used as shown by Pl. 12, Figs. 1 and 2, are "compression" members, or "struts," that make it possible to shorten the "span" of the rafters by preventing the rafters from sagging. Therefore, the outward thrust of the roof in such cases is resisted by the attic joists (which serve as tie members), while the inward thrust is resisted by the collar beams.

84. Collar Beams as Ties — Under no conditions should suitable "tie" members (see Par. 83) be omitted and collar beams be used as tie members. Under such conditions the collar beams would no longer be *collar beams* in "compression" but would serve as *ties* in "tension". This would result in the portion of rafter below the collar beam bending outwards, due to the thrust of the roof (see Fig. 7). Also, the nails would probably be pulled out of the collar beams at their ends.

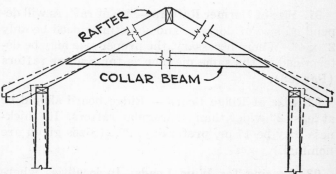

Fig. 7.—*Collar Beams, Unless Placed Near to the Plate, Should Not be Depended Upon for Ties, as There is a Tendency for the Rafters to Bend and the Building to Spread as Indicated by the Dotted Lines. The Nails are Likely to Pull Out at the Ends of the Collar Beam, Also.*

85. Type of Roof Recommended — As pointed out in Par. 19, P. 24, a gable roof (without dormers) makes the simplest, cheapest, and strongest type of sloping roof. Therefore, it is recommended that such a roof be used where practicable.

86. Material and Grade (All Rafters) — Same as for joists (Par. 35).

87. Spacing — 16" spacing (center to center) is recommended for regular rafters and jack rafters.

88. Determining Rafter Size — The procedure is practically the same as for joists, and is as follows:

First Step—Determine the rafter span by refering to Par. 81, and scaling the house plans.

Second Step—Determine the *combined* live and dead loads for which to provide. The required live load may be ascertained from your local building code. [The live load for which the roof should be designed should, ordinarily, be a vertical load of 30 pounds per square foot of horizontal projection ("rafter span") for roofs having a rise of 4" or less per foot, and 20 pounds for roofs having a rise of more than 4" but less than 12" per foot. If the rise exceeds 12" per foot, provision should be made for a wind force acting in a normal direction, on one slope at a time, of 20 pounds per *sloping* square foot]. The required dead load may be obtained from Fig. 3, P. 92.

Remaining Steps—These are the same as the similar steps for joist calculation (Par. 38). It should be kept in mind, however, that the combined load per square foot on the rafters is treated as a "live" load when using the joist tables.

89. Size of Jack Rafters — Same as for regular rafters.

90. Size of Hip and Valley Rafters—These rafters should be the same size as the regular rafters for spans not exceeding 3 feet; should be 2" wider or 1" thicker, than regular rafters for spans of 3 to 12 feet; and should be double the thickness of the regular rafter for spans greater than 12 feet.

91. Size of Dormer Rafters—Size of rafters will depend on size of dormer, and sometimes need be only 2" x 4". Where necessary, the proper size may be determined in the same manner as for regular rafters (Par. 88).

92. Size of Ridge Board — Ridge board should be at least 2" wider than the regular rafters. Its thickness may be 1" or, preferably, 2". (Sizes given are nominal.)

93. Bracing for Wind Loads—In localities where roof will be subjected to heavy wind or snow loads, extra bracing may be required.

SUB FLOOR

94. Definition—A sub floor (see Pls. 7, 10, and 11) is a wood floor of dressed lumber which is laid over the floor joists, and over which the finish floor is laid.

95. Function — A sub floor serves the following purposes: (1) It prevents finish floors from sagging under normal loads, and serves as a nailing base. (2) When laid diagonally (see Pls. 7, 10, and 11), it stiffens the building. (3) It adds to the insulation of the room (Table 4, P. 136). (4) It makes a room more soundproof. (5) It helps prevent dust from rising from the basement, through the first floor. (6) It serves as a working platform during construction, thereby saving the finish floor from premature use and defacement.

96. Where Needed—A sub floor under each finish floor is recommended. Also, even though a finish floor is omitted from the attic, a sub floor is recommended, where practicable, to stiffen the building and serve as a storage platform.

97. When Sub Floor Is Omitted in Attic—When both sub floor and finish floor are omitted from attic, one or more strips of sub flooring at least 3 feet wide should preferably be installed in the attic over the attic joists, to serve as walkways, storage space, etc.

98. Material—Any species recommended for joists, studs, or other framing may be used.

99. Grade—No. 1 common is preferable, but No. 2 common is sufficient for the average building.

100. Size—1" x 6" nominal (25/32" x 5½" actual) size is recommended. The use of a width greater than 6" is not advisable, due to the greater warpage and shrinkage of wider boards.

101. Type of Boards — Matched (tongued and grooved) sub flooring is desirable for the first floor to help keep out dust. These boards may also be end-matched at little extra cost, as end-matching of boards saves both labor costs and material. Ordinary square-edged boards will be sufficient for the second and attic floors.

102. Building Paper—See Par. 9, P. 135.

EXTERIOR WALL SHEATHING

103. Definition—Exterior wall sheathing consists of dressed boards nailed to the framework, as shown by Pl. 14, Fig. 11.

104. Function—Wood sheathing serves the following purposes: (1) It provides a base upon which the finish siding, shingles, brick veneer, etc., may be nailed or attached. (2) It adds greatly to the strength and stiffness of the building. (3) It serves as a good insulation against heat and cold (Table 4, P. 136).

105. Diagonal Versus Horizontal Sheathing—Tests show that diagonal sheathing is from 4 to 7 times as stiff, and from 7 to 8 times as strong as horizontal sheathing.

106. Recommended Direction of Boards — All sheathing should be applied diagonally at 45°, except for stucco exteriors. In the latter case, horizontal sheathing and let-in braces (Par. 11, P. 145) should be used.

107. Material—The same species and grade as for sub floors is recommended (Pars. 98 and 99).

108. Size—1″ x 6″ nominal (25/32″ x 5½″ actual) size is recommended. The use of a width greater than 8″ is not advisable.

109. Type of Boards — Matched (tongued and grooved) sheathing is preferable. Such boards may also be end-matched at little cost due to the saving in labor costs and material when using end-matched lumber. For the average house, however, ordinary square-edged boards will serve the purpose.

110. Special Sheathing Materials—Before substituting any "special" wall boards for wood sheathing, the home builder should check such material for the following points: (1) Is it *really* as strong as diagonal wood sheathing, or do nail heads pull through it easily? (Make some tests yourself.) (2) Is it a better insulator than wood, or actually less? (See Table 4, P. 136.) (3) Does it make a suitable nailing base, or can you pull nails out with your fingers? (4) Has it been made rot and vermin proof by impregnating it with poisons (such as arsenic) that are harmful to human beings?

111. Building Paper—See Par. 9, P. 135.

ROOF SHEATHING

112. Definition—Roof sheathing consists of dressed boards applied over the rafters, as shown by Pls. 7, 10, and 11.

113. Function—Roof sheathing provides a support and nailing surface for the roofing material. It also stiffens and braces the roof framing, and provides thermal insulation.

114. Material, Grade, Size, and Types of Boards—See Pars. 107 to 109.

115. Building Paper—See Par. 9, P. 135.

GROUNDS FOR PLASTER

116. Definition — Grounds are strips of dressed lumber nailed to the framework at critical points, to serve as a guide for the plasterer. See Pl. 14, Fig. 14, and Pls. 16 to 18.

117. Function—Grounds provided wherever baseboards, windows and door trim, interior cornices, etc., are nailed against the plaster, serve the following

purposes: (1) Insure that the adjacent plaster surfaces are flat and true, by serving as a "gauge" for plasterer. (2) Provide a nailing strip for the trim.

118. Use of Wood Lath as Grounds—Although in cheap construction wood lath are sometimes used as temporary grounds, such practice is highly objectionable because: (1) They are easily knocked out of alignment. (2) They are too short to use in one piece. (3) It is difficult to keep the edges perfectly straight. (4) A permanent nailing strip is not provided. (5) It is a "sloppy", makeshift method at the best.

119. Use of Door Frames as Grounds — In cheap construction, the finished door frame is sometimes set in place before plastering, and such frame used as a ground. This practice has the following objections: (1) The kiln-dried lumber of the frame will soak up moisture from the plaster. (2) The frame will become roughened from the grinding action of the plaster and sand. (3) The frame is likely to become injured, due to workmen passing materials through the door, etc.

120. Use of Window Frames as Grounds—The use of window frames as grounds has the same objections as the use of door frames (Par. 119). However, it is practically necessary to install the window frames before plastering, so as to make the house weatherproof. Thoroughly priming the frames will help protect them against moisture, and the use of grounds (see Pl. 16) will help protect them against the abrasive action of the plaster and sand.

121. Material and Grade—No. 2 common grade of practically any species is suitable. However, grounds should be straight, uniform, and fairly clear.

122. Size—A 1″ x 2″ strip, dressed to proper thickness, is usually sufficient.

FURRING

123. Definition—Furring, as herein defined, consists of strips of dressed lumber applied to the interior of outside masonry walls so as to provide nailing strips for the plaster base, paneling, etc. See Pl. 7.

124. Function—Furring serves the following purposes: (1) Prevents moisture which condenses on, or passes through, the masonry wall from wetting the interior plastered or paneled wall. (2) Provides added insulation for the wall by the creation of an airspace (see Table 4, P. 136).

125. Use of Furring Recommended—The inside of all exterior masonry walls should be furred, as a commonsense precaution against leaks and condensation of moisture on the interior face of the walls. Also, in cold climates, the added insulation afforded by the furring will reduce the fuel bill sufficiently to pay for the added cost of such furring in a few years.

126. Material—As furring is subject to dampness, a durable species of wood such as tidewater red cypress or California redwood, is recommended (Table 1, P. 106).

127. Grade—As the sapwood of no species is decay resistant, the use of a No. 1 or No. 2 common heart grade is recommended.

128. Size—1″ x 2″ (dressed size) is sufficient for average conditions.

129. Wall Plugs for Attaching Furring—Metal wall plugs should be hot-dipped galvanized, and wooden wall plugs (if used) should be of a durable type of wood.

130. Nails—As the nails will be subjected to dampness, it is recommended that all nails for attaching the furring to the masonry wall be hot-dipped galvanized (Table 20).

FRAMING OF ANNEXED BUILDINGS

131. Usual Faults—Due to a lack of proper detail drawings, annexed or attached portions of the house (such as sunrooms, heater rooms, attached garages, etc.) are often attached to the main portion of the residence in a weak and flimsy manner.

132. Suggested Methods—Where the house plans are deficient in details, and there is doubt as to how the contractor will frame any of the annexed portions, it is recommended that he be required to furnish sketches indicating the methods he proposes to use.

WOODEN PORCHES

133. General Recommendations — Porches should be framed in a strong, substantial manner (see Pars. 131 and 132) ; and should be of suitable materials to withstand exposure to the elements.

134. Sills—See Pars. 4 to 13.

135. Floor Joists — See Par. 35 for species and grade. Determine size in same manner as for joists of residence (Pars. 38 and 39), using the proper joist table for the type of wood selected, and using 40 pounds per square foot floor load. The joist table used should be based on "No Plastered Ceiling Below".

136. Girders—Species and grade should be the same as for porch floor joists. Determine size in same manner as for house girders (Par. 22) using 40 pounds per square foot live load, plus 10 pounds per square foot dead load.

137. Ceiling Joists—No. 1 common grade of any framing lumber listed in Par. 19, P.108, is suitable A 2″ x 6″ size, spaced 16″ center to center, is sufficient for the average porch.

138. Rafters—Same as for ceiling joists; except for heavy roofs, the size should be increased as required. See Par. 88.

139. Carriages for Wooden Steps — Species and grade same as for floor joists. For size and spacing, see Pl. 19, Fig. 7.

ROUGH HARDWARE

140. Definition — Rough hardware includes nails, sash weights, sash cord, and similar rough items of hardware.

141. Importance of Nails—As nails are what hold the house together, due consideration should be given to the size, material, holding power, number used, etc.

142. Cement-Coated Nails—Such nails consist of wire nails that are coated with a resinous gum, and have the following advantages: (1) Have a holding power about twice that of ordinary nails. (2) Due to their protective coating, they have an useful life about twice that of ordinary nails. (3) Require less force to drive. (4) Less likely to split the wood. (5) Due to their slightly smaller size in comparison to ordinary nails, their cost per pound is very little more than for ordinary nails.

TABLE 20.—*Nails Recommended for Dwelling Construction*

Use of Nail	Type and Material of Nail
All rough carpentry	Cement-coated wire nails, preferably; otherwise, regular wire nails.
Building paper	Hot-dipped galvanized roofing nails
Furring (interior and exterior)	Special, hot-dipped galvanized nails designed for attaching furring
Interior finish floors	Steel cut casing nails
Interior trim	Wire finishing nails
All exterior finish carpentry	Hot-dipped galvanized nails, or brass or bronze brads

FINISH CARPENTRY AND MILLWORK

GENERAL RECOMMENDATIONS

1. Exterior Millwork—All exterior millwork, such as exterior doors, windows, siding, porch work, cornice, moldings, etc., should preferably be of a naturally durable, paint retaining wood, so that the necessity for painting will be infrequent; and so that if the paint becomes impaired, little or no damage will result. Such millwork should be assembled by skilled mechanics; and only the use of hot-dipped galvanized nails, and bronze or brass brads, should be allowed. In other words, the exterior of the house should be made permanently weatherproof, so as to require a minimum of upkeep.

2. Interior Millwork — Interior millwork, such as interior trim, paneling, stairwork, finish flooring, etc., should be selected in accordance with the personal taste and desires of the home builder. Such millwork may be simple and inexpensive, or pretentious and exceedingly costly. In either case, it is important to use thoroughly kiln-dried lumber that is primed (given initial coat of paint) before erection, and to have the erection done only by skilled mechanics, *after* the building is thoroughly dry. All work should be sanded smooth, and should be free of defects or defacements.

3. Materials and Grades—See Pars. 2 and 3, P. 116.

4. "Stock" Millwork Items — Several large companies make stock millwork items, such as interior trim, doors, sash, window and door frames, etc., which are distributed through local mills. The home builder should consult with his architect or a reputable lumber mill in regard to the availability of stock items in the material desired, and the comparative costs of such items, etc. If, for some reason, "stock" moldings and trim are not used, it is generally advisable to ascertain what cutters the local mills have on hand, and then specify contours of moldings and trim accordingly.

WINDOWS (GENERAL)

5. Importance of Windows—Windows are very important items in a home. They not only vitally affect the architectural appearance of a home, but also the health and comfort of the occupants. Windows, therefore, should be given careful consideration.

6. Number of Windows — Each room should be equipped with at least two windows, so located as to provide cross-ventilation and sufficient lighting for the room. The number and location of the windows should also harmonize with the architectural requirements of the house. The use of too many windows in cold climates will result in excessive fuel bills, unless they are fitted with storm sash or the glass in the regular sash are of the insulating type.

7. Type of Window — Double-hung windows are recommended. If casement windows are used, they should be of the out-swinging type.

8. Material—Wood is recommended. Metal, if used, should be of a non-corrodible type.

WINDOW FRAMES

9. Types of Construction—See Pl. 16, Figs. 1 to 11.

10. Material—All portions exposed to the weather, and all concealed portions in contact with masonry, or otherwise subject to dampness, should be of heartwood of a decay resistant species (see Table 1, P. 106). Southern pine or Douglas fir are recommended for pulley stiles, on account of their good wearing qualities.

11. Grade—"Clear Heart" grade is recommended for sills, and "Clear Heart Face" grade for all portions of frames exposed to the weather.

12. Minimum Thicknesses of Material—See Pl. 16.

WOOD SASH

13. Types of Construction—See Pl. 17, Figs. 27 to 32, and 38 to 42.

14. Material for Sash—A decay resistant, paint retaining species is recommended (see Par. 19, P. 108). Otherwise, the wood should be given an approved rot-proofing treatment. Of the woods in which stock sash are usually available, sugar pine, Idaho white pine, and Arkansas soft pine are probably the best.

15. Grade—"Clear Heart" grade is recommended.

16. Minimum Thickness—A thickness of 1¾" is preferable, and is the minimum thickness for sash that are to be fitted with an insulating type of glass. However, the usual 1⅜" stock sash thickness will give long service.

17. Number of Lights—The number of lights (Pl. 17, Figs. 27 to 32) is dependent on the architectural requirements.

18. Meeting Rail—The beveled and rabbetted meeting rail (Pl. 17, Fig. 40) is recommended, especially if weather stripping is to be omitted.

19. Putty Groove—Putty grooves (Pl. 17, Figs. 38 to 42) are recommended for all sash.

20. Glass—An approved brand of "Grade A" drawn glass is recommended, as it costs only slightly more than inferior grades. "Grade B" should be the minimum quality used. (Some brands of Grade B are very good. Examine various grades at a local hardware store.) Single strength glass is suitable for sizes up to 14" x 20".

21. Glazing—All sash should first be thoroughly kiln-dried, with the rebates primed, and the priming thoroughly dry. Glass exposed to the weather should then be bedded in putty (back puttied) and face puttied.

DOOR FRAMES

22. Types of Construction—See Pl. 17, Figs. 1, 2, 3, and 50.

23. Type of Jamb—The solid type (Pl. 17, Fig. 50, B) is recommended for exterior doors. Any of the types shown by Pl. 17, Figs. 50, A, B, or C, are suitable for interior doors.

24. Material and Grade—Requirements for exterior door frames are the same as for window frames (Pars. 10 and 11). For interior frames see Par. 19, P. 108.

INTERIOR AND EXTERIOR DOORS

25. Design and Style—It is recommended, for the sake of economy, that stock doors of a reputable manufacturer be used. The design and style should be in harmony with the architectural requirements, of course. Several types of interior stock doors are shown by Pl. 17, Figs. 33 to 37.

26. Construction—Construction details (Pl. 17, Fig. 44 to 49) will vary in accordance with type of door selected.

27. Minimum Thicknesses—These should be 1¾" for exterior doors, and 1⅜" for interior doors.

28. Material—A decay resistant, paint retaining wood should be used for all exterior doors (see Table 1, P. 106). The interior doors may be constructed of soft pine, oak, birch, etc. See Pars. 2 to 4.

29. Glass Panels—Glass panels in exterior doors provide added light for the entrance hallway, and permits vision through the door. Such glass, if used, should be retained in manner shown by Pl. 17, Fig. 43.

GARAGE DOORS

30. Type—Due to the sagging, swelling and binding, damage from wind, etc., usually experienced with swinging type garage doors, it is recommended that either a "sliding" or an "up-an-over" type door be used, where the budget will permit.

31. Thickness—1¾" is usual thickness.

32. Material—See Par. 28.

SIDING

33. Type of Siding—Pl. 15, Figs. 6 to 10, shows various types of wood siding. Wide bungalow siding of the type shown by Pl. 15, Fig. 7, is preferable from a standpoint of appearance.

34. Material—Either "edge grain" or vertical grain (V. G.) wood siding of a durable, paint retaining species, such as tidewater red cypress or California redwood (see Par. 19, P. 108), or cement-asbestos siding, is recommended.

35. Grade—"Clear Heart" grade is recommended for wood siding.

36. Size—For wood bungalow siding, a thickness of 9/16" x 3/16" or 11/16" x 3/16", and a dressed width of 7½", 9½", or 11½" are suitable.

37. Corner Construction—For wide, wood bungalow siding, a mitered corner as shown by Pl. 15, Fig. 11 is recommended for the sake of appearance. The other types shown by Pl. 15, Figs. 12 to 14, are somewhat more durable, however. For cement-asbestos siding, the corner construction should be in accordance with the manufacturer's recommendations.

SHINGLES FOR SIDE WALLS

38. Staining and Painting—Wood side-wall shingles may be either stained, painted, or left in the natural state. Staining or painting, however, will make the shingles last longer, and give the owner a choice of colors.

39. Unpainted Shingles—Unpainted wood shingles of a durable species should last from 50 to 75 or more years on the average side wall. Such shingles are less fire-resistant than stained or painted shingles, however (see Par. 9, P. 142). The colors of weathered, unstained or unpainted shingles are as follows:

(a) Tidewater red cypress and Port Orford cedar shingles, when weathered, have a light gray color and silvery sheen.

(b) Western red cedar and California redwood shingles, when weathered, have a dark gray color and little or no sheen.

40. Material and Grade—Either wood shingles as listed below, or cement-asbestos shingles, are recommended:

(a) "Certigrade" western red cedar shingles, No. 1, or No. 2 grade.

(b) Tidewater red cypress shingles, "Bests" grade.

(c) California redwood shingles, No. 1 grade.

(d) Northern white cedar, "Extra A" grade.

41. Grain — All wood shingles should be "edge grain" or vertical grain (V. G.), as such shingles have less tendency to warp, expand and contract, or split, than do flat grain shingles.

42. Size—Wood shingles are made in 16″, 18″, and 24″ lengths and should not be less in thickness than five butts to 2″. Sizes should be specified as follows: 16″-5/2; 18″-5/2¼; or 24″-4/2.

43. Corner Construction—Corner construction for wood shingles may be as shown by Pl. 15, Figs. 18 to 21. Mitered corners (Pl. 15, Figs. 19 and 21) are neater in appearance. For cement-asbestos shingles, the corner construction should be in accordance with the manufacturer's recommendations.

44. Number of Courses — Single course construction (Pl. 15, Fig. 15) should be sufficient for the average home.

WATERTABLES

45. Definition—A watertable is a slight projection on the outside wall, a few feet above the ground, as shown by Pl. 15, Figs. 1 to 5, and Pl. 19, Figs. 21 and 22.

46. Function—The function of watertables is to deflect the storm water, which runs down the side walls, away from the foundation of the house. Watertables are especially desirable for houses having basements.

47. Types of Construction—See Pl. 15, Figs. 1 to 5, and Pl. 19, Figs. 21 and 22.

48. Material—See Par. 1.

PORCH FINISH

49. Porch Flooring—Tongued and grooved flooring of 1¼″ nominal (1-1/16″ actual) thickness is recommended. A durable, paint retaining species suitable for flooring (see Par. 19, P. 108), of at least "B and Better Vertical Grain Heart" grade is preferable. Where non-durable wood is used, a "B and Better Vertical Grain" grade, pressure treated with zinc chloride, is recommended. Porch flooring should be laid at right angles to the wall of dwelling, and should slope away from dwelling at the rate of ¼″ per foot.

50. Porch Ceiling—Tongue and grooved ceiling of 1″ nominal (25/32″ actual) thickness is recommended. Practically any species of softwood, such as yellow pine, is suitable in grades of "No. 1 Ceiling" or "No. 2 Ceiling". The ceiling should be applied at right angles to the ceiling joists; or, in other words, it should, ordinarily, be run lengthwise the porch (parallel to wall of building).

51. Treads and Risers for Steps—For sizes see Pl. 19, Fig. 7. For species and grade see Par. 19, P. 108.

52. Porch Columns — The following is recommended:

Type of Construction—See Pl. 15, Figs. 30 to 32.

Material—A decay resistant wood, such as tidewater red cypress, California redwood, etc., is recommended. See Par. 19, P. 108.

Grade—"Clear Heart" grade is recommended.

Anchoring—The base of columns should be securely anchored, to prevent dislodgement. Also, base should be arranged to allow water to drain from under column or to evaporate quickly, so as to prevent decay. For best results, a suitably ventilated, non-corrodible, metal base is recommended.

CORNICES

53. Definition—A cornice is the projection at the top of a finished wall. See Pl. 15, Figs. 22 to 29.

54. Function—Cornices are essentially architectural embellishments which, when properly designed architecturally, add greatly to the appearance of a dwelling.

55. Open Timber Cornices—This type (Pl. 15, Figs. 22 to 24) is generally used only for cheaper types of houses.

Advantages—Slightly less first cost than boxed cornices.

Disadvantages—(1) "Cheap" appearance, architecturally. (2) Ends of rafters, which are, ordinarily, not of a naturally durable or paint retaining species of wood, are exposed to weather. (3) Difficult to paint.

56. Boxed Cornices—This type (Pl. 15, Figs. 25 to 29) is generally used for the better type of houses.

Advantages — (1) Pleasing appearance. (2) No framing members exposed to the elements. (3) Easy to keep painted.

57. Type Recommended—The use of boxed cornices, instead of open timber cornices, is recommended.

58. Architectural Design — The design should be suited to the particular type of house selected, and should be shown on the house plans. When changing from an open timber to a boxed cornice (on your house plans), an architect should be consulted.

59. Types of Construction—A weatherproof construction equal to that shown by Pl. 15, Figs. 22 to 29, is recommended, regardless of type of cornice used.

60. Material—See Par. 19, P. 108.

INSECT SCREENS

61. Openings Requiring Screens—This guide recommends the use of insect screens at the following points: (1) In all window and door openings of residence, to prevent the entry of all types of insects. (2) In basement window and ventilator openings, to prevent the entry of insects (including winged termites), rats, mice, etc. (3) In attic louver frames, to prevent the entry of insects, birds, bats, etc.

62. Type of Screens—The following is recommended for the various screens:

Windows—Full-length screens, hung at top with hot-dipped galvanized screen brackets, and held at the inner bottom-end by two rust-proofed hooks and eyes.

Doors—Door screens should be fitted with suitable protective grille in lower panel.

Foundation Ventilators—Frames for such screens should be a close, snug fit in openings of foundation wall.

Attic louvers—Wire cloth tacked to the inner face of the louver frame is generally sufficient.

63. Frame Material—A durable, paint retaining wood of "Clear Heart" grade is recommended. See Par. 19, P. 108.

64. Wire Cloth Material—Bronze screening material is recommended. All tacks, staples, and brads should be of bronze or copper.

INTERIOR TRIM (GENERAL)

65. Wood Most Generally Used—Soft pine, southern pine, Douglas fir, oak, birch, and gum are the woods most generally used for interior trim.

66. Window and Door Trim—Several types of construction are shown by Pl. 17, Figs. 24 to 26. If mitered trim is used (Pl. 17, Fig. 25), it should be of a narrow type; and the mitered corners should preferably be splined and glued at the mill, to prevent the joint from opening.

67. Baseboards—Baseboards may be two-piece or three-piece construction (see Pl. 15, Figs. 1 to 5, and Pl. 18, Fig. 36). The three-piece construction is recommended, as it may be fitted into corners and against the wall more effectively.

68. Fitting Baseboard Into Corners—Referring to Pl. 17, the method shown by Fig. 22 is best; that shown by Fig. 23 is second best; and that shown by Fig. 21 is third best. The interior corners of baseboards should never be mitered, as the joint will open up.

69. Method of Nailing Baseboard—See Pl. 18, Figs. 36 and 37.

WOOD PANELING

70. Use of Paneling Recommended—The judicious use of paneling in a home is highly recommended by this Guide. Those desiring paneling should refer to Refs. R25-4 to R25-9, Sec. 38, and should also consult their architect in regard to its proper use.

71. Advantages of Paneling—Wood paneling for interior walls and ceilings of homes, has the following advantages: (1) Imparts a "rich", homelike atmosphere. (2) Eliminates plaster, with its troublesome cracks.

72. Disadvantages of Paneling—If too much paneling of a dark color is used in a room, the lighting in the room may be impaired. (2) The cost is generally slightly more than for plastered walls.

73. Material—The material may be clear pine, "knotty" pine, clear cypress, "pecky" cypress, redwood, Douglas fir, etc. (Consult your architect or lumber mill.)

74. Type of Paneling—Type may be as shown by Pl. 18, Figs. 1 to 28, or other miscellaneous types illustrated in the literature of the various lumber associations.

75. Type of Construction—For methods of erecting paneling, see Pl. 18, Figs. 1 to 28.

STAIRWORK

76. General—Stairwork should be of such material and construction that it will stand up under the wear and abuse that it will normally receive, without deterioration.

77. Type of Stair—Stairs may be either of the closed string or open string type (Pl. 18, Figs. 29 and 30). The type chosen should depend upon the architectural requirements and the choice of the owner.

78. Type of Construction—See Pl. 18, Figs. 29 to 35.

79. "Rise" and "Run"—The RISE (height from top of one step to top of the next) should be 7″ to 7½″. The RUN (horizontal distance from the face of one riser to the face of the next) should be approximately 10″. The *sum* of the RISE and the RUN should be 17″ to 17½″. If these dimensions vary much, the stair will not only be difficult to walk up and down, but may be dangerous, as well.

80. Material for Treads — Tread material should usually match that of the flooring, and should have a 1-1/16 minimum thickness, and a round nosing.

81. Material for Risers—This material may match that of treads or may be any species of interior finishing wood desired. A relatively hard species (yellow pine, Douglas fir, etc.) of a 1-1/16" minimum thickness is recommended, as the toes of a person's shoes will dent wood that is too soft.

82. Material for Miscellaneous Parts—Miscellaneous stair parts, such as newels, rails, balusters, etc., are generally obtained from large millwork concerns as stock parts; and may be obtained in a choice of materials such as pine, oak, and birch. See Pars. 2 to 4.

FINISH FLOORING

83. Oak Flooring—Oak flooring is the most desirable flooring for residences.

Grades Available—There are six grades, as follows: (1) Clear, quarter sawed. (2) Sap clear, quarter sawed. (3) Select, quarter sawed. (4) Clear, plain sawed. (5) Select, plain sawed. (6) No. 1 common, plain sawed.

Sizes Available—Flooring, tongued and grooved at sides and ends, is available in the following sizes: 25/32" thick by 1½", 2", 2¼" or 3¼" wide.

84. Maple Flooring—Maple flooring will probably withstand more rough usage than any other type.

Grades Available — There are three standard grades: First, Second, and Third.

Sizes Available—Standard sizes are 25/32" thick by 1½", 2", 2¼", or 3¼" wide.

85. Softwood Flooring — The so-called softwoods are sometimes used for finish flooring, especially those to be painted or covered by linoleum, etc.

Species and Grades—See Par. 19, P. 108.

Sizes Available — The standard thicknesses are 25/32", 1-1/16", and 1-5/16". The face widths, which vary for the different species of wood, include: 1½", 2⅜", and 3¼" for Southern pine flooring; 2⅜", 3¼", and 5-3/16" for Douglas fir and Western hemlock flooring; and 2¼", 3¼", and 5¼" for Western larch flooring.

86. Suggested Materials—The material used should depend on the home builder's personal preferences, and the amount he wishes to spend on flooring. The following suggestions are offered, however, for flooring the average home:

Living-Room, Dining-Room, and Hall—White oak or red oak flooring of "Clear, Plain Sawed", or "Select, Plain Sawed" grade.

Kitchen—Softwood flooring (such as southern yellow pine) of a "B" and Better or "No. 1" grade, covered with heavy, inlaid linoleum.

Bedroom—Oak, maple, or softwood flooring of desired grade.

87. Thickness—A floor thickness of 25/32" is recommended. The thinner types cost slightly less for material but are more expensive to lay; will "squeak" and become warped; will soon become unsightly in appearance; and will have insufficient thickness to allow for future scraping and sanding.

88. Width—A 2¼" width for the oak and maple, and 2¼" or 2⅜" width for the softwoods, are good average widths. The less the width, the less danger of cracks, warping, squeaking, etc.

FINISH HARDWARE

89. Definition — Finish hardware consists of door hinges and locks, window pulls and locks, screen brackets, door closers, and all similar exposed hardware.

90. Importance of Good Hardware — A person's home may well be judged to a great extent by the quality of the finish hardware. For, when one visits a home where all the exposed hardware is rusty and dilapidated in appearance, he may safely estimate that the builder "cut corners" at other points, too. To build a home for a lifetime's use and yet install in it finish hardware that will become unsightly in a year or so is, self-evidently, a short-sighted policy. It is recommended, therefore, that all finish hardware be of a good grade of a reputable brand.

91. Selecting Hardware—The home builder should take his house plans to several hardware stores to obtain "bids" for the hardware needed. (The hardware dealers will gladly go over the plans and list the items that are necessary.) Bids should be for competitive brands of equal quality.

92. Kind and Quality—This will depend upon the desires of the home builder, and the amount he spends. The following recommendations are offered, however:

Exterior Hinges — All exterior exposed hinges should have hot-dipped galvanized butts and brass pins.

Interior Hinges—Hinges with loosely-fitted steel butts and pins, and primed with a coat of flat paint, are recommended.

Door Locks—Locks with bronze or brass exposed parts are recommended throughout the residence, except that in the kitchen and bathroom the knobs may be chromium plated; and in the bedrooms, the knobs may be of glass.

INSULATION OF DWELLINGS

GENERAL DISCUSSION

1. Importance of Insulation — Properly insulated dwellings are more comfortable in both winter and summer, as the insulation helps prevent heat from passing *out* of the house in cold weather, or *into* the house in warm weather. Also, insulated dwellings are much more economical to heat in the winter.

2. Heat Losses—Heat is lost from a dwelling in two ways, as follows:

Air Leakage—Cold air leaking through cracks or crevices in or around windows, doors, walls, etc., tends to cool off the house in the winter.

Heat Transmission—Heat passing through the materials of the walls, floors, and roof tends to make the house cold in winter, and hot in summer.

TABLE 1.—*Approximate Fuel Savings in Dwelling Houses*

(Expressed in Percentage of Fuel Which Would Have Been Required for Similar House Without Insulation or Weather Stripping)	SAVING
	Per Cent
No Insulation, Weather Stripped	15 to 20.
Same With Double (Storm) Windows	25 to 30.
½-Inch Insulation, Not Weather Stripped	20 to 30.
½-Inch Insulation, Weather Stripped	About 40.
½-Inch Insulation, With Double Windows	About 50.
1-Inch Insulation, Not Weather Stripped	30 to 40.
1-Inch Insulation, Weather Stripped	About 50.
1-Inch Insulation, With Double Windows	About 60.

(Expressed in Percentage of Fuel Which Would Have Been Required for Similar House Without Insulation But With Weather Stripping)	Per Cent
With Double Windows, No Insulation	10 to 15.
½-Inch Insulation Only	25 to 35.
½-Inch Insulation, With Double Windows	40 to 45.
1-Inch Insulation Only	35 to 45.
1-Inch Insulation With Double Windows	50 to 55.

(Reprinted from Reference R11-2, Sec. 38)

BUILDING PAPER

3. Definition—Building paper consists of a felt or paper for use between sub floors and finish floors, exterior wall sheathing and exterior wall finish, and roof sheathing and roof covering. See Pl. 15, Item 4.

4. Function—Building paper should not only protect the wood underneath from moisture, but should reduce to a minimum the passage of air through the floors, walls, or roof.

5. Desired Properties — Building paper should be strong, moisture-proof, resistant to air penetration, and rot-proof. Also, it should not expand and contract an appreciable amount when the weather varies, as excessive expansion will cause tears around nail heads. Table 2 indicates the relative desirability of the several types of building paper, from a standpoint of the first three requirements.

TABLE 2.—*Physical and Mechanical Properties of Building Paper*

GROUP	Weight of 1,000 Square Feet	Tensile Breaking Strength, Pounds Per Inch	Tearing Resistance	Time Required for Penetration of Water Through Paper	Air Permeability (20-Mile Wind), Cubic Feet Per Square Foot Per Minute
A (Asphalt Saturated):	Pounds	Width		Minutes	
1	163	30.1	726	900	0.007
2	66	31.2	181	60	.006
3	101	57.2	319	2,500	None
P (Paraffin Saturated):					
1	35	60.8	146	35	None
2	26	36.4	99	17	None
3	18	29.6	58	7	None
L (Laminated Papers):					
1	63	97.2	362	2,500	None
2	47	60.9	245	1,100	None
3	44	34.8	102	13	.004
M (Machine-finished Papers):					
1	188	22.4	528	4	.365
2	40	28.0	111	3	.013
3	111	65.2	637	30	.022

(Reprinted from Reference R11-6, Sec. 38)

6. Control of Air Leakage—Building paper, properly applied to the sheathing of a frame house, will practically eliminate all air infiltration, as indicated by Table 3.

TABLE 3.—*Air Infiltration Through Frame Walls*[1]

(Average Wind Velocity of 15 Miles Per Hour)

TYPE OF CONSTRUCTION	Infiltration in Cubic Feet Per Hour Per Square Foot Area	TYPE OF CONSTRUCTION	Infiltration in Cubic Feet Per Hour Per Square Foot Area
D and M Sheathing	12.3	24-Inch Shingles, Paper and Sheathing	.13
Insulation A	16.1	Sheathing and Paper	.31
Insulation B	9.1	Wood Lath and Plaster	.17
Corrugated Steel Siding	26.8	Wood Lath, Plaster, and Wall Paper	.10
Drop Siding, Paper and Sheathing	.19	Metal Lath and Plaster	.23
Bevel Siding, Paper and Sheathing	.28	Siding with 2 Coats Paint, Paper, Sheathing, Wood Lath, and Plaster	.16
16-Inch Shingles, Paper and Ship-Lap	.17		

[1]The air infiltration through frame wall construction, containing building paper or plaster properly applied, is negligibly small.

(Reprinted from Reference R11-6, Sec. 38)

7. Where Needed—It is recommended that all sub floors and sheathing be covered with a building paper of the minimum weights and qualities specified in Par. 9. All paper should be of a reputable brand.

8. Methods of Application—See Pls. 7, 15 to 20, and 23.

9. Material and Weights—The following materials and *minimum* weights are recommended:

Floors — First choice (on account of fire-proofness): Asbestos felt weighing not less than 14 lbs. per 100 sq. feet. Second choice: Asphalt-saturated rag felt of same weight.

Exterior Wall Sheathing—Same as "second choice" above, except that for brick veneer construction a minimum weight of 30 lbs. per 100 sq. feet is recommended; and for wood shingle side walls rosin-sized paper, weighing not less than 4 lbs. per 100 sq. feet, is recommended.

Roof Sheathing—An asphalt-saturated rag felt is recommended for all roof areas; except that for wood shingle roofs a rosin-sized paper, weighing not less than 4 lbs. per 100 sq. feet, is recommended. A minimum felt weight of 15 lbs. per 100 sq. feet is recommended for light weight roofs, and 30 lbs. per 100 sq. feet for heavier roofs. The latter weight felt for all roofs is preferable.

CAULKING

10. Definition — Caulking, as herein defined, consists of applying an elastic caulking compound (usually by means of pressure) around the outer edges of exterior door and window frames. See Pls. 16 and 17.

11. Function—The function of caulking is to prevent moisture and air from entering around the door and window frames. This helps to prevent the wood frames from decaying, and makes the house warmer in winter.

12. Faults of Caulking Compounds—Most caulking compounds deteriorate, due to a loss of adhesiveness and elasticity caused by the oils in the compound evaporating, oxidizing, or being soaked up by the adjacent masonry or wood. U. S. Government tests indicate that it is not sufficient to specify caulking compounds by brand alone, as even some of the best brands may vary in quality due to lack of systematic and rigorous control of the raw materials comprising the compound.

13. Where Needed—The joints of all door and window frames set in masonry should be caulked in the manner shown by Pls. 16 and 17. Also, it is advisable, but not always absolutely necessary, to have the

underside of all window sills set in wood frame construction caulked as shown by Pl. 16, Figs. 1, 2, 3, and 8.

14. Material—For types of material (elastic caulking compound, oakum, and roofers cement) to be used at various points, refer to Pls. 16 and 17. All caulking compound used should be of a reputable, time-tested brand which should have the following qualities, in so far as possible: (1) Adhesiveness. (2) Permanent elasticity. (3) Waterproofness. (4) Minimum shrinkage with age. (5) Permanence.

15. Workmanship—Caulking is a fairly simple procedure, when one gets the "hang" of it, and need not necessarily be performed by a highly paid mechanic. It should be performed, however, by a person who is thoroughly conscientious, reliable, and capable of making a clean-cut, first-class job.

16. Supplementing Caulking — Caulking, where needed is indispensable from the standpoint of preventing decay and corrosion. However, as even the best caulking compound eventually requires replacing when exposed to the elements, all cracks to be caulked should be made as watertight as possible by other permanent means (such as copper flashing) in addition to the caulking.

WEATHER STRIPPING

17. Definition—Weather stripping consists of the proper fitting of strips (usually of metal) around doors and windows to minimize the air infiltration at these points.

18. Advantages — Weather stripping will, under average conditions, reduce by 15% to 20% the amount of fuel required for a house that is not especially insulated (see Table 1). Therefore, for all except very mild climates, weather stripping should pay for itself in a very few years.

19. Type of Weather Stripping—There are a number of good weather strips on the market; and as each type has its own special features, only the following general recommendations for minimum requirements are given:

Exterior Doors—Use a weatherproof type bronze sill, in combination with an interlocking bronze weather strip, at the bottom; and use flat, spring bronze strips at the top and sides.

Double-Hung Sash—Use an interlocking type of weather stripping at the sides and meeting rails; and use a vertical strip, designed to enter a groove in the sash, at the sill and head.

20. Material—Phosphor bronze or zinc are suitable, the bronze being preferable for exterior doors. All nails should be permanently rust-proof.

21. Specifying Weather Stripping—The home builder should allow representatives of several well-known brands of weather stripping to show him their working models and make suggestions as to the type best suited to his needs. He can then make an itemized list and description of the various weather stripping of each brand that he may be interested in, and arrange for a bid on each brand. (It is much cheaper to install weather stripping when the house is being built than afterwards.)

22. Selecting a Representative—Only representatives who install reputable brands of weather stripping should be considered. Then, only such representatives who have a reputation for satisfactory installations should be allowed to bid. Check up on their previous jobs through the home owner, and through reliable general contractors.

23. Good Workmanship Necessary—The proper installation of weather stripping requires the services of a skillful, conscientious workman who is not only an expert at handling a wood plane but also at trimming, fitting, and nailing the strips. An inferior type of weather stripping, expertly installed, is far better than the best weather stripping poorly installed.

THERMAL INSULATION

24. Definition—Thermal insulation, as herein defined, is the proper use of insulating materials in a dwelling for the purpose of reducing heat transmission (see Par. 2).

25. Advantages—In view of the great saving in fuel afforded by thermal insulation, its use in cold climates is almost necessary from a standpoint of economy, alone. Even in mild or warm climates, its use in the attic (or under the roof) is advisable from a standpoint of comfort in summer as well as in winter.

26. Where to Insulate—It is estimated that the total saving in fuel for an insulated house (exclusive of weather stripping) is obtained approximately as follows: (1) Insulation of attic or roof = 60% saving. (2) Insulation of outside walls = 20% saving. (3) Insulation of windows by use of storm sash = 20% saving. Therefore, it is seen that the insulation of the attic or roof is of greater importance than that of the side walls and windows combined.

27. Types of Insulation—Table 4 gives the relative insulating value of a number of common building and insulating materials. For a complete list of such materials, see Ref. R10-4, Sec. 38. Only several of these materials will be discussed here.

28. Storm Sash—Storm sash used in combination with the regular sash provide an air space, which is a good thermal insulation (see Tables 1 and 4).

29. Erroneous Beliefs—Although it is popularly supposed that solid masonry walls are good insulators against heat and cold, such beliefs are erroneous as will be seen from Tables 4 and 5.

TABLE 4.—*Resistance to Heat Loss, or Insulating Value, of Building Materials*

(The greater the resistance, the greater the insulating value)

Material	Thickness (Inches)	Insulating Value (Resistance)
Air Space (Over ¾″ in Width) Faced With Ordinary Building Materials		0.91
Aluminum Foil: (a) Air Space (Over ¾″ in Width) Faced on One Side With Bright Aluminum Foil		2.17
(b) Air Space Divided Into Two Spaces With a Single Curtain of Bright Aluminum Foil (Both Sides Bright). Each Space Over ¾″ Wide		4.35
Balsam Wool	0.55	2.10
Brickwork	4	0.80
Cabots Quilt	0.35	1.39
Celotex	7/16	1.39
Compressed Cement-Asbestos Sheets	1	0.37
Concrete	6	0.72
Flax-li-num	0.56	1.80
Gyplap	½	0.38
Hollow Building Tile	4	1.16
Inso Board	7/16	1.33
Insulite	½	1.47
Masonite	7/16	1.33
Mineral Wool or Glass Wool	1	3.70
Sheet Rock	⅜	0.27
Stucco	1½	0.187
Wood Sheathing	25/32	0.98

TABLE 5.—*Heat Loss Through Different Wall Types*

(The smaller figures indicate higher insulating values)

Wall Type	Heat Loss
1. Frame Wall, Wood Siding, Building Paper, Wood Sheathing, Wood Lath and Plaster	.190
2. Frame Wall, Wood Siding, Building Paper, ½-Inch Rigid Insulating Board Sheathing, Wood Lath and Plaster	.175
3. Frame Wall, Wood Siding, Building Paper, Wood Sheathing, ½-Inch Rigid Insulating Board Plaster Base, Plaster	.156
4. Frame Wall, Wood Siding, Building Paper, Wood Sheathing, Wood Lath and Plaster, With ½-Inch Felt or Quilt Insulation Between Studs	.125
5. Frame Wall, 4-Inch Brick Veneer, Building Paper, Wood Sheathing, Wood Lath and Plaster	.175
6. Frame Wall, 4-Inch Brick Veneer, ½-Inch Rigid Insulating Board Sheathing, Wood Lath and Plaster	.160
7. Frame Wall, 4-Inch Brick Veneer, Building Paper, ½-Inch Rigid Insulating Board Plaster Base and Plaster	.145
8. Frame Wall, 4-Inch Brick Veneer, Building Paper, Wood Sheathing, Wood Lath and Plaster, With ½-Inch Felt or Quilt Insulation Between Studs	.118
9. 8-Inch Brick Wall, ¾-Inch Plaster on Brick	.420
10. 8-Inch Brick Wall, ¾-Inch Plaster on Wood Lath, Furred	.280
11. 8-Inch Brick Wall, Plaster on Rigid Insulation Board, Furred	.208
12. 8-Inch Hollow Building Tile Wall, Stucco Exterior Finish, ¾-Inch Plaster on Tile	.280
13. 8-Inch Hollow Building Tile Wall, Stucco Exterior Finish, ¾-Inch Plaster on Wood Lath, Furred	.210
14. 8-Inch Hollow Building Tile Wall, Stucco Exterior Finish, Plaster on ½-Inch Rigid Insulating Board, Furred	.167

(Reprinted from Reference R11-6, Sec. 38)

30. Mineral Wool—There are several types of this material. Although all types have practically the same insulating value, some types are more fire resistant than others.

Advantages—Mineral wool has the following advantages: (1) High insulating value (see Table 4). (2) Fire resistance. (3) Vermin-proofness. (4) Permanence.

Disadvantages—Some types of mineral wool have the following disadvantages: (1) When used in a closed space (such as a studded side wall) it tends to become saturated with dampness, which reduces its insulating value, and promotes decay of the adjacent woodwork. (2) When used in side walls it tends to "settle", and thus leave spaces in the wall that are not insulated.

31. Aluminum Foil—Aluminum foil is used to increase the insulating value of air spaces, by reducing heat transfer by radiation. Aluminum foil should always *face* or *divide* an air space that is at least 3/4" wide. It is most effective when *dividing* an air space (see Table 4), as it will increase the insulating value of the original (single) air space by an amount equivalent to about 1 1/4" of insulating board; it is half as effective when *facing* an air space; and it has no insulating value when placed between solid materials, such as between sheathing and clapboards or shingles, etc.

Advantages—Aluminum foil insulation has the following advantages: (1) Good insulating qualities when used properly. (2) Moisture-proofness. (3) Waterproofness. (4) Vermin-proofness. (5) Permanency under ordinary conditions. (6) Forms a "vapor barrier" (Par. 34) between the warm, humid inside air of house and the air in side walls and attic, and thereby minimizes the accumulation of condensation in the side walls and attic.

Permanency—Tests indicate that, under average conditions, aluminum foil will retain its insulating properties indefinitely. Tests also indicate that an average amount of dust accumulation on the foil does not materially reduce its efficiency. (See Ref. R12-3, Sec. 38.)

32. Suggested Insulation — When selecting any type of insulation, the following requirements should be kept in mind: (1) Good insulating qualities. (2) Moisture-proofness and waterproofness. (3) Vermin-proofness. (4) Permanency.

With the above requirements in mind, the following recommendations are offered:

Attic (No Floor)—For attics without floors and which have the joists exposed, a standard (3 5/8") thickness of mineral wool placed between all joists, is recommended.

Attic (With Floor, but no Ceiling)—For such attics, it is recommended that a standard (3 5/8") thickness of mineral wool be placed between the rafters.

Attic (Finished-Off for Living Quarters) — For such attics, where mineral wool (if used) would be entirely enclosed and, therefore, subject to becoming damp, the following is recommended: (1) Provide a sheet of aluminum foil insulation between the rafters and side wall studding of the attic in such a manner that the air space formed by the roof and ceiling, and the air space formed by the interior side walls and outside sheathing, will be divided approximately in half (see Table 4); or, (2) use a fibrous insulating board (see Table 4) to form the ceiling and side walls of attic. Such insulating board may be merely painted, or it may be plastered.

Side Walls—Aluminum foil insulation is recommended for all exterior side walls, as it provides a good insulation without the danger of its becoming moisture-soaked, and thus causing decay, as might be the case with some types of insulation. For best results, a sheet of aluminum foil placed in the studded wall in such a manner as to divide the air space approximately in half, is recommended. However, where one-half this amount of insulation will be satisfactory, an insulating type of plaster base (metal lath, gypsum board, etc.), which has a sheet of aluminum foil attached to the backside of it, may be used. (See Table 4.)

33. Windows—In cold climates, the insulation of windows by the use of storm sash is recommended from a standpoint of comfort and economy.

34. Vapor Barrier—Where mineral wool insulation is enclosed in studded side walls or the attic, a "vapor barrier" should be provided *between the warm, humid inside air of the house and the mineral wool,* so as to minimize condensation within the mineral wool. This vapor barrier should preferably consist of a sheet of aluminum foil placed between the plaster base and the supporting framework (side wall studs, attic joists, etc.). Also, the attic should be suitably ventilated. (See Ref. R12-5 and R12-6, Sec. 38.)

SHEET METAL WORK

FLASHINGS

1. Definition—Flashings are strips of metal used as shown by Pls. 19 to 21, to form a leakproof seal at various vulnerable points of a dwelling.

2. Importance of Flashings—Flashings are one of the most important items of a dwelling, as may readily be surmised from Par. 1, above. Any dwelling that is not properly flashed will be a source of constant worry and expense to its owner, due to leaks and subsequent stained walls, cracked plaster, decayed woodwork, etc. The only safe method of economizing on flashings is to select a simple type of dwelling construction that does not require many flashings. See Par. 19, P. 24.

3. Usual Defects — The flashings of the average dwelling usually have some, or all, of the following defects: (1) Flashings omitted from vital points. (2) Material too thin, and of a type that corrodes away in a few years. (3) Insufficient overlap for flashings. (4) Edges of flashings for chimneys, etc., merely "stuck" into a shallow groove in the masonry by means of a short-lived elastic cement (see Par. 12, P. 135), instead of being *built* into the masonry.

4. Metals Used for Flashings—These are as follows:

Copper—Copper is the ideal metal for flashings as it is, in most cases, permanent (Table 1, P. 75), is easily fabricated, and requires no painting. When used in locations where the fumes of ammonia or certain acids are in the air, copper may deteriorate rapidly; otherwise, its only disadvantage is its slight extra cost as compared, for example, to galvanized iron or tin.

Galvanized Sheet Steel — Galvanized sheet steel ("galvanized iron") consists of a sheet of mild steel coated with zinc. Due to the fact that zinc is anodic, and not cathodic to iron (Par. 4, P. 73), the sheet steel core will not be subject to rapid corrosion due to *small* cracks or scratches in the protective coating or due to cut edges. However, this material is unsuited for items having sharp bends because of the likelihood of cracking the zinc coating; and it should be kept painted, for best results.

Tin—This material usually consists, not of pure tin, but of sheets of mild steel plated with tin. Once the soft tin coating is broken, the steel core corrodes very rapidly due to electrolysis (Par. 4, P. 73). "Tin" flashings should be kept painted, especially the uncoated cut edges; however, in most cases, it is practically impossible to paint all the surfaces requiring paint.

Lead—Lead, when used for flashings, has a number of disadvantages as it is heavy, expensive, and subject to serious corrosion if exposed to an accumulation of coal cinders or decaying organic matter (leaves, etc.) that might accumulate on, or around, the flashings.

5. Material Recommended—16-ounce copper is recommended. The additional cost for this material will be insignificant in comparison with the repair bills that it will save you.

6. Type of Construction Recommended — See Pls. 19 to 21.

7. Workmanship—All flashings should be installed in a careful and workmanlike manner. Where practicable, all flashings inserted in masonry shall be *built in* as the masonry work progresses, instead of being inserted into a shallow groove in the finished masonry and "stuck" there with elastic cement. The latter type of construction may not only leak, but will require periodic repair and replacement of the elastic cement.

GUTTERS AND LEADERS (DOWNSPOUTS)

8. Why Necessary—Gutters and leaders are necessary for catching the storm (rain) water that falls upon the roof areas, and for conducting such water into a suitable drainage system.

9. Usual Defects — The usual defects of gutters, leaders, and their accessories are: (1) Material too thin, and of a type that corrodes away in a few years. (2) Gutters too small. (3) Outlets too small and of improper shape. (4) Gutters improperly supported. (5) Gutter supports, or attachments, of a type that deteriorates rapidly. (6) Expansion and contraction not provided for. (7) Lack of scuppers or over-flow drains. (8) Improper provision for snow and ice. (9) Failure to connect the leaders to a suitable drainage system.

10. Kinds of Gutters—There are two general classes of gutters. These are "hanging gutters" and "box gutters". See Fig. 1 and Pl. 22, Fig. 33.

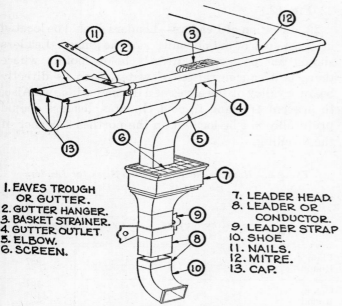

I. EAVES TROUGH	7. LEADER HEAD.
OR GUTTER.	8. LEADER OR
2. GUTTER HANGER.	CONDUCTOR.
3. BASKET STRAINER.	9. LEADER STRAP
4. GUTTER OUTLET.	10. SHOE.
5. ELBOW.	11. NAILS.
6. SCREEN.	12. MITRE.
	13. CAP.

FIG. 1.—*Half-round Hanging Gutter*

11. Hanging Gutters—This class of gutters is free from the roof and requires suitable support brackets (Fig. 1). A discussion of the several types of hanging gutters follows:

Half-Round Hanging Gutter—This type (Pl. 22, Figs. 1 to 3) is usually the most economical and, consequently, is the most widely used type of all gutters. Standard sizes of this type are usually carried in stock by the sheet metal contractor. The most serious disadvantage of this type of gutter is the fact that it sticks out from the roof like a "sore thumb", partly hiding (and thereby spoiling) the effect of any adjacent cornice.

Molded Gutters—This type of gutter (Pl. 22, Figs. 4 to 11) is more ornamental and pleasing in appearance than is the half-round type. Molded gutters may be slightly more expensive than half-round gutters—their cost depending, of course, on the particular shape required.

12. Box Gutters—This class of gutters includes the various types of gutters that are formed by a metal lining built into solid supporting framework at the edge of the roof (Pl. 22, Fig. 33). Box gutters are

used on better-class residences where it is desired to obtain proper roof drainage without marring the beauty of the cornice. Such gutters are special and expensive; and if not properly designed and installed, they are likely to be a source of trouble and expense due to leaks, overflow, etc.

13. Types of Gutters Recommended—These are:

Gutter for Low Cost Dwellings—A stock type of molded gutter is recommended, as such gutters cost very little more than half-round gutters, and their use will add considerably to the appearance of the dwelling. See Pl. 22, Figs. 4 to 11.

Gutter for Medium Cost Dwellings—An appropriately shaped molded gutter is recommended. See Pl. 22, Figs. 4 to 11.

Gutter for High Cost Dwellings—An appropriately shaped molded gutter is recommended. For the more pretentious type of dwelling, the built-in type of gutter may be considered; however, such gutters should be designed and built with the greatest of care to guard against leaks due to cracks, overflow, etc.

14. Material Recommended—See Par. 5.

15. Factors That Determine Size of Gutters—The following factors should be considered when selecting the size of gutters: (1) Area of the roofs to be served. (2) Pitch of roof. (3) Class and type of gutter. (4) Size, number, and location of leaders. (5) Severity of local rainfalls.

16. Rules for Selecting Size of Gutters—For gutters that are free to overflow occasionally without harmful effects, the minimum size may be selected on the following basis:

Minimum Size—A gutter less than 4″ wide should never be used, due to the difficulty and expense of soldering such gutters. Also, a gutter should never be smaller than the leaders (Par. 20 and Table 2). If a half-round hanging gutter is used, a 5″ minimum size is recommended for average use.

Leader Spacing 50 Feet or Less—When the leaders are spaced 50 feet or less, the gutters may be of the same size as leaders.

Leader Spacing More Than 50 Feet—When the leaders are spaced more than 50 feet, the gutter should be 1″ larger than the leader for every additional 20 feet (or fraction thereof) of such additional leader spacing.

Ratio of Depth to Width for Box Gutters—Box gutters should have a depth of from ½ to their mean (average) width.

Widths and Depths of Molded Gutters—Standard proportions are given in Table 1.

TABLE 1.—*Recommended Proportions for Molded Gutters*
(For Figs. 4 to 11 referred to below, see Pl. 22)

Fig. No.	Width (Inches)	Depth (Inches)	Girth (Inches)
4	5 6 7	3½ 4¼ 4½	12 14 16
5	6 7 8	4 5 5¾	15 18 20
6	6 7 8	5½ 6½ 7	18 20 22
7	6 7 8	4 4¾ 5½	14 16 18
8	6 7 8	4½ 5½ 7	15 18 22
9	6 7 8	5½ 5¾ 6	18 20 22
10	5 5¼ 5½	2¾ 3½ 4¼	10 12 14
11	6 7 9	5¾ 6½ 8	18 20 24

17. Slope of Gutters—Gutters should be pitched not less than 1/16″ per foot, if possible, for proper drainage. For box gutters and molded gutters, a lesser amount of pitch may be necessary for architectural or mechanical reasons. Each half of a long gutter should slope in an opposite direction towards its leader.

18. Accessories for Gutters—Miscellaneous gutter accessories are shown by Pl. 22. All such accessories should preferably be of copper, brass, or bronze, so as to give a lifetime of service.

19. Location of Gutters at Eaves—Hanging gutters should be so placed that a straightedge laid along the roof (in the direction of slope) will bear lightly against the upper, outer edge of the gutter. If gutters are too low, the roof water will pass over them; and if gutters are too high, they will act as a barrier for snow that may collect on the roof, and may thus become damaged.

20. Size of Leaders—As in the case of gutters, the proper size of leaders (also called conductors and downspouts) depend on many variable factors. It is safe, however, to figure on approximately one square inch of leader cross-sectional area for each 100 square feet of roof area (computed area based on measurements taken along slope of roof). The sizes given in Table 2 are based on this rule.

21. Shape of Leaders—The most economical leader shape is the plain round. However, for cold climates where freezing of water in the leader is likely, a shape such as the corrugated round, that will allow a certain amount of "stretch", is recommended. See Pl. 22, Fig. 13.

22. Location of Leaders—Leaders should be located near the ends of outside mitres of the gutter. Leaders should not be located directly below points where there is a concentration of water, such as directly below a valley or the eaves of a dormer window. Also, to prevent freezing in cold climates, leaders should preferably not be located on the northeast corner of the dwelling.

TABLE 2.—*Recommended Minimum Sizes for Leaders*
(Refer to Pl. 22, Figs. 12 to 15)

Type	Nominal Size (Inches)	Area (Sq. In.)	Roof Area Drained (Sq. Ft.)
Plain Round	3 4 5	7.07 12.57 19.63	707 1257 1963
Corrugated Round	3 4 5	5.94 11.04 17.72	594 1104 1772
Plain Rectangular	1¾ x 2¼ 2 x 3 2 x 4 3 x 4 4 x 5	3.94 6.00 8.00 12.00 20.00	394 600 800 1200 2000
Corrugated Rectangular	1¾ x 2¼ (2) 2⅜ x 3¼ (3) 2¾ x 4¼ (4) 3¾ x 5 (5)	3.80 7.73 11.70 18.75	380 773 1170 1875
Polygon or Octagonal	3 4 5	6.36 11.30 17.65	636 1130 1765

23. Inside Leaders—All leaders, when placed within the walls of the dwelling, should be cast iron, or extra heavy galvanized wrought iron pipe.

24. Connecting Leaders to Underground Drains—See Par. 13, P. 159.

TABLE 3.—*Thickness and Weights of Copper and Galvanized Steel Sheets*

Material	Size	Thickness (Inches)[1]	Weight Per Sq. Ft. (Pounds)
Copper	16-oz. 18-oz. 20-oz.	.0216 .0243 .027	1 1⅛ 1¼
Galvanized Steel	26-Ga. 25-Ga. 24-Ga. 16-Ga.	.0184 .0214 .0245 .0613	.768 .902 1.017 2.553

[1]Thickness given for steel does not include zinc coating.

ROOFING

1. Usual Defects of Roofing—These are: (1) Insufficient pitch of roof, especially porch and dormer roofs, for type of roofing material used. (2) Use of a "cheap" grade of asphalt composition shingle that blisters and curls up under the sun's rays; lifts up and stands on-end during heavy storms; and, after a few years exposure, presents a very sorry appearance. (3) Roof of a hideous color, architecturally. (4) Roof improperly constructed, and improperly flashed.

TYPES OF ROOFING

2. General—The types of roofing that will be discussed here are: Slate, rigid cement-asbestos, clay tile, Portland cement tile, sheet metal, asphalt-felt, and wood. For probable useful life of roofing, see Table 2, P. 173.

3. Slate Shingle Roofs — Slate shingle roofs may consist of: (1) A "Standard" slate roof for which the "Commercial Standard" slate shingle (having a thickness of approximately 3/16") is used. (2) A "Textural" slate roof, for which a rough textured slate having uneven butts and a variation of size and thickness (thickness does not generally exceed ⅜") is used. (3) A "Graduated" slate roof, which is a textural roof for which larger sized slate, having a greater variation in thickness, size, and color, are used.

Advantages—(1) Beauty. (2) Permanence. (3) Fire-resistance.

Disadvantages—(1) Cost. (2) Weight (makes heavy framing members necessary). (3) High heat conductivity (poor insulation). (4) Susceptibility to damage from hail or frost action, or by being walked upon directly. (5) Difficult to repair or alter.

4. Rigid Cement-Asbestos Shingles — These shingles are available in three styles, which are: American Method, Dutch Lap Method, and Hexagonal Method. Each style is laid in a different manner, as shown by Pl. 23, Figs. 9 to 11. Thicknesses vary from 3/16" for Standard grades, to 5/16" for Heavy grades.

Advantages—(1) Pleasing appearance (may be obtained to imitate wood shingles). (2) Long life. (3) Fire-resistance. (4) Moderate cost.

Disadvantages—(1) Susceptibility to damage from hail or frost action, or by being walked upon directly. (2) Difficult to repair or alter. (3) Color of some types tend to fade, causing roof to have a dingy appearance.

5. Clay Tile Roofs — Clay tile is architecturally suited to certain types of houses.

Advantages (Hard Tile)—(1) Permanence. (2) Fire-resistance. (3) Has an insulating value better than slate. (4) Is easier to repair than slate.

Disadvantages—(1) Cost. (2) Weight (makes heavy framing members necessary). (3) Driving rains may get under tile, thus making the use of a watertight under-roofing necessary.

6. Cement Tile Roofs—This material has practically the same advantages and disadvantages of clay tile, except that it has the added advantage of being moderate in cost, and the added disadvantage of being somewhat lacking in strength.

7. Sheet Metal Roofs — Sheet metal is sometimes used for roofs, especially low pitched and flat roofs.

Advantages—If 10-ounce (or heavier) copper is used and properly installed, the roof should have a long life.

Disadvantages—(1) High heat conductivity (poor insulation). (2) Iron and steel roofs are subject to corrosion, and require periodic painting. (3) Copper roofs are relatively high in cost.

8. Asphalt-Felt Roofs—There are three types of this roofing, which are: Roll Roofing, Builtup Roofing, and Flexible Shingles. The life of such roofing may vary from 5 to 20 years. A shorter life may be expected in hot climates than in cold or moderate climates.

Roll Roofing—This roofing is cheaper than the other two types, but is less durable, and requires periodic repair.

Built-Up Roofing—This roofing is economical, and is satisfactory for covering flat roofs that are not exposed to view. If installed in accordance with the best practice, such roofing may last 15 years or longer.

Flexible Shingles—Such shingles are made from roll roofing and, in the heavier and better grades, have the following advantages: (1) Fairly pleasing appearance. (2) Fair amount of fire-resistance. (3) Moderate cost. (4) Moderately long life. (5) Fairly easy to repair or alter.

The cheaper grades have the following disadvantages: (1) Short life. (2) Curling under the sun's heat. (3) Tendency for ends to be lifted up by driving rains, due to lack of rigidity.

9. Wood Shingles—The use of wood shingles for roofs is prohibited by law in many states and municipalities, due to their fire hazard. This fire hazard is greater than the average person realizes, because, as the shingle weathers and certain soluble portions are washed away, fine fibers are left standing which are readily ignited by any stray spark. For further discussion, see Ref. R8-6, Sec. 38.

TABLE 1.—*Costs of Roofing Materials and Application, Per Square, on a Simple Pitched Roof With No Valleys, but Including Chimney Flashings. (In Urban Centers in Southeastern States)*

[Data obtained from the Home Owners' Loan Corporation]

MATERIALS	WEIGHT PER SQUARE	COST PER SQUARE[1]		
		Minimum	Maximum	Average
ASPHALT SHINGLES:	POUNDS			
Giant Individual, 12″ × 16″, American Method	325	$ 9.50	$14.50	$10.65
Standard Individual, 9″ × 12¾″, American Method	255	8.25	13.50	9.45
4-Tab Square Butt Strip, 12½″ × 36″	266	8.25	10.40	9.00
3-Tab Square Butt Strip, 12″ × 36″ Overlay	211	6.75	9.10	7.95
2-Tab Hexagonal Strip, 11⅜″ × 36″	167	5.25	7.15	6.35
Individual Recover—Dutch Lap	125 to 140	5.25	6.90	5.85
Individual Recover—Hexagonal	125 to 140	5.25	6.80	5.90
ASPHALT ROLL ROOFING:				
Mineral-Surfaced	90	3.00	6.50	4.35
Smooth-Surfaced	55	2.50	5.90	3.55
CEMENT-ASBESTOS SHINGLES (GRAY COLOR ONLY):				
American Method		13.75	24.00	19.00
Hexagonal Method		9.50	15.25	12.35
Dutch Lap		10.80	16.75	13.00
Slate		14.00	40.00	21.00
Wood Shingles		6.00	15.00	9.15
METAL ROOFINGS:				
Shingles (Galvanized)		7.50	12.50	9.05
Five V-Crimp Sheets (Galvanized)		6.00	7.15	6.40
Standing Seam "Tin", 25-lb., Unpainted		8.25	14.00	11.70
Flat Lock and Soldered "Tin", 25-lb., Unpainted		9.25	15.00	12.80
TILE ROOFING:				
Ceramic Shingle Tile		14.40	30.00	20.20
Cement Tile		14.00	22.50	16.75
BUILT-UP ROOFING:				
Five-Ply Coal-Tar-Pitch, Surfaced With Slag or Gravel		6.75	12.00	9.55
Five-Ply Asphalt, Surfaced With Slag or Gravel		7.00	12.00	9.65

[1]100 square feet of roof surface.

(Reprinted from Reference R19-2, Sec. 38)

RECOMMENDED PRACTICE

10. General—Roofs should not only be made storm-proof and fire-resistant but, like all other exterior portions of the house, should be made as permanent and free of upkeep costs as is practicable.

11. Type of Roof Construction—The first step in securing an economical, trouble-free roof is to use a simple, practical type of roof construction (such as a gable roof), and avoid the use of "cut-up" roofs having dormers, valleys, etc. See Pl. 12, Fig. 1, and Par. 19, P. 24. The roof should also have sufficient slope for the type of roofing selected (see Table 3).

12. Type of Roofing—The choice of the roofing material depends, of course, upon the preference of the owner; the proportionate sum that is available for roofing; and the type of house being constructed. Tables 1 to 3 may prove helpful when selecting roofing.

TABLE 2.—*Guide for Selection of Roofing*

TYPE OF HOUSE	TYPE OF ROOFING	
	For Sloping Roof	For Flat Roof[1]
High Cost[2]	A, B, C, D	I
Medium Cost[3]	E, F, G, H	I, J, K
Low Cost[4]	F, G, H	J, K

[1]Any roof with less than 4″ rise in 12″, is termed a flat roof.
[2]Houses costing more than $8,000.00.
[3]Houses costing between $5,000.00 and $8,000.00.
[4]Houses costing less than $5,000.00.

Key to Table 2

A = Slate shingle (heavy weight).

B = Rigid cement-asbestos shingle, American Method (heavy).

C = Slate shingle ("Commercial Standard" thickness).

D = Rigid cement-asbestos shingles, American Method (standard weight).

E = Rigid cement-asbestos shingle, Dutch Lap Method.

F = Rigid cement-asbestos shingle, Hexagonal Method.

G = Asphalt composition shingle (heavy).

H = Asphalt composition shingle (standard weight).

I = Copper roofing (10 oz. minimum weight).

J = Built-up asphalt-felt roofing.

K = "Tin", or galvanized, copper-bearing sheet steel roofing.

13. Hips and Ridges—The choice of hips and ridges (see Pl. 23) will depend upon the preference of the owner. From a standpoint of economy, the following hips and ridges are recommended for the various types of shingle roofs:

Slate—Saddle hip and saddle ridge (Pl. 23, Figs. 1 and 5).

Rigid Cement-Asbestos—Boston hip and Boston ridge (Pl. 23, Figs. 14 and 17).

Asphalt Composition—Saddle hip and saddle ridge.

14. Valleys—Open valleys (Pl. 20, Figs. 13 and 14) are more economical, and more "fool-proof" from a standpoint of becoming clogged with leaves, etc.; whereas, closed valleys may have a somewhat better appearance. This Guide recommends the use of open valleys for the average roof.

15. Asphalt Composition Shingles — Where such shingles are used, the *minimum* weights used should be as follows:

Square Butt Shingles—210 pounds per 100 square feet, laid.

Individual Shingles—253 pounds per 100 square feet, laid.

Hexagon Shingles (If Used)—187 pounds per 100 square feet, laid.

16. Shingle Clips—Large-size asphalt composition shingles should be clipped on each outer corner with a special copper shingle clip to prevent the shingles from being lifted by high winds.

17. Roofing Felt—See Par. 9, P. 135.

18. Flashing and Gutters—See Sec. 27, P. 138.

TABLE 3.—*Minimum Slopes for Roofs*

Type of Roofing Used	Minimum Slope, Pitch, and Angle of Slope[1]		
	Slope Per Foot (Inches)	Pitch[2]	Approx. Angle of Slope (Degrees)
Slate Shingle: 3" Headlap	8	1/3	33¾
4" Headlap	4	1/6	18½
Rigid Cement-asbestos Shingle: American Method	4	1/6	18½
Dutch Lap Method	5	5/24	22½
Hexagonal Method	5	5/24	22½
Asphalt Shingle	4	1/6	18½
Clay Tile	4½	9/48	20½
Wood Shingle	6	1/4	26½
Sheet Copper Roofing: Corrugated	4	1/6	18½
Batten Seam	3	1/3	14
Standing Seam	2½	5/48	11¾
Flat Seam	¼	1/96	1¼
Built-up, Asphalt-felt Roofing	2	1/12	9½

[1]A **greater** slope than the "minimum" slope should always be used, if possible.
[2]Pitch = Height of roof divided by span; or slope in 12" divided by 24

EXTERIOR STUCCO

1. Usual Defects—These are: (1) Supporting wall of improper type and poor construction, resulting in cracks and deterioration. (2) Oversanded mortar, resulting in cracks and deterioration. (3) Imperfect embedment of metal lath, resulting in rusting and deterioration of lath. (4) Lack of proper metal flashings, resulting in leaks, decay, etc. (5) Floating of sand finish (when used) while mortar is too soft, resulting in "map" cracks.

2. Types of Stucco Bases—The following types of stucco bases are listed in numerical order, in accordance with their comparative merits as established by U. S. Government tests: (1) Monolithic concrete, *not* coated with a bituminous compound. (2) Metal lath, applied directly to the studs of a frame house and back-plastered. (3) Brick and tile. (4) Metal lath over wood sheathing. (5) Wood lath. (6) Gypsum block and plasterboard.

3. Metal Lath for Stucco—The following materials for metal lath are listed in numerical order in accordance with their comparative merits as established by U. S. Government tests: (1) Lath galvanized *after* fabrication. (2) Lath cut from galvanized sheets. (3) Painted ingot iron lath. (4) Painted steel lath. (5) Sherradized steel lath. (6) Plain ingot iron lath. (7) Plain steel lath.

4. Wood Lath—Wood lath is entirely unsuitable for use as a base for Portland cement stucco.

FINISHES FOR STUCCO

5. Importance of Finish—The type of finish used for stucco is important from both a standpoint of appearance and possibility of surface cracks. U. S. Government tests indicated that smooth sand-float finish is susceptible to fine cracks, unevenness of texture, blotches, and other small defects, more so than are rougher finishes.

6. Miscellaneous Finishes — The following comments are offered in regard to such finishes:

"Rough Cast" or "Pebble Dash", "Spatter Dash", and "Sand Spray" or "Broom Dash" Finishes—These finishes are known as wet dashes, and have the following advantages: (1) Are readily applied by workmen of ordinary skill, and thus are low in cost. (2) Their rough texture hides any fine shrinkage cracks that may develop.

"Dry Dash" Finish—Clean Pebbles, stone chips, or pieces of shell may be used for this finish. Such finishes are quite difficult to apply properly, but produce a finish of different color and texture from the wet dashes, when properly done.

Float Finish—This is a "smooth" type of finish and has the following disadvantages: (1) One of the most difficult finishes to obtain. (2) Imperfections show up conspicuously (Par. 5). (3) Highly skilled workmen are required.

Textured Finishes—Such finishes are obtainable in countless textures and colors, and make it possible to avoid the monotony of the dashes and the difficulties of applying float finishes.

Exposed Aggregate Finish — Colored aggregate ranging from ⅛" to ¼", or more, in size, depending upon the architectural features and effects desired, may be used for this finish. Such finishes are held in high regard; and the coarse aggregate, due to its density, tends to eliminate many of the usual structural defects. This finish has the disadvantage of being difficult to obtain, and requires the services of highly skilled workmen.

RECOMMENDED PRACTICE

7. Basic Requirements — Government tests indicate that, if certain basic requirements are fulfilled, it is possible to obtain stucco construction that is structurally sound, durable, and capable of giving satisfactory service over long periods with low maintenance costs. These requirements are: (1) The building must be properly designed and constructed. (2) Stucco must be applied to a suitable base. (3) The mortar must be properly proportioned and carefully mixed from good materials. (4) The stucco must be applied by *skilled workmen*.

8. Type of Construction (General)—The type of construction used should provide overhanging roofs, gutters, suitable flashings, drip grooves, cappings, etc., so as to prevent the entrance of water back of the stucco, and prevent a concentrated flow over the face of the walls. All surfaces, other than vertical, to which stucco is to be applied should be given the greatest possible slope in order to shed water readily. Sills, cornices, and copings should preferably be made of wood or cast (monolithic) concrete. Stucco on the lower edges of side walls (frame *or* masonry) should be stopped at least 12″ above grade to protect it from ground moisture.

9. Stucco on Masonry—The type of masonry backing to be used may be selected from Par. 2. Substantially constructed walls of concrete masonry should be practically as suitable a base for stucco as monolithic concrete, since the material and amount of expansion and contraction is nearly the same (and similar to stucco) in each case. Masonry walls to receive stucco should have raked joints.

10. Stucco on Wood Frame (Back-Plastered)—As noted in Par. 2, stucco applied directly to the studs of a wood frame, and back-plastered, is the best method of applying stucco to a wood frame base. This type of construction, however, has disadvantages, inasmuch as the bracing and insulating values of the sheathing (which must be omitted) are lost. Also, if building paper is omitted, dampness passing through the stucco will affect the wood studs. Therefore, if this type of construction is used, the following is recommended:

Type of Locality—It is recommended that back-plastered stucco be used only in mild, dry climates.

Type of Framing—Use type shown by Pl. 10.

Bracing—1″ x 4″ let-in bracing should be provided for all side walls. See Pars. 69 to 73, P. 124.

Building Paper—Building paper, used in the usual manner, would make back-plastered stucco ineffective, inasmuch as it would defeat the purpose by preventing the complete and positive covering of the metal lath from the rear, and by preventing the formation of panels of mortar between the studs which serve to stiffen the framework. Building paper for back-plastered stucco should, therefore, be cut into strips and wrapped partially round each stud in a manner to protect the stud from dampness, yet not to interfere with the back-plastering.

Attachment of Metal Lath—Attach directly to studs (over building paper) by means of nails or clips that will hold the reinforcement ⅜″ away from the studs.

Back-Plastering—The backside of the reinforcement should be thoroughly embedded in mortar applied from the inner side.

Insulation—To compensate for the loss of the insulating value of the sheathing, a sheet of aluminum foil or other moisture-proof insulation should be provided in the space between the studs, so as to form an additional airspace and provide insulation. See Par.

32, P. 137, and Table 4, P. 136.

11. Stucco on Wood Frame (Sheathed)—It is recommended that the average frame house that is to have stucco sidewalls, especially houses located in cold or damp climates, be *sheathed* and otherwise constructed as follows:

Type of Framing—Use type shown by Pl. 10.

Sheathing—Use horizontal sheathing. See Pars. 106 to 110, P. 126.

Bracing—Use 1″ x 4″ let-in bracing for all side walls. See Par. 69 to 73, P. 124.

Building Paper—Use heavy, waterproof type. See Par. 9, P. 135.

Attachment of Metal Reinforcement—Attach to sheathing (over building paper) by means of nails or clips that will hold the reinforcement ⅜″ away from sheathing, and thus allow the stucco to be forced behind the reinforcement and thus thoroughly embed it. Do not use wood furring strips under the metal reinforcement.

12. Specifying Metal Lath—All metal lath (metal reinforcement) should be made from galvanized (hot-dipped, preferably) copper bearing steel. The types and minimum weights recommended are as follows:

Back-Plastered Stucco—Use an expanded metal lath, weighing not less than 3.4 pounds per square yard, and having a thickness of not less than No. 24 gage (.025″).

Sheathed Construction—Use either an expanded metal lath weighing not less than 3.4 pounds per square yard, and having mesh openings about 1½″ by 3″ in size, or a woven wire lath having a wire size of not less than No. 18 gage (.0475″), and 2½ meshes to the inch.

13. Stucco—The proportions for all coats of stucco should be 1 part Portland cement to 3 parts aggregate, measured by Volume, to which may be added hydrated lime in an amount not to exceed 10 pounds per sack of cement. The requirements for materials, methods of mixing, etc., for stucco are the same as for cement mortar (Sec. 14, P. 84).

14. Number of Coats—Three coats of stucco should be used on frame structures and two coats on masonry. In fact, three coats should also be used for masonry that is not sufficiently true for two-coat work.

15. Type of Finish—The type of finish (Par. 6) will depend upon the preferences of the owner, of course. It is recommended that the sand float finishes, due to their exceptionally bad features, be avoided if possible.

INTERIOR LATHING AND PLASTERING

1. Definition—Interior lathing and plastering consists, briefly, of applying a suitable plaster base to the inside walls and ceiling of the house, and then applying the plaster (3 coats, usually) to the plaster base. See Pls. 10 and 11, Item 30.

2. Function — The primary function of interior plastering is that of decoration, but it also serves the following purposes in varying degrees: (1) It adds rigidity to the building. (2) It adds insulation value to the walls by creating an airspace (Table 4, P. 136).

3. Objectionable Features — The chief objections to plastered walls are the following: (1) The wet plaster contains hundreds of gallons of water which must evaporate inside the building, thus tending to warp the wooden framework. (2) Most plaster has a tendency to crack.

4. Usual Defects—The chief causes of cracks in plaster are the following: (1) Flimsy construction, such as undersized footings, defective framework, etc. (2) Use of an inferior plaster base, such as a poor grade of wood lath. (3) Improper mixing of plaster. (4) Omission of metal reinforcing from interior and exterior corners.

TYPES OF PLASTER BASES

5. General — The following plaster bases will be discussed: (1) Metal lath, (2) gypsum lath, (3) fiber insulating lath, and (4) wood lath.

6. Metal Lath—There are three general classes of metal lath which are: Perforated sheet, expanded metal, and woven or welded wire. Such lath may be plain or self-furring and may, or may not, have a backing of paper or other material, such as aluminum foil insulation. Also, such lath may be obtained of copper bearing metal which is asphalt-painted or galvanized.

Advantages—(1) Reduces plaster cracks. (2) Reduces fire hazard.

Disadvantages—(1) High heat conductivity (poor insulating properties). (2) Cost.

7. Gypsum Lath—Gypsum lath (or board) consists of a core of gypsum and wood fiber, sandwiched between two sheets of strong cardboard. This cardboard covering allows it to be sawed or nailed and provides the necessary strength. Gypsum lath sheets are available in several sizes and thicknesses, and may be plain, or may be perforated to give a better plaster bond. Insulating gypsum lath, which is gypsum lath with a sheet of aluminum foil cemented to the backside, is available also. *Lime plaster and Portland cement plaster should not be applied to gypsum lath, as they do not bond to it properly.*

Advantages—(1) Reduces plaster cracks considerably, compared to wood lath. (2) Fire-resistant. (3) Prevents the wooden supporting members from becoming water-soaked when plaster is applied. (4) Moderate in cost.

Disadvantages—The non-perforated type of lath has no particular disadvantages, if properly installed. However, the perforated type of lath may allow the wooden supporting members to become wet when the plaster is applied.

8. Fiber Insulating Lath—Such lath (boards) are made of a variety of materials, such as wood fiber, exploded wood fiber, sugar-cane fiber, wood-pulp fiber, etc. The usual size is 18″ x 48″ by ½″ thick.

Advantages—(1) Good insulating properties (see Table 4, P. 136) which is approximately equal to that of a single sheet of aluminum foil insulation.

Disadvantages — (1) Lacks fire-resistance. (2) Some types absorb moisture from the air, causing buckling with resultant plaster cracks and reduction of insulating value.

9. Wood Lath—Wood lath, though one of the oldest plaster bases, may now be considered practically obsolete, due to its many bad features.

Advantages—(1) Low cost (slightly less than gypsum lath). (2) Moderate insulating value.

Disadvantages—(1) Must be thoroughly soaked with water before use. (2) Allows the wooden supporting members to become wet, when plaster is applied. (3) Has a tendency to warp and buckle, thus cracking the plaster. (4) Not fire-resistant.

TYPES OF INTERIOR PLASTERS

10. General—Two general types of plaster will be discussed. These are: (1) Gypsum plaster and, (2) lime plaster.

11. Gypsum Plaster—Gypsum plaster is available in the following forms: (1) Plaster of Paris which, due to its quick-setting properties, is used in small quantities to "gauge" (produce rapid setting of) other plaster materials. (2) Hard wall plaster (suitable for the "scratch" and "brown" coats) which contain such retarders as animal blood and glue, and such fillers as shredded wood fiber, hair, etc. (3) Hard finish plasters, such as Keene's cement, which are slightly moisture-resistant due to their alum or borax content.

Advantages—(1) Easy to mix. (2) Sets rapidly (the hard wall plaster sets in about two hours), which makes it suitable for use over gypsum lath or fiber insulating lath. (3) Fire-resistant. (4) Fairly strong.

Disadvantages—(1) Cannot endure dampness.

Adhesion to Various Backings—It adheres to various backings with a factor of safety many times in excess of actual requirements When used with gypsum lath, this factor of safety is 144; or, in other words, a force of 144 times the weight of the plaster is necessary to break the bond.

12. Lime Plaster—Lime is available as lump (unslaked) lime or hydrated (slaked) lime. Lump lime must be kept in air- and moisture-proof containers, as it will deteriorate when exposed to the air.

Advantages of Lime Plaster—(1) Costs slightly less than gypsum plaster. (2) A large proportion of lime putty in finish-plaster coats increases the plasticity of the plaster, and produces a smooth finish.

Disadvantages of Lime Plaster—(1) Hardens slowly, making it unsuited for scratch coat on fiber boards. (2) Weak. (3) Shrinks considerably when hardening. (4) Will not bond properly to gypsum lath.

RECOMMENDED PRACTICE

13. General—Plastering may be regarded as a necessary evil in house building, at the present time, for the only way to avoid its use is to resort to paneling or special wall board throughout the house. However, all plastering that is used should consist of a good plaster base and good plaster, installed by first-class mechanics. This will insure the home owner a minimum of plaster cracks and subsequent upkeep, and will give him a greater and more lasting satisfaction in his home. General recommendations are given in Table 1.

TABLE 1.—*Guide for Selection of Plastering Materials*

TYPE OF HOUSE	PLASTER BASE				PLASTER		
	Outer Walls	Other Walls	Ceiling First Floor	Ceiling Second Floor	First Coat	Second Coat	Finish Coat
High Cost[1]	A, C	B, D	B, D	A, C	G	G	H, I
Medium Cost[2]	C	D	D	C	G	G	H, I
Low Cost[3]	E, F	E, F	E, F	E, F	F, G	F, G	F, H, I

[1]Houses costing more than $8,000.00.
[2]Houses costing between $5,000.00 and $8,000.00.
[3]Houses costing less than $5,000.00.

Key to Table 1

Plaster Base:
  A=Metal lath, with paper and aluminum foil backing
  B=Metal lath, with paper backing.
  C=Gypsum lath, with aluminum foil backing.
  D=Gypsum lath, plain.
  E=No. 1 wood lath, of white pine.
  F=Insulating wall board, with plaster omitted.

Plaster:
  G=Gypsum plaster (may be unfibered for gypsum lath or fiber insulating lath).
  H=Smooth white finish.
  I=Sand float finish.

14. Type of Finish—A tinted, sand float finish is suitable for all of the rooms except bathrooms and kitchen.

Bathroom—All plastering above the tile work (assuming bathroom is tiled) should be Keene's cement hard white finish, or smooth white finish.

Kitchen—Plaster in kitchen should also be plain white as noted for bathroom, as a sand float finish will soon collect grease which will be hard to remove. Very often an imitation tile effect is provided in the kitchen (and bathroom, too) by using Keene's cement hard white finish for the lower portion of walls, scored to form squares about 4" in size. The scored wall generally extends to a height of about 4'-6", at which height a chair rail (flat molding) is provided to form a separating border between the scored and unscored plaster.

Selecting Finish—Examine the plastered walls of your friends so as to help you decide upon proper tint, texture, etc.

15. Plastering Around Chimney — The plans or specifications should indicate whether the plaster is to be placed directly on the chimney, or whether studs and a 2″ air space are to be used. Pl. 8, Fig. 1, illustrates both methods. Plastering directly on the chimney is the cheapest method, but is not recommended, as the chimney may settle slightly, and crack the plaster where it bonds to the regular wall plaster. For most "exterior" type chimneys (see Par. 2, P. 100) a studded air space is *necessary* due to the possibility of leaks or moisture formed by condensation, as these would stain and crack the plaster.

16. Specifying Metal Lath—All metal lath should be painted or galvanized *after* fabrication, and should have a waterproofed paper backing to prevent moisture in the plaster from soaking into the wooden supporting framework. Such lath should be of a proper design and sufficient weight to give it stiffness. See a reputable local Building Supply man for samples, recommended brands, weights, etc. Table 2 will serve as a guide for minimum requirements.

TABLE 2.—*Minimum Recommended Weights for Metal Lath*

(All supporting members assumed to be spaced 16″, center to center)

Type of Lath	Minimum Recommended Weights (Pounds Per Sq. Yd.)	
	Walls and Partitions	Ceiling
Expanded	2.5	3.4
Flat Rib	2.75	3.0
⅜″ Rib	2.5	2.75

17. Specifying Gypsum Lath—The standard type lath (not perforated), ⅜″ thick, and of a reputable brand, is recommended.

18. Specifying Fiber Insulating Lath or Insulating Board—Such material, when used, should be of a type that is not readily affected by moisture (see Ref. R17-3, Sec. 38), and of a type that has not been impregnated with poisons (such as arsenic) that are harmful to human beings.

19. Metal Reinforcements—It is of the utmost importance that all exterior plastered corners be provided with a metal corner bead, and all interior plastered corners be provided with a metal "cornerite". Here, again, see your Building Supply man.

20. Number of Plaster Coats—Except as noted by Par. 21, three coats should be used. These are: (1) First, or scratch coat. (2) Second, or brown coat. (3) Finish coat.

21. Plastering Basement—All plastering on inside of exterior walls of basement should be Portland cement plaster, especially if applied directly to masonry walls.

Plaster over Furnace—Whether the entire ceiling of basement is plastered or not, it is well to provide a slab of Portland cement plaster on metal lath base, at least 8′-0″ square, over the top of the furnace to serve as a fire barrier (Fig. 3, P. 124).

Number of Coats—Two-coat work is sufficient for the average basement.

PAINTING AND FINISHING

1. Purpose of Painting—Painting serves the following purposes: (1) Provides an attractive decorative coating. (2) Protects exterior surfaces from the weather. (3) Makes interior surfaces more sanitary, and usually makes dark rooms lighter.

2. Usual Defects—Some of the most usual defects are the following: (1) The species of wood used for exterior finish has poor paint retaining qualities. (2) The wood used for exterior finish (especially siding) is "flat" grain instead of vertical or "edge" grain, thereby reducing its paint retaining qualities. (3) Due to faulty construction, proximity of woodwork to ground, improper drying of the interior plaster, condensation in the side walls, etc., moisture finds its way behind the coat of paint, and causes it to peel and blister. (4) At time of painting, surfaces to be painted are damp (due to lack of seasoning or recent wetting from rain), or otherwise not properly prepared for painting. (5) Paint of an inferior grade is used. (6) Paint is improperly mixed and is *thinned down too much*. (7) The priming coat is too "stingy". (8) Paint is not properly brushed out, nor worked into the pores of the wood. (9) Paint is omitted from surfaces that are not readily seen by the owner, such as the tops and bottoms of doors and window sash.

3. Low-Grade Paints—Low-grade "bargain" paints cause home owners great financial loss annually, due to poor protection afforded. Fig. 1 shows, graphically, why some paints are sold as "bargain" paints, and also why such paints are soon "gone with the weather".

PAINT MATERIALS

4. White-Lead-and-Oil Paint—The following discussion applies to a paint mixture of white lead and linseed oil, with possibly a small amount of turpentine and liquid drier added. The white lead for such paint may be basic carbonate white lead or basic sulphate white lead (sublimed white lead). Basic sulphate white lead is somewhat less poisonous, but has less hiding power than the basic carbonate white lead.

Advantages—(1) Spreads and hides well. (2) Decays by chalking instead of cracking, thus provides a very good (chalky) surface for repainting over. (This makes it unnecessary to remove any neglected portion of the paint by scraping, burning, etc.) (3)

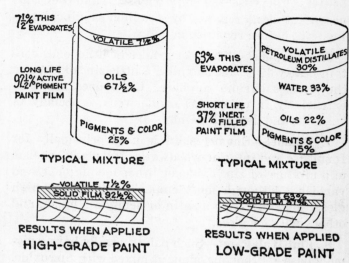

FIG. 1.—*The Difference Between High-Grade and Low-Grade Paints*

Is considered to be one of the two best primers for new wood (aluminum paint is the other). When used as a primer, it may be tinted to suit the finish coat, thus making a two-coat job possible, where so desired.

Disadvantages—(1) Not quite so durable as some "harder" types of paint. (2) Has a greater tendency to take up dirt than is the case of harder types of paint. (Any dirt collected is soon eliminated, however, due to the chalking of the paint.) (3) If taken into the human system (by breathing in the dust caused by sandpapering of painted surfaces, etc.), it may cause lead poisoning.

5. Lead-Zinc, and Titanium-Lead-Zinc Paints—The lead pigment of such paints has mild chalking tendencies; and the titanium (a pigment that is extremely opaque, very white in color, very fine in size, and available in three varieties which contain varying degrees of titanium oxide), when used, has pronounced chalking tendencies. Therefore, the addition of zinc oxide to such paints as a hardener has certain advantages.

Advantages—(1) Spreads and hides well. (2) More durable than lead-and-oil paints (lasts longer, stays white longer, or holds color longer). (3) Does not collect dirt as rapidly as lead-and-oil paints. (4) Somewhat less poisonous than lead-and-oil paints.

Disadvantages—When paint of this type is used which contains low percentages of white lead and titanium, the surfaces protected with such paint must be promptly repainted when the old coats become brittle. Otherwise, the paint may scale and peel, thus necessitating its removal by scraping, sanding, burning, etc., before repainting.

6. Lithopones—The best grades of lithopones contain nearly 30% zinc sulphide, a little zinc oxide, and the balance barium sulphate. Lithopones are used extensively in paints for inside work, especially in enamels, and flat wall paints.

7. Enamel—Enamel paint is used principally for furniture and interior woodwork. It usually consists of a mixture of zinc oxide, or lithopone pigment, and varnish. Although most enamels dry with a high gloss, some dry with a satin or semigloss finish, and others without gloss.

8. Flat Wall Paint—Such paints usually have a pigment base of lithopone, alone or mixed with zinc oxide. The vehicle is usually about ⅓ nonvolatile matter (such as varnish) and ⅔ volatile thinner (such as turpentine, etc.).

9. Varnish—Varnish, generally speaking, is a liquid which contains no suspended matter (pigment), and which is used for a decorative or protective coating, and is capable of being spread in a thin, homogeneous film which will dry out to form a hard coating. Varnishes that are water-resistant are known as "spar" varnishes.

10. Shellac—Shellac, which consists primarily of lac resin and highproof alcohol, is obtainable in a number of grades, and in two colors — white (bleached) and orange. Shellac has poor waterproof qualities, but is resistant to mineral oils, turpentine, and most turpentine substitutes.

11. Colored Paints—The darker colored paints are somewhat more durable than white or light colored paints.

RECOMMENDED PRACTICE

12. General—The first step in securing first-class, low-upkeep paintwork is to use a paint retaining wood for all painted portions of the dwelling that are exposed to the weather (see Fig. 2 and Table 1, P. 106). The next step is to use a type of construction and workmanship that will prevent water from entering the wood and getting behind the paint. The final and equally important steps are to use good paint materials applied by conscientious and expert workmen. It is also well to remember that painted surfaces having a southern exposure will be affected the most, due to the deteriorating action of sunlight on paint.

FIG. 2.—*Typical Paint Failure on Wood That Has Inferior Paint Retaining Qualities*

13. Exterior Finish—The *type* of paint should be carefully selected before the first finish coat is applied. All finish coats and all repaint coats in the future should then be of the same type, and, preferably, of the same brand of paint; for when paint of one type is applied over paint of another type, poor results are apt to be obtained.

Priming Coat—For a paint retaining species of wood, a priming coat of white-lead-and-oil paint *or* aluminum paint is recommended. For such woods as yellow pine, Douglas fir, etc., that lack paint retaining qualities, aluminum paint is recommended.

Finish Coats—For dwellings where the paint may possibly be neglected for considerable periods, a pure white-lead-and-oil paint is recommended as being the most satisfactory. For dwellings which are certain to be repainted promptly when the old coatings become brittle, the lead-zinc and titanium-lead-zinc paints are somewhat superior.

14. Interior Finish—The type of painting material used for the interior of the house will depend upon the preferences of the owner. The following general recommendations and comments are offered, however:

Paints Containing Lead—It is recommended that no paint containing lead be used for interior finish, due to the hazards of lead poisoning.

Interior Trim—The use of a flat, or semi-gloss enamel is recommended.

Finish Floors—Hardwood floors are often finished (after sanding and scraping) by first applying a filler, and then one or two coats of white (bleached) shellac followed by a coat of floor wax. Ref. R9-4, Sec. 38, however, advises against the use of shellac or varnish on oak floors due to the fact that when such finishes become worn or scratched the whole floor must be sanded and refinished, and advises the use of one of the following floor finishes after the filler has been aplied: "Bruce Floor Finish", "Dura-Seal", "Hil-Seal", "Permatite", or "Pyra-Seal".

Interior Walls—It is not advisable to paint plastered walls that are less than a year old, as the lime in the plaster may cause the paint to blister and peel. If such walls *must* be painted before aging, they should first be treated with a solution made by dissolving 2 to 3 pounds of crystallized zinc sulphate in 1 gallon of water. Then, after the plaster has become thoroughly dry, a priming coat of good water-resistant (spar) varnish "size" (containing no glue), thinned with turpentine or mineral spirits, should be applied. For the finish coats, two coats of flat wall paint of "egg shell" texture are recommended. Before selecting paint for interior plaster, however, it will be well to consider the use of one of the various water-mixed paints for plaster that have recently been placed on the market, and which are economical to use. Interview people who have used them, and examine walls so painted.

Stairwork—The treads are usually finished similar to the floors; the risers and balusters are usually enameled; and the rail is often stained a mahogany, or other suitable color, and varnished.

15. Painting Radiators
Painting Radiators—Paint for radiators should consist of a good radiator paint that does not contain aluminum or bronzing pigments. The application of aluminum or bronzing coats to a radiator serves as a reflective insulation, and thus lowers the efficiency of the radiator.

16. Painting Bare Ferrous Metal (Iron and Steel)
Painting Bare Ferrous Metal (Iron and Steel)—Red lead is one of the best paints for bare ferrous metal items, such as steel lintels that have not been galvanized, and should be used as a priming coat on metal in cases where aluminum paint is used for a finishing coat.

17. Selection of Materials—Be sure that all paint materials meet the following three basic requirements: (1) They should be of a reputable source of manufacture. (2) The kind and proportion of the ingredients should be plainly indicated on the label. (3) The kind and proportion of ingredients should conform, in general, to those of other well-known brands, or, otherwise, to Federal Specifications for the type of paint in question. (See Ref. R16-14, Sec. 38.)

18. Mixed Paint *Versus* Semipaste Paint—While the use of semipaste paint is somewhat cheaper, the use of ready mixed paint is much safer. For, in the latter case, the pigment and vehicle have been properly proportioned by the manufacturer; thus there is less danger of the painter improperly proportioning the paint. The priming coat and initial finish coat may have to be thinned somewhat, but the manufacturer furnishes specific directions for this procedure.

19. Thickness of Coating — Each coat of paint should be spread evenly, and should be well brushed out. Such coats should be neither too thin nor too thick, and the combined (total) thickness of all coats should be about 1/200 of an inch (.005").

20. Maintenance of Painted Surfaces—It is well to mention here (for future use) that the too frequent application of paint to painted surfaces will make it difficult to maintain the paint in good condition over a period of years; for, as the paint coating should be maintained at a thickness of about 1/200 inch (Par. 19), it is necessary for the old paint to chalk, or wear away, before applying a new coat. The condition of any coat of paint will change according to climatic conditions, and other variables; but the following rules will serve as a general guide for repainting: (1) Surfaces painted with a "soft" type of paint should receive one coat of paint every three years, or two coats every four years. (2) Surfaces painted with a "hard" type of paint should receive a preliminary spot coating over patches where loose paint has been scraped off, and one coat of paint, every four years.

TILE WORK

1. Tile Walls and Floors—The use of tile as a finish for walls and floors of bathrooms is very prevalent at the present time, especially in bathrooms where a combination tub and shower bath are provided. Tile wall and floor finishes are highly desirable, if they can be afforded. However, in the case of medium cost construction, it is certainly more desirable to eliminate interior "luxuries" than it is to economize too much on the exterior construction of the house (Pars. 7 and 8, P. 66).

Advantages—Tile walls and floors have the following chief advantages: (1) Pleasing appearance. (2) Waterproof. (3) Easy to keep clean (sanitary).

Disadvantages—The chief disadvantages of tile walls and floors are: (1) Cost. (2) Floors are "cold" (tend to conduct heat from one's body).

2. Selection of Tile—Your architect or any reputable local tile contractor will be helpful in assisting you in the selection of a suitable tile pattern. Also, the various tile manufacturers are usually glad to offer suggestions. A partial list of such manufacturers, who are members of The Tile Manufacturers' Association, Inc., are as follows:

NAME	ADDRESS
American Encaustic Tiling Co., Inc.	101 Park Ave., New York, N. Y.
The Atlantic Tile Manufacturing Co.	Matawan, N. J.
Carlyle Tile Company	Ironton, Ohio
Franklin Tile Company	Lansdale, Penna.
B. Mifflin Hood Company	Daisy, Tenn.
Mosaic Tile Company	Zanesville, Ohio
Murray Tile Company	Cloverport, Ky.
Olean Tile Company	Olean, N. Y.
Sparta Ceramic Company	East Sparta, Ohio
United States Quarry Tile Company	Canton, Ohio

3. Color of Tile—The color combination should suit the desires of the owner. One color combination that is neat, simple, and very pleasing in appearance, is black-and-white. A *typical* arrangement, using these two colors, is as follows:

Floor—Use unglazed tile, arranged to form a basket-weave pattern. This pattern may consist of a series of squares about 2½" x 2½", with each of such squares consisting of four pieces of ¾" x 1½" white tile clustered around a ¾" x ¾" black tile center.

Walls—Use glazed tile for walls. The base or cove may be bright black tile; the wainscot may consist of white tile approximately 4¼" x 4¼" in size; and the wainscot cap may be bright black tile. Also, immediately below the top row of white tile a continuous strip of bright black tile ½" wide (consisting of ½" x 6" tile) may be used.

4. Height of Tile Walls—A good height for the tile wainscot is 4'-0", except around the bathtub, where it should be from 5'-6" to 6'-0" high.

5. Support for Tile—All floors and walls that support tile should be rigidly constructed so as to prevent cracks in the tile. See Pl. 14, Fig. 10.

6. Tile Substitutes—Before using substitutes for tile, it is well to determine the water-resistance and life expectancy of such substitutes.

ELECTRICAL WORK

1. Advantages of Proper Wiring — Electricity is one of the most useful and remarkable servants that a man can have in his home. Therefore, with our knowledge of its present usefulness and the certainty that this usefulness is sure to increase year by year, it is quite evident that every modern home should be adequately wired, for not only the needs of today, but for those of tomorrow as well.

2. Importance of Wire Size—Copper wires offer a resistance to the flow of electricity, the same as does the special resistance wire of an electric iron, electric toaster, etc., except on a much smaller scale. The electrical energy consumed in overcoming such resistance is dissipated in the form of heat, but must be paid for by the consumer. As small copper wires offer more resistance to electrical energy than do larger wires, it is important that the wires for each circuit be of at least the minimum accepted standard size for the type of service that it must render. Otherwise, the system will be subject to fire hazards, and will be inefficient and expensive to operate.

3. Types of Wiring—The following types of wiring are recommended for various parts of the system:

Service Entrance Conductors (Overhead)—Service conductors run in a hot-dipped galvanized rigid metal conduit, or electrical metal tubing, are preferable. For the average house, however, an approved brand of waterproof service entrance cable will suffice.

Service Entrance Conductors (Underground)—Where such conductors are run underground, it will be well to obtain expert opinion as to the nature of the soil and its probable corrosive action on the type of cable that you contemplate using.

Miscellaneous Conductors—For the feeder conductors, branch circuits, and circuits from panelboard to individual appliance circuits, wiring run in rigid conduits, or electrical metal tubing, is preferable. For the average house, however, it is sufficient to use BX armored cable for dry locations, and BXL (lead-sheathed) armored cable for damp locations. The use of knob-and-tube wiring is not recommended by this Guide, due to the fire hazard that it presents.

Circuit to Garage—For overhead conductors to a detached garage, the use of an approved brand of line wire is recommended.

4. Size of Service Conductors—The size of service conductors, and the rating of service equipment, should not be less than that specified in Table 1.

TABLE 1.—*Recommended Minimum Sizes and Ratings for Service Entrance Equipment*

FLOOR AREA OF DWELLING (Square Feet)[1]	NUMBER OF ROOMS	SIZE OF SERVICE CONDUCTOR WIRES (Gauge No.)	RATING OF SERVICE EQUIPMENT (Amperes)		
			Switch	Fuse	Circuit Breaker
Up to 1,000	4	6	60	50	50
1,000 – 1,500	5	4	60	60	70
1,500 – 3,000	6 – 9	4	100	70	70
3,000 – 4,000	10 – 13	2	100	90	90

[1]For computing floor area of dwelling, use the **outside** dimensions of the house and include all areas except open porches and unfinished spaces in the basement and attic.

5. Fifteen-Ampere Branch Circuits—The number of branch circuits, exclusive of "appliance" branch circuits (Par. 6), should be determined by providing one circuit for every 500 square feet of floor area of the house. (Compute floor areas in manner specified by Table 1.) The wire size for these circuits should not be smaller than No. 14.

6. Appliance Branch Circuit—At least one branch circuit should be installed for supplying all convenience outlets in the dining room, breakfast nook, and kitchen; and at least one branch circuit should be installed for supplying all convenience outlets in the laundry. These circuits should not supply any other outlets, nor should the wire size be smaller than No. 12.

7. Individual Appliance Circuits—An individual circuit, of not less than No. 12 wire size should be provided for the electric range, electric hot-water heater, oil burner or stoker motor, and similar items.

TABLE 2.—*Summary of Minimum Residential Outlet Requirements*

Location	Lighting Ceiling Outlets	Lighting Wall Outlets	Convenience Outlets	Switch Outlets	Remarks
Front Entrance.........	1 or	2 or 1		1	Choice depends on entrance architecture.
			1		Weatherproof.
Other Entrances........		1			For illuminated house number; may be combined with Lighting Outlet.
	1 or	1		1	
Covered Porches........	1 min.			1	1 Lighting Outlet for each 100 sq. ft. or major fraction.
Terraces, Patios, Covered Porches, etc....			1 min.		1 Convenience Outlet along each 15 ft. of wall or major fraction.
Stairways..............	2 or	2		2	1 Lighting Outlet at head and 1 at foot of each stairway, with separate 3-way control for each at head and foot.
Halls..................	1 min. or	1 min.		1	Required if halls not illuminated by stairway light. 1 Lighting Outlet for each 15 ft. of hallway.
			1 min.		1 Convenience Outlet for each 20 ft. of hallway.
Living Room, Library, Den, Reception Halls, Bedrooms, Sun Room, Recreation Room, etc....	1			1	Additional control (3-way, etc.) if other important entrances are more than 10 feet from main entrance.
			(a)		(a) At least 1 Convenience Outlet for each 12 ft. of wall unbroken by doorway, and at least one in each wall space 3 ft. or more in length at floor line.
		(b)			(b) Outlets for wall brackets as desired.
Dining Room...........	1		1	1	Flush in mantel shelf. Multiple control for important entrances more than 10 ft. apart, plus additional Convenience Outlets to provide 1 in every wall space suitable for buffet, etc.
			2 min.		
Breakfast Room, Dinette, etc..............	1			1	
			1		
Kitchen...............	1			1	
	(c) or	(c)			(c) Lighting Outlets for each important work area along wall. Sufficient Convenience Outlets to serve all fixed appliances (refrigerator, clock, etc.) plus each work area.
			3 min.		
Pantry................	1 or	1	1		
Bathroom.............	1	2		1	Ceiling Outlet may be omitted in small bathrooms.
Lavatory..............			1		Located away from bathtub.
	1 or	2		1	
Closets...............	1 or	1			For closets over 10 sq. ft. in area.
Laundry..............	1			1	
	(d) or	(d)			(d) Lighting Outlets for each important work area along wall. Sufficient Convenience Outlets to serve each work area.
			2 min.		
Basement.............	1			1	With pilot light on switch plate on floor above.
	(e) or	(e)			(e) Lighting Outlets for furnace, work bench, and each separate enclosed space.
Attic.................			1		With pilot light on switch plate on floor below.
	1			1	(f) 1 Lighting Outlet for each enclosed space.
	(f) or	(f)			
Garage...............	1			1	Additional requirements for garages of more than 1-car capacity.
	1			2	Exterior light—controlled by 3-way switch from house and garage.
			1		

(Reprinted through the courtesy of the publishers of Handbook of Interior Wiring Design)

8. Telephone Outlets—At least one outlet box, with concealed wiring for outside telephone service, is recommended for each active floor. Your local telephone company should be consulted before specifying types of outlets.

9. Radio Outlets—A minimum of three radio outlets (complete with antenna and ground connections) are recommended for houses of six rooms or less, and a greater number of outlets for larger houses. These outlets are usually installed in the living-room, kitchen, bedrooms, and recreation room. They should preferably consist of a combination radio and convenience outlet; otherwise, they should be located adjacent to a standard convenience outlet so as to obtain current for operating the radio. Consult your local radio dealer in regard to the best type of antenna to specify for your radio.

10. Lighting Fixtures (General) — The electrical specifications usually require the contractor to include in his bid a certain specified allowance for lighting fixtures which are to be selected by the home builder and are to be paid for by the contractor. Such fixtures, like finish hardware (Par. 90, P. 133), should be selected with as much care and discrimination as possible, for they serve as an index to the quality of a house.

11. Selection of Lighting Fixtures — The home builder may take his house plans to several reputable electrical dealers who have well-known brands of lighting fixtures on display. The home builder can discuss his requirements with each dealer, and make a tentative selection from the fixtures sold by the dealer. Each dealer can then make him an offer, or "bid", for furnishing the fixtures selected. Such bids should be for competitive brands of equal quality, and the home builder should remain free to accept or reject any, or all, of such bids.

12. Miscellaneous Electrical Material—All electrical material, such as wiring, outlet boxes, switches, etc., should be of a reputable brand. When specifying such materials, it is advisable to consult with your local electrical dealers who handle the products of the companies selected, or else refer to the companies' catalogues. Also, it is advisable to specify several alternate brands of equal quality as this will allow the subcontractor to obtain the material at a better price and pass the saving on to you.

PLUMBING

1. Definitions—The following definitions are copied verbatim from Ref. R18-1, Sec. 38:

Plumbing—Plumbing is the art of installing in buildings the pipes, fixtures, and other apparatus for bringing in the water supply and removing liquid and water-carried wastes.

Plumbing System — The plumbing system of a building includes the water supply distributing pipes; the fixtures and fixture traps; the soil, waste, and vent pipes; the house drain and house sewer; the storm-water drainage; with their devices, appurtenances, and connections all within or adjacent to the building.

Water-Service Pipe — The water-service pipe is the pipe from the water main to the building served.

Water-Distribution Pipes — The water-distribution pipes are those which convey water from the service pipe to the plumbing fixtures.

Plumbing Fixtures—Plumbing fixtures are receptacles intended to receive and discharge water, liquid, or water-carried wastes into a drainage system with which they are connected.

Trap—A trap is a fitting or device so constructed as to prevent the passage of air or gas through a pipe without materially affecting the flow of sewage or waste water through it.

Trap Seal—The trap seal is the vertical distance between the crown weir and the dip of the trap.

Vent Pipe—A vent pipe is any pipe provided to ventilate a house-drainage system, and to prevent trap siphonage and back pressure.

Local Ventilating Pipe—A local ventilating pipe is a pipe through which foul air is removed from a room or fixture.

Soil Pipe—A soil pipe is any pipe which conveys the discharge of waterclosets, with or without the discharges from other fixtures, to the house drain.

Waste Pipe and Special Waste—A waste pipe is any pipe which receives the discharge of any fixture, except water-closets, and conveys the same to the house drain, soil, or waste stacks. When such pipe does not connect directly with a house drain or soil stack, it is termed a special waste.

Main—The main of any system of horizontal, vertical, or continuous piping is that part of such system which receives the wastes, vent or back vents, from fixture outlets or traps, direct or through branch pipes.

Branch—The branch of any system of piping is that part of the system which extends horizontally at a slight grade, with or without lateral or vertical extensions or vertical arms, from the main to receive fixture outlets not directly connected to the main.

Stack—Stack is a general term for any vertical line of soil, waste, or vent piping.

House Drain—The house drain is that part of the lowest horizontal piping of a house drainage system which receives the discharge from soil, waste, and other drainage pipes inside the walls of any building and conveys the same to the house sewer beginning 5 feet outside of the inner face of the building wall.

House Sewer—The house sewer is that part of the horizontal piping of a house drainage system extending from the house drain 5 feet outside of the inner face of the building wall to its connection with the main sewer or cesspool and conveying the drainage of but one building site.

Size and Length—The given caliber or size of pipe is for a nominal internal diameter, except that other than iron pipe size, brass pipe is measured by its outside diameter. The developed length of a pipe is its length along the center line of pipe and fittings.

Dead End—A dead end is a branch leading from a soil, waste, vent, house drain, or house sewer, which is terminated at a developed distance of 2 feet or more by means of a cap, plug, or other fitting not used for admitting water to the pipe.

2. Basic Plumbing Principles—The U. S. Government publication (Ref. R18-1, Sec. 38), entitled "Recommended Minimum Requirements for Plumbing", contains the following twenty basic principles for designing and installing the average plumbing system:

(1) All premises intended for human habitation or occupancy shall be provided with a supply of pure and wholesome water, neither connected with unsafe water supplies nor cross connected through plumbing fixtures to the drainage system.

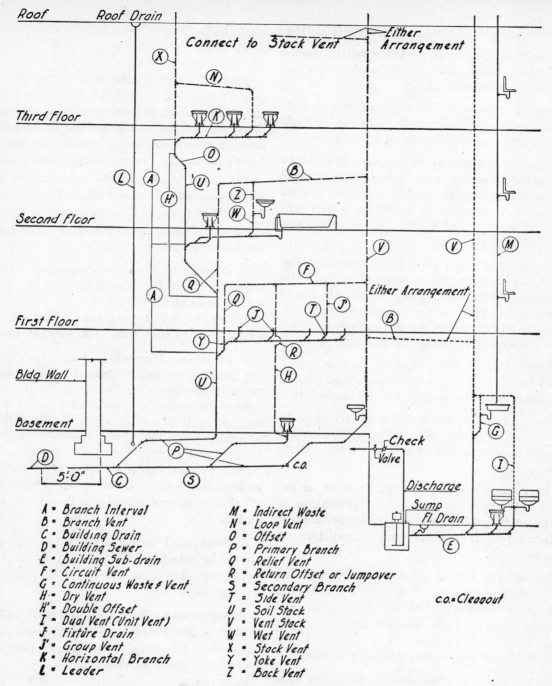

Roof   Roof Drain

Connect to Stack Vent   Either Arrangement

Ⓧ
Ⓝ
Third Floor   Ⓚ
Ⓛ Ⓐ   Ⓞ   Ⓑ
Ⓗ'   Ⓤ
Ⓩ
Second Floor   Ⓦ   Ⓥ Ⓥ Ⓜ
Ⓐ Ⓠ   Ⓕ   Either Arrangement
Ⓐ   Ⓓ Ⓙ Ⓣ Ⓙ'   Ⓑ
First Floor   Ⓨ
Ⓡ
Ⓤ   Ⓗ
Bldg Wall
Basement   Ⓖ
Check Valve
Ⓓ   Discharge
5'0"   Ⓟ   c.o.   Sump Fl. Drain   Ⓘ
Ⓒ   Ⓢ   Ⓔ

A = Branch Interval
B = Branch Vent
C = Building Drain
D = Building Sewer
E = Building Sub-drain
F = Circuit Vent
G = Continuous Waste & Vent
H = Dry Vent
H' = Double Offset
I = Dual Vent (Unit Vent)
J = Fixture Drain
J' = Group Vent
K = Horizontal Branch
L = Leader

M = Indirect Waste
N = Loop Vent
O = Offset
P = Primary Branch
Q = Relief Vent
R = Return Offset or Jumpover
S = Secondary Branch
T = Side Vent
U = Soil Stack
V = Vent Stack
W = Wet Vent
X = Stack Vent
Y = Yoke Vent
Z = Back Vent

c.o. = Cleanout

FIG. 1.—Illustration of Definitions

(Reprinted from Ref. R18-2, Sec. 38.)

(2) Buildings in which water-closets and other plumbing fixtures exist shall be provided with a supply of water adequate in volume and pressure for flushing purposes.

(3) The pipes conveying water to water-closets shall be of sufficient size to supply the water at a rate required for adequate flushing without unduly reducing the pressure at other fixtures.

(4) Devices for heating water and storing it in "boilers", or hot-water tanks, shall be so designed and installed as to prevent all dangers from explosion, and also prevent a back flow of hot water through a meter connected with a public water supply.

(5) Every building intended for human habitation or occupancy on premises abutting on a street in which there is a public sewer shall have a connection

with the sewer, and, if possible, a separate connection.

(6) In multiple dwellings provided with a house drainage system, there shall be for each family at least one private water-closet.

(7) Plumbing fixtures shall be made of smooth non-absorbent material, shall be free from concealed fouling surfaces, and shall be set free of inclosures.

(8) The entire house drainage system shall be so designed, constructed, and maintained as to conduct the waste water or sewage quickly from the fixture to the place of disposal with velocities which will guard against fouling and the deposit of solids and will prevent clogging.

(9) The drainage pipes shall be so designed and constructed as to be proof for a reasonable life of the building against leakage of water or drain air due to defective materials, imperfect connections, corrosion, settlements or vibrations of the ground or building, temperature changes, freezing, or other causes.

(10) The drainage system shall be provided with an adequate number of cleanouts so arranged that in case of stoppage the pipes may be readily accessible.

(11) Each fixture or combination fixture shall be provided with a separate, accessible, self-scouring, reliable water-seal trap placed as near to the fixture as possible.

(12) The house-drainage system shall be so designed that there will be an adequate circulation of air in all pipes and no danger of siphonage, aspiration, or forcing of trap seals under conditions of ordinary use.

(13) The soil stack shall extend full size upward through the roof and have a free opening, the roof terminal being so located that there will be no danger of air passing from it to any window, and no danger of clogging of the pipe by frost, or by articles being thrown into it, or of roof water draining into it.

(14) The plumbing system shall be subjected to a water or air pressure test and to a final air-pressure test in such a manner as to disclose all leaks and imperfections in the work.

(15) No substances which will clog the pipes, produce explosive mixtures, or destroy the pipes or their joints shall be allowed to enter the house-drainage system.

(16) Refrigerators, ice boxes, or receptacles for storing food shall not be connected directly with the drainage system.

(17) No water-closet shall be located in a room or compartment which is not properly lighted and ventilated to the outer air.

(18) If water-closets or other plumbing fixtures exist in buildings where there is no sewer within reasonable distance, suitable provision shall be made for disposing of the house sewage by some method of sewage treatment and disposal satisfactory to the health authority having jurisdiction.

(19) Where a house-drainage system may be subjected to back flow of sewage, suitable provision shall be made to prevent its overflow in the building.

(20) Plumbing systems shall be maintained in a sanitary condition.

3. Amount to Spend for Plumbing—The cost of the complete plumbing system should, as a general rule, range from about 8% to 10% of the total cost of the dwelling, except in very small dwellings, where the proportionate cost will be somewhat greater.

4. Materials (General)—Refer to Table 1, P. 75, for general recommendations. For other materials, refer to the following Paragraphs. In selecting miscellaneous materials, such as pipes, traps, faucets, etc., especial attention should be given to the *weight* of such items. The heavy grades of these items may be obtained at only a slightly higher price than the lighter grades, but will outlast the lighter grades an appreciable length of time. For probable useful life of plumbing equipment and materials, see Table 2, P. 173.

5. Selecting Plumber—The plumbing subcontractor should be selected with the utmost care, so as to insure your obtaining a first-class, trouble-free, long-lived system.

6. Inspection—It is recommended that the home builder obtain a copy of the plumbing code that is applicable to his locality, and familiarize himself with local requirements; also, that he observe, in particular, the nature of the inspection tests that the system is supposed to pass. Where the tests outlined in the code are inadequate, they should be supplemented by the tests outlined in Ref. R18-2, Sec. 38.

HOUSE DRAIN AND SEWER

7. General—A complete drainage system, including all necessary mains, branches, soil stacks, vents, traps, cleanouts, or other items, should be provided from all fixtures or floor drains of the residence to the house sewer

8. House Sewer—The house sewer should begin 5 feet outside of the inner face of the building wall; should be of vitrified, salt glazed clay sewer pipe; and should connect with the sewer in the street, or with the septic tank, etc.

9. Floor Drain (for Basement and Garage)—Drains are usually of cast iron. For trap material see Table 1, P. 75. See your local plumbing dealer for various suitable types.

10. Grease Trap—A grease trap is advisable when a septic tank is used. When a grease trap is required, a separate drain should be run underground from the kitchen to the grease trap, and the grease trap should then be connected to the sewer line. No sewage from the water-closet should go into the kitchen drain and grease trap. A grease trap may be purchased "ready-made" of metal suitably treated to prevent corrosion, or it may be of concrete as shown by Pl. 2, Fig. 14.

11. Cesspool—A cesspool is not recommended, due to the probability of it being unsafe from a hygienic standpoint.

12. Septic Tanks—Septic tanks are recommended where a sanitary sewer is not available. The septic tank may be purchased "ready-made" of metal suitably treated to prevent corrosion, or it may be made of concrete as shown by Pl. 2, Figs. 7 to 13. Table 5, P. 83, and Pars. 62 to 65, P. 83, give information in regard to required sizes, etc. The drainage field (which, incidentally, requires considerable ground area) should never be placed on hillsides above the level of wells or springs that supply drinking water, even though such wells or springs are at considerable distance from the drain tile.

STORM-WATER AND SUBSOIL DRAINAGE SYSTEMS

13. Storm-Water Drainage System—The importance of draining the storm water that discharges from the gutters and downspouts away from the foundation of the house is discussed in other Sections of this Guide (Par. 9, P. 98, and Sec. 27, P. 138). The rain conductors (downspouts) should preferably be fitted with cast iron shoes; and these shoes, in turn, should connect to a drainage system of vitrified, salt glazed clay pipe which should meet at a corner of the building, or other suitable point, and be connected to a vitrified, salt glazed clay sewer pipe. The sewer pipe should discharge into a storm sewer if one is available, otherwise into a drywell, gutter, etc. No storm water should drain into a septic tank; and, in most localities, storm water is not allowed to be drained into the sanitary sewer.

Where an underground drainage system is not used, a stone or concrete spill block should be so placed under the shoe of each downspout as to drain the storm water away from the foundation of the house.

14. Subsoil Drainage System—The importance of a subsoil drainage system has been discussed in other Sections of this Guide (Par. 10, P. 98). The system (when used) may be "single" or "double", as shown by Pl. 1, Figs. 4 and 5, and 11 to 14; and it should be fitted with a trap and protected against back pressure by a bronze or brass automatic back-pressure valve accessibly located between the system and the discharge sewer. Such systems may, ordinarily, discharge through the cellar drain. However, subsoil drains below the main sewer level should discharge into a sump or receiving tank, and the contents should be automatically lifted by an automatic pump or an automatic, water-operated ejector which has a ball float, and which is attached to the main water supply.

WATER SUPPLY SYSTEM

15. Material—See Table 1, P. 75. It is recommended that *no* lead pipe be used in *any part* of the water supply system, due to the danger of lead poisoning.

16. Minimum Pipe Sizes—The water-service pipes should be of sufficient size to permit a continuous, ample flow of water simultaneously on all floors. The minimum size for the water-service pipe from the curb to the residence should be ¾″, and the minimum size of water-service pipes inside the residence should be as follows.:

Main supply line	¾″	Sinks	½″
Risers	½″	Lavatories	⅜″
Sill cocks	½″	Bathtubs	½″
Hot-water boilers	½″	Water-closet tanks	⅜″
Laundry trays	½″		

17. Control Valves — The water supply system should preferably include the following control valves:

(a) A brass stop and waste cock on the service pipe where it enters the building.

(b) A brass compression type stop and waste valve on lower end of each hot- and cold-water riser near mains.

(c) A brass compression type stop valve on each supply pipe at each fixture, tank, boiler, or similar item. (These valves should be installed in addition to any faucets that may be required for the usual operation of fixtures.)

(d) A brass compression type drain valve, threaded for hose connection, on the bottom of hot-water tank.

(e) Brass compression type hose bibbs on exterior of residence (and possibly in garage) ; and, on the interior of the residence, an accessibly located brass compression type stop and waste valve on each pipe supplying a hose bibb.

18. Hot-Water Storage Tank—If the boiler or furnace selected for the heating system is arranged to supply domestic hot water on a year-round basis (Par. 49, P. 169), only a hot-water storage tank, for connecting to the boiler or furnace, will be required. Otherwise, in addition to the tank, a suitable hot-water heater utilizing gas, electricity, oil, or coal, will also be required.

The tank should, in any case, be insulated with not less than 1½ inch of asbestos, or equivalent insulation, and should be provided with a drain opening at the bottom for draining off any accumulation of sludge.

If the tank is connected to a hot-water heater, it should also be sufficiently strong to withstand a hydrostatic pressure of 300 pounds per square inch; it should be equipped with a safety pressure-and-temperature relief valve, unless the hot water can safely back up into the water supply system in case the water in the tank becomes overheated; and, for the sake of economical operation, it should preferably be equipped with a thermostat to maintain the water at a temperature not to exceed 140° F.

19. Pipe Covering—All hot-water pipes should be covered with insulation, so as to conserve heat. All exposed pipes under houses without basements should be insulated to prevent the pipes from freezing and bursting during cold weather.

PLUMBING FIXTURES

20. General Recommendations—It is recommended that the prospective home owner visit several plumbing supply houses that carry a reputable brand of plumbing fixtures on display and make a tentative selection of the fixtures that are needed. Each dealer will be glad to furnish an itemized list of the fixtures selected (including catalogue number, material, etc.),

thus enabling the prospective home owner to list several *alternate* brands of plumbing fixtures in the specifications of his home. This method will assure the plumbing contractor of better prices on the fixtures, and thus allow him to submit a lower bid for the plumbing. A few general suggestions for selection of fixtures are given below.

Kitchen Sink—A "cabinet" type sink is preferable, especially from a standpoint of appearance. Consideration may also be given to such a sink outfitted with a built-in dishwasher unit and a built-in garbage disposal unit. The fittings may include a swinging spout faucet and mixing valve with all-metal trim, open strainer with stopper, and removable crumb cup and strainer.

Bathtub—A white, porcelain enameled cast iron, recess built-in tub, 5'-6" long, fitted with over rim tub spout, two-valve fitting with all-metal trim, and 1½" connected drain and overflow, is suitable for the average home. If combination shower is desired, a two-valve, all-metal, self cleansing shower head, and a shower curtain with supporting rod and flanges, should be specified.

Lavatory—A white, porcelain enameled cast iron, or vitreous china, lavatory of a design to match tub, is suitable. Fittings may include a mixing faucet, pop-up waste, and 2 chromium-plated brass supporting legs.

Water-Closet—A white, vitreous china, two-piece washdown closet combination; having syphon action bowl with jet, and of a design to match the tub and lavatory, is suitable. Noiseless, one-piece closets are available at extra cost.

21. Enameled Pressed-Steel Fixtures — Such fixtures, when made of light gauge material, are not recommended for permanent construction, due to the likelihood of them becoming damaged.

22. Colored Fixtures—White is the most satisfactory color for fixtures from a standpoint of obsolescence, as fixtures of various colors may become obsolete and outmoded in a shorter period of time.

23. Finish for Trim — All exposed metal parts should be chromium plated.

24. Acid Resisting Fixtures — It is recommended that all porcelain enamel for the kitchen sink be of an acid-resisting type.

HEATING

WARM AIR HEATING SYSTEMS

1. Space Heaters—Such heaters consist of the ordinary fireplaces, fireplaces having a special built-in warm air circulating chamber, stoves or "parlor furnaces" of various types, and floor furnaces (Fig. 1).

Advantages—(1) Low first-cost. (2) Most of these heaters (except the "ordinary" fireplace) are fairly economical to operate in small houses located in mild climates. (3) No pipes or radiators to become frozen.

Disadvantages—(1) Uneven heat distribution. (2) Inadequate for large houses, or houses in cold climates. (3) Difficult or impossible to obtain domestic hot water efficiently as a by-product.

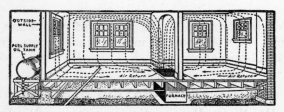

FIG. 1.—*Floor Furnace Installation, Showing Heat Flow*
(Courtesy of Home Builders' Research Institute, Inc.)

2. Gravity Warm Air Furnace Heating System—The warm air furnace consists of a combustion chamber (usually of cast iron, in the cheaper types) surrounded by a sheet metal casing, and is usually installed in the basement. When the system is operating, air enters the space between the combustion chamber and the sheet metal casing, is heated, expands and rises to the top of the furnace, and from there is conducted through one or more sheet metal ducts to the various rooms. The air is replaced at the furnace partly by outdoor air, and partly by recirculated room air.

Advantages—(1) Moderate first cost. (2) Fresh air may be conveniently introduced in the desired amount, by suitable dampers. (3) Air filters may be used to cleanse the air. (4) The air may be readily humidified. (5) Heat may be obtained quickly. (6) The system is suitable for all heating requirements, such as high heat output in cold weather, and low heat output in mild weather. (7) Economical to operate. (8) No pipes or radiators to become frozen. (9) Circulation of air in winter obtained without opening the windows.

Disadvantages—(1) Furnace must be installed very nearly in the center of the basement (and house) for proper operation, thus considerable basement space (especially overhead) is taken up by the ducts. (2) If filters are omitted, the system will circulate throughout the house dirt and dust collected from the basement and outside air. (3) If a suitable humidifier is not used, the air will be "dry" and unhealthful. (4) Unless the entire system, especially the ducts, is very carefully *designed* and *installed*, it will fail to operate properly. (5) Difficult to obtain domestic hot water efficiently as a by-product.

3. Mechanical Warm Air Heating System — This system (Fig. 2), which is sometimes misleadingly called air conditioning, is basically the same as the gravity system, except for the addition of a fan which mechanically forces the heated air through the ducts.

Advantages—The mechanical operated system has the following advantages over the gravity operated system: (1) The furnace need not be centrally located. (2) Ducts and registers may be smaller. (3) Air circulation is positive and more uniform. (4) Better humidity control is obtainable. (5) Air may be cleaned by washers *or* filters. (6) A cooling effect is possible in the summer merely through air circulation. (7) Heat extraction from the fuel is more efficient.

Disadvantages—(1) Difficult to obtain domestic hot water efficiently as a by-product. (2) Installation of the ducts sometimes requires that important framing members, such as ribbands, cap plates, etc., be cut to provide the necessary clearance. (3) Annoying sounds and noises may be transmitted through the ducts.

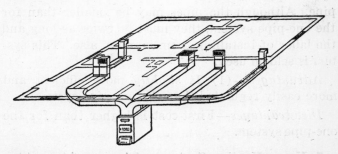

FIG. 2—*Warm Air Heating System, Forced Circulation*
(Courtesy of Home Builders' Research Institute, Inc.)

STEAM HEATING SYSTEMS

4. Steam Heating Systems (General)—Such systems usually employ steam at atmospheric pressure or at a slightly greater pressure. The temperature of the steam will vary from 212° F. for atmospheric pressure to 227° F., or more, for greater pressures.

Advantages (General) — (1) Will provide heat quicker than a gravity hot-water system. (2) Requires smaller radiators.

Disadvantages (General)—(1) Lacks heat-storage capacity. (2) When fire dies down to a point where water stops boiling, no heat is delivered to the radiators above. (3) A hot fire must be maintained at times when heat is required, even in mild weather, thus resulting in waste of fuel. (4) Such systems are not readily adapted to the addition of air-filtering or humidification equipment. (5) Air escaping from the air vents and "hot" dust rising from around the radiators create unpleasant odors. (6) Heat obtained is a "dry", uncomfortable heat. (7) Requires frequent examination and cleaning of traps, air vents, etc.

5. One-Pipe Steam System — In this system the steam rises to the radiators, gives off sufficient heat to become condensed, and the condensate then returns to the boiler through the *same* pipe. The single pipe of this system must be sufficiently large to provide for these two counter-directional flows.

Advantages—Low first-cost.

Disadvantages—(1) Requires special care in design and operation. (2) Expensive and unsatisfactory to operate. (3) Difficult to obtain uniform temperature regulation. (4) The piping must be pitched downward all the way from the radiators to the boiler. (5) System is likely to be noisy.

6. Two-Pipe Steam Heating System—In this system, the steam rises to the radiator through one pipe and the condensate (usually separated from the steam by a trap) returns to the boiler through a separate pipe. Although the pipes may be smaller than for the one-pipe system, they must be twice as long and the labor of installing them is more, also. This system is seldom used.

Advantages—(1) Is *slightly* more efficient and more easily regulated than the one-pipe system.

Disadvantages—First-cost is higher than for the one-pipe system.

7. Vapor Heating System — The one-pipe or two-pipe steam heating system may be converted into a vapor system by making such system air-tight and replacing the air-venting valves on the radiators with special vacuum valves. The operation of this system is the same as for the ordinary steam system up to the point where the fire dies down and the steam is not supplied to the radiator as fast as that in the radiator is condensed. At this point (in the vapor system) a vacuum is created in the radiators, which causes a continuation of the heat supply to the radiators, even though the temperature of the water in the boiler is below the ordinary boiling point of water.

Advantages—More efficient and economical to operate than the ordinary steam system.

8. Vacuum Heating System — Such a system is similar to the vapor system, except for the addition of a vacuum pump which maintains a vacuum on the return side. Such systems (using pump) are sometimes used for large, expensive residences.

Advantages—More efficient than vapor steam systems.

Disadvantages—(1) High cost of equipment and fittings. (2) Amount of maintenance necessary for succesful operation.

HOT-WATER HEATING SYSTEMS

9. Hot-Water Heating Systems (General)—In the average hot-water system, the operation is as follows: The water is heated in the boiler in the basement, passes up through the pipes to the radiators, gives up its heat, and returns through another set of pipes to the bottom of the boiler where it becomes heated and continues the cycle. Such systems are very well suited for heating of residences.

Advantages (General)—(1) Supplies a pleasant and comfortable type of heat which is free from odor. (2) Simple and economical to install and operate. (3) Well suited to varying load requirements caused by outside weather variations. (4) Has a large heat storage capacity, which helps to make its heat output constant and unaffected by small fluctuations of the heat in the boiler. (5) Such a system will supply a comfortable amount of heat long after the fire has been banked.

Disadvantages (General)—(1) Difficult to obtain large amounts of heat *quickly*. (2) System cannot be cooled down quickly when weather becomes suddenly mild. (3) Such systems are not readily adapted to the addition of air-filtering or humidification equipment.

10. Gravity, Open Type Hot-Water Heating System—The piping in such a system (Fig. 3) connects with an expansion tank located under the roof in the attic. This tank is provided with an overflow pipe which is open to the atmosphere and free to discharge on the roof. The system is usually filled to a point where the expansion tank just overflows slightly. The tank then serves as a reservoir, allows for the expansion and contraction of the water, and allows steam to escape from the system if the water becomes overheated. Such a system operates in the manner described in Par. 9.

Advantages—Simplest and most fool-proof type of hot-water heating system.

Disadvantages—Refilling the system (to allow for evaporation, etc.) must be done manually by operating a valve on the water supply pipe. (Such refilling should be required at very infrequent intervals, however.)

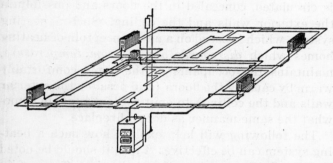

FIG. 3.—*Two-Pipe Hot-Water Heating System, Gravity Circulation*

(*Courtesy of Home Builders' Research Institute, Inc.*)

11. Gravity, Closed Type Hot-Water Heating System

—This system is similar to the "open" type, except that the system is closed and operates under pressure. The expansion tank, which may be located adjacent to the boiler, contains air which is compressed by the water and serves as a cushion as the water expands and contracts due to temperature changes. A pressure-reducing and filler valve is often used on the cold water line supplying the boiler, so as to automatically keep the system filled with water at a safe working pressure. A relief (safety) valve is required (usually placed in the line between reducing valve and boiler) to safeguard the system from excessive pressures.

Advantages—(1) The closed type system will generally have a better circulation than the open type, *provided* that the pipes of the two systems are of the same size. (2) The closed system is automatically filled.

Disadvantages—(1) Not as fool-proof as the open type. (2) More mechanical parts to wear out.

12. Forced Circulation Hot-Water Heating System

—Such a system (Fig. 4) is similar to the "closed" system except that an electrically operated pump is placed in the system for the purpose of circulating the hot water mechanically. The operation of this pump is usually automatically controlled by a thermostat located in one of the rooms of the residence.

Advantages—(1) Smaller pipe sizes may be used. (2) Circulation of water more positive and rapid. (3) More even heat distribution. (4) Better heat regulation.

Disadvantages—(1) Not as fool-proof as the gravity type system. (2) Operating cost will be higher than for gravity type system. (The pump will consume electrical energy and will depreciate more rapidly than the remainder of the system.)

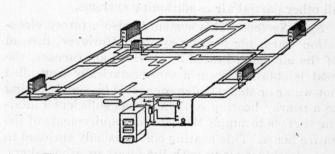

FIG. 4.—*Two-Pipe Hot-Water Heating System, Forced Circulation*

(*Courtesy of Home Builders' Research Institute, Inc.*)

AIR CONDITIONING SYSTEMS

13. Definition—Complete air conditioning involves control over (1) *air temperature,* (2) *air movement,* (3) *moisture content of the air,* and (4) *air purity* with the elimination of *odor, noise,* and *vibration. Any equipment which does not provide for the control of the elements mentioned above cannot be considered complete air conditioning.* As mechanical warm air furnaces (Par. 3) are sometimes misleadingly referred to as "air conditioning" units, it is of importance to know the difference between the two. Also, if the system is only equipped to condition the air in summer (has no provisions for heating and humidifying) it is a summer partial air conditioning system, only. If the system is only equipped to condition the air in winter (has no provision for cooling and dehumidifying the air) it is a winter partial air conditioning system, only.

14. Types of Equipment—There are three general classes of such equipment on the market today. These are: (1) Self-contained air conditioners designed to take care of one room; (2) Unit-type air conditioners that are designed for one room, and which must have connection to a remotely located heating plant and refrigerating machine; and, (3) Central air conditioning system designed to air condition the entire house. (This latter type is the one best suited to new homes.)

15. Winter Partial Air Conditioning — The two chief systems of winter air conditioning of the central air conditioning system type are the "direct" system and the "split" system.

Direct System—This system is simply a mechanical warm air heating system provided with humidifier, filter or air washer, and automatic, thermostatically controlled heating equipment. This system is usually the simplest in form, and the least costly of all other partial air conditioning systems.

Split System—This system is also a forced circulation warm air heating system. However, instead of the air being heated by a warm air furnace, the heat is obtained from a thermostatically controlled hot-water or steam boiler connected by simple piping to a nearby heating coil which has sufficient radiating surface to supply the heating requirements of the entire house. This heating coil is usually enclosed in a steel cabinet along with the filters or air washers, humidifier, and circulating fan. As in the direct system, the air is circulated through ducts. One feature of the split system is that it allows the use of hot-water or steam radiators, instead of air ducts, in such rooms as the bathroom and kitchen from which the recirculation of air would be objectionable.

Advantages and Disadvantages of Winter Partial Air Conditioning—Same as for mechanical warm air heating systems (Par. 3).

16. Summer Partial Air Conditioning — Methods for providing summer partial air conditioning (using the "direct" or "split" systems) are very similar to those used for partial winter air conditioning, except that means must be provided for cooling and dehumidifying the air before circulating it. For a discussion of various methods of cooling and dehumidification, refer to Refs. R10-5 and R10-11, Sec. 38.

Advantages—(1) Air may be cooled in summer (the air should never be cooled to more than 10° F. below the outside temperature, however). (2) Air may be dehumidified. (3) Air may be circulated.

Disadvangtaes—(1) High installation cost. (2) High depreciation cost. (3) High operating cost.

(4) Annoying sounds and noises may be transmitted through the ducts.

RADIANT AND SOLAR HEAT

17. General—In view of the publicity that has been given to the possibility of heating our future homes by means of radiant or solar heat, it is believed that a brief discussion here in regard to these types of heat will be helpful to the prospective home owner.

18. Radiant Heat—A radiant heating system, as now proposed for homes, consists essentially of a conventional steam or hot-water heating system (preferably a hot-water heating system with circulating pump), with the conventional radiators replaced by coils of pipe, through which the steam or hot water is circulated, concealed in the floors and possibly in the exterior walls and the ceiling. Such a heating system, which is based on a new concepto in of heating homes which *disregards air or room temperature*, maintains the occupants of the home comfortably warm by causing the floors (and possibly the exterior walls and the ceiling) to emit radiant heat, in somewhat the same manner as does a fireplace.

The following will help explain how such a heating system can be effective: First, it should be noted that our bodies must continuously give off a certain amount of heat in order for us to remain comfortable or healthy. This body heat is lost by conduction, evaporation, convection, and radiation, with the latter two methods of heat dissipation (convection and radiation) accounting for about 75% of the body heat that is given off. Present-day heating systems heat the air in our homes to such a relatively high temperature that the body cannot lose the desired proportionate amount of heat by convection, and therefore must lose most of its excess heat by radiation to cooler objects, such as cold floors, walls, and ceilings. Radiant heat, however, due to the fact that it raises the room temperature to only about 60° F., or less, allows us to lose a greater proportion of our excess body heat by convection, and also prevents the loss of our radiant body heat, as such heat is reflected instead of being absorbed by a cold floor, wall, or ceiling.

Advantages Claimed for Radiant Heating Systems —(1) Provide a more comfortable type of heat. (2) Cleanliness (no air currents to circulate dust). (3) Provide a practically uniform heat from floor to ceiling. (4) Allow a better arrangement of furniture by elimination of radiators. (5) Operating costs may be considerably less than for conventional types of heating systems.

Present Disadvantages of Radiant Heating Systems—(1) Still in experimental stage. (2) Difficult to install the necessary heating coils in usual types of floors, walls, or ceilings. (3) Cost of installing heating coils greater than cost of installing conventional radiators. (4) Difficulty of heating or cooling heating panels (floors, walls, or ceiling) *quickly,* tends to make heat control difficult. (5) Because the room temperature remains relatively low (about 60° F.), there is a natural tendency for occupants (especially those who look at the thermometer) to *imagine* they are cold.

19. Solar Heat—It is natural, in view of present-day talk about radiant heat and the use of large glass areas in the side walls of homes, that the question should arise as to how best to utilize the radiant heat from the sun for heating our homes.

Tests along this line indicate that, if the *south* walls of a home have large glass areas, consisting of two- or three-ply *insulated* glass, the amount of solar heat that passes into the house, through the glass area, during the day may be approximately equal to the amount of heat that passes out of the house, through the glass area, during the night. The results of such tests indicate two things: (1) It may be possible to have large, insulated-glass areas in certain side walls of your home without increasing your fuel bill. (2) Until special methods and equipment (special reflectors, etc.) are devised for utilizing the sun's heat more effectively, solar heating of homes can make only limited progress.

A summary of the advantages and disadvantages of utilizing solar heat by the use of large, insulated-glass areas in the home are as follows:

Advantages—(1) Added light. (2) Better view of the out-of-doors. (3) Pleasant sensation of basking in the sunlight in winter. (4) The solar heat obtained may off-set any heat loss through the glass areas.

Disadvantages—(1) An insulated type of glass must be used, with resultant additional cost. (2) An overhanging type of roof and suitable shades must be used, so as to partially shade the glass area from the hot, summer sun. (3) Sun shining through glass may create glare. (4) Tends to make home somewhat hotter in summer.

MISCELLANEOUS HEATING EQUIPMENT

20. Oil Burners—There are two main types of oil burners — the "vaporizing", and the "atomizing" types. There is also another type of burner, known as the blue-flame rotary burner, which combines vaporization with some degree of atomization. The several types of burners are shown and described in Ref. R10-14, Sec. 38. Each type works better in one type of boiler than in another type.

Atomizing Gun-Type Burner—This type of burner may be used in round, square, or elongated types of fire pots, but does best in elongated types. Such burners at the present time use oil as heavy as No. 3. Due to the simplicity, and the ease of design and manufacture of gun type burners, they are being adapted by more and more manufacturers; and the present indications are that they may gradually supersede other types.

Vaporizing Pot Type Burner—Such burners may be used in various types of fire pots. This type burns No. 1 or No. 2 oil.

Vertical Rotary Burners—Such burners operate best in round boilers, or those in which the length does not exceed 75% or 100% of the width. The type of oil used is No. 1 or No. 2.

21. Automatic Coal Burning Equipment — Such equipment may consist of ordinary coal-fired boilers equipped with mechanical stokers, or may consist of magazine feed coal-burning boilers. The chief advantages of such equipment are: (1) Partial elimination of manual labor. (2) More efficient operation (when using the mechanical stokers). (3) Cheaper grades of coal may be burned.

22. Convecters (Concealed Radiators)—A convector consists of a radiator unit concealed in a wall or arranged within a cabinet in such a manner that air enters the compartment at the bottom, is heated, expands, and flows out the upper end. This cycle is continuous, so long as heat is supplied to the radiator unit. The heat is termed "convected" heat. Such convectors, when built into the wall, save space; but they cost more than ordinary radiators. When concealed convectors are used, make sure that all air valves, etc., on the concealed radiator are readily accessible by means of suitable trap doors, in the front grille, so as to make the removal of the grille unnecessary when bleeding air out of the radiator.

FUELS

23. Wood—Wood is seldom used for heating residences at the present time.

Advantages—(1) Cleanliness. (2) Cheerful fire. (3) Quick increase in heat. (4) Cheap, in some localities.

Disadvantages—(1) Low heat value. (2) Large storage space necessary. (3) Labor in preparation. (4) Scarcity. (5) Does not hold fire long. (6) Unsteady heat.

24. Coal (General)—Coal is one of the most widely used fuels for the heating of residences.

Advantages—(1) Readily available in most localities. (2) Some grades are medium in cost. (3) Requires only simple combustion equipment.

Disadvantages—(1) Coal dust, ashes, and smoke tend to smudge not only the basement, but other parts of the house. (2) Hand firing is generally required. (3) The ashes must be disposed of. (4) Efficient heat regulation and fuel consumption is difficult, if not impossible, without special equipment and controls.

25. Anthracite Coal—The use of this coal is becoming restricted, due to its steadily increasing cost.

Advantages—(1) Comparative cleanliness. (2) Easy control of fire. (3) Efficient combustion. (4) Steady heat.

Disadvantages—(1) High cost. (2) Difficulty of obtaining. (3) Slow response to change of drafts.

26. Bituminous Coal—Such coals vary greatly in composition, physical characteristics, and heat value.

Advantages—(1) Low cost. (2) Availability. (3) High heat value (in the best grades). (4) Low percentage of inert matter (in the best grades).

Disadvantages—(1) Dirty. (2) Produces smoke. (3) More attention to fire and furnace necessary than with anthracite.

27. Sub-Bituminous Coal, Lignite, and Peat—These fuels are generally used within comparatively short distances from where they are produced.

Advantages—(1) Relatively low price. (2) Responds quickly to opening of drafts.

Disadvantages—(1) Slakes and deteriorates on exposure to air. (2) *Takes fire spontaneously in piles.* (3) Heat value generally low. (4) Burns inefficiently. (5) Fires do not keep well. (6) Gases generated over fire pot sometime burn in smoke pipe, causing excessive heating.

28. Coke—Coke consists of bituminous coal from which all volatile gases have been extracted by the process of heating in an oven or retort.

Advantages — (1) Cleanliness. (2) Responds quickly to opening of drafts. (3) Fairly high in heat value.

Disadvantages—(1) Bulkiness. (2) Liability of fire going out if not properly handled. (3) Fire requires rather frequent attention unless fire pot is deep.

29. Fuel Oil—Fuel oil is becoming widely used for residential heating. The grades suitable for this type of heating are Nos. 1 to 3. The higher the grade number, the heavier the oil, the greater the heat content, and the less the cost.

Advantages—(1) High heat value. (2) Cleanliness. (3) Operation is usually fully automatic. (4) Close, uniform temperature regulation is readily obtainable. (5) The fuel may be burned very efficiently.

Disadvantages—(1) Special equipment and controls are necessary. (2) Cost of operation is greater than for some grades of coal.

30. Gas—Gas is often used, where it can be obtained economically. Natural gas costs much less than artificial gas and has a higher heat content.

Advantages—(1) Ease of control. (2) Cleanliness. (3) Convenience. (4) Immediate increase of heat. (5) No storage space required.

Disadvantages—Cost is too high in most localities.

31. Electricity — Electricity provides ideal heat (100% efficient), but its cost is usually prohibitive.

HUMIDITY IN HOUSE HEATING

32. Relative Humidity—Relative humidity is the relation between the actual moisture content of the air at a given temperature and its capacity for holding moisture at that temperature. Raising the temperature of air increases its moisture capacity. The average relative humidity over the land of the earth is 60%, and over the oceans is about 85%. In Death Valley, California, where there is one of the driest atmospheres in North America, the relative humidity has been observed to be 23%.

33. Desirable Relative Humidity—The relative humidity of artifically heated air should be between 40% and 50%. In many heated homes, however, the air is drier than that of the driest desert.

34. Effect of "Dry" Heated Air—"Dry" air (air having relative humidity less than 40%) at ordinary room temperature has the following objections: (1) Drys up the mucuous membranes of the nose, throat, and lungs, thus weakening the resistance of these organs to disease germs. (2) Has a harsh, drying effect upon the hair and skin. (3) The dry air causes an excessive loss of moisture and heat from the skin, and thus necessitates the maintenance of high room temperatures for warmth. The high temperatures, in turn, cause a person to become enervated, nervous, and irritable, and also adds materially to the cost of heating the house (Table 4). (4) Such air is also injurious to woodwork, paintings, furnishings, fabrics, etc.

35. Effect of "Moist" Air—"Moist" air (air having a relative humidity in excess of 50%) has the following objections: (1) Gives one a sultry, stuffy feeling. (2) Prevents normal evaporation of moisture from the skin, thus weakening bodily resistance to sudden temperature changes, such as encountered when going out into the outside air. (3) Causes frosting of window panes; causes excessive condensation of moisture on walls; encourages mildew, etc.

36. Humidifying Equipment—Such equipment may vary in complexity from such simple devices as a pan of water on the stove, radiator, etc., to special, automatically controlled devices on the heating furnace.

37. Checking Humidity—This can best be done by installing a reputable make of Wet and Dry Bulb Hygrometer, as it is impossible to accurately measure the humidity by the sense of feel.

MISCELLANEOUS HEATING DATA

38. General—Tables 1 and 2 give approximate data in regard to first-cost and operating costs of heating systems. First-costs and fuel costs will vary in different parts of the country, and the average efficiency obtained will vary for different types of equipment, and for different types of house construction. These tables, therefore, should be used as a general guide only.

TABLE 1.—*Estimated Comparative Costs of Heating Systems*
(The One-Pipe Steam System is Used as a Basis of Comparison)[1]

TYPE OF HEATING SYSTEM	COMPARATIVE COST
One-Pipe Steam	100%
Convection Heaters or Stoves	15%
Pipeless Furnace	35%
Piped Furnace (Gravity Warm Air)	65%
Two-Pipe Vapor	125%
Two-Pipe Hot-Water	125%
Mechanical Warm Air, Gas or Oil-Fired Furnaces	150%
Air Conditioning, With Summer Cooling	250%

[1]The costs of one-pipe steam systems in the colder climates range from 15% for $2,000 homes to 10% for $9,000 homes; and in the milder climates from 10% for $1,500 homes to 5% for $7,000 homes.

TABLE 2.—*Comparative Fuel Consumption of Different Kinds of Heating Systems in Terms of Fuel Required for One-Pipe Steam System*

TYPE OF FUEL AND METHOD OF FIRING	ONE-PIPE STEAM	TWO-PIPE VAPOR	HOT-WATER	PIPED FURNACE	PIPELESS FURNACE
Hard Coal, Hand Fired	100%	90%	85%	80%	75%
Soft Coal, Hand Fired	100%	90%	85%	80%	75%
Fuel Oil, Automatic Control	100%	90%	85%	80%	75%
Gas, Automatic Control	100%	90%	85%	80%	75%

NOTE: Tables 1 and 2 are based on data contained in "House Design, Construction and Equipment", published by the Conference on Home Building and Home Ownership.

SELECTION AND INSTALLATION OF HEATING SYSTEM

39. Basic Requirements — The basic requirement of a heating system in a home is to maintain the air in the livable parts of the house at a temperature that will protect the health, and maintain the comfort of the occupants. Even an inefficient heating system will perform this function better in a well-built house than will the very best system in a poorly built house. Other requirements are as follows: (1) Economy of installation. (2) Economy of operation. (3) Freedom from mechanical failures. (4) Ease of operation. (5) Availability of prompt and competent servicing.

40. Air Conditioning—True, year-round air conditioning is emerging from the experimental stage, but may cost too much for the average home-owner to operate. The mechanical warm air furnaces (so-called air-conditioning systems) are recommended, however, to those who want warm, filtered, and humidified air in winter, and a circulation of uncooled, filtered air in the summer. Those who wish to obtain a cooling effect in the summer without using a forced air system employing ducts, may well consider installing a large fan or blower in the attic.

41. Type of Fuel—Before selecting a heating system, it is well to consider the type of fuel to be used. Such fuel should be selected on the basis of its continued availability locally at a reasonable price. Just how much of a premium one should pay for the privilege of using the cleaner or more convenient types of fuels is a matter for each prospective home owner to decide.

42. Estimating Heating Costs—When considering the various types of fuels and heating systems from a standpoint of operating costs, the following should be considered:

Cost of Fuel—Both the present cost and the probable future cost of fuels should be considered. A competent heating engineer can readily estimate the yearly fuel consumption by refering to "degree-day" charts, that have been compiled for most sections of the country, and then using the proper correction factor.

Depreciation of Equipment—It is important to consider the probable life of the equipment (see Table 2, P. 173), for it is evident that if a $1,000.00 heating system is obsolete in 20 years, its yearly cost due to depreciation is $50.00, without even considering the additional interest losses on the $1,000.00, which will be considerable. Also, it is necessary to obtain trustworthy assurance that spare parts will be obtainable during the useful life of the equipment.

Special Operating Costs—The cost of operating electrical equipment (motors, spark ignition, etc.), cost of gas for pilot lights, and other similar costs, should be estimated and added to the operating cost. Such costs may amount to several dollars per month.

Service and Maintenance Costs—It is safe to estimate that such costs will be in proportion to the complexity of the equipment used. Such costs may amount to $25.00, or more, a year.

43. Type of Heating System—It is an accepted rule that the cost of the heating system should range from about 8% to 10% of the total cost of the home. This would mean, for example, that the heating system for a $4,000 home should not cost more than $400.00. Some people, however, may prefer an elaborate heating system in a very modest home, or vice versa. It should be borne in mind, however, that heating systems are *mechanical equipment,* and that almost any type of system installed (except the portion consisting of durable pipe work) will wear out long before the remainder of the house; therefore, weather-resisting construction for the exterior of the house should not be sacrificed for the sake of temporary gadgets and convenience (Par. 8, P. 66). The recommendations of Table 3 may prove helpful in making a selection.

TABLE 3.—*Guide for Selection of Heating System*

| TYPE OF HOUSE | TYPE OF SYSTEM | | TYPE OF FUEL | TYPE OF CONTROL |
	Mild Climate	Cold Climate		
High Cost[1]	A, B, C, D	A, B, C, E	Gas or Oil	Automatic
Medium Cost[2]	B, C, D, G	B, C, D, F	Gas, Oil, or Coal	Automatic or Manual
Low Cost[3]	D, G, H, I	F, G, H	Coal or Wood	Manual

[1]Houses costing more than $8,000.00.
[2]Houses costing between $5,000.00 and $8,000.00.
[3]Houses costing less than $5,000.00.

Key To Table 3

A=Year-round air conditioning.
B=Mechanical warm air system with provision for winter air conditioning and circulation of air in summer.
C=Hot-water system with circulating pump and provision for year-round hot-water supply.
D=Hot-water system, gravity type.
E=Two-pipe vapor system.
F=One-pipe vapor system.
G=Gravity warm air system.
H=Pipeless furnace.
I=Convection heater or stove.

44. Humidity Requirements — It is recommended that provisions be made to maintain the air in the house at a relative humidity of between 40% and 50% during the times that the heating system is operated, so as to make the indoor air more healthful and comfortable, and to economize on heat. (See Table 4.)

TABLE 4.—*Variation of Heating Costs with Decrease or Increase of Inside Temperature Below or Above 70° F.*

INSIDE TEMPERATURE	VARIATION OF COST (Compared to Cost for 70° Temperature)[1]	INSIDE TEMPERATURE	VARIATION OF COST (Compared to Cost for 70° Temperature)[1]
68° F.	− 6.2%	75° F.	+15.6%
69° F.	− 3.1%	76° F.	+18.7%
71° F.	+ 3.1%	77° F.	+21.9%
72° F.	+ 6.2%	78° F.	+25.0%
73° F.	+ 9.4%	79° F.	+28.0%
74° F.	+12.5%	80° F.	+31.0%

[1]Each degree that the inside temperature is increased above 70° F. increases the fuel consumption about 3%.

45. Design of System—Where possible, the services of a professional heating engineer, who has nothing to sell but his services, should be employed to design the heating layout, including the computation of radiation required.

46. Design Temperature — The heating system should be of adequate capacity to maintain a temperature of 70° F., at a distance of not more than 2'-6" above the floor, in all habitable portions of the dwelling when the outside temperature is 10° F. above the lowest recorded minimum for the locality.

47. Heating Systems Using Air Ducts — The following is recommended relative to such systems:

(a) Bathrooms and kitchens should each have a separate outside air vent to prevent the circulation of odors.

(b) The air ducts for warm air furnaces, etc., should be made of galvanized copper-bearing sheet steel, not less than No. 26 Ga. (.0184") in thickness, or the average dwelling. For more pretentious homes, copper may be considered for all ducts that are hidden in the wall and are inaccessible for replacement.

(c) Where possible, ducts should be installed in such a manner as to allow them to be replaced if, and when, it becomes necessary.

(d) All framing members cut away to allow installation of the ducts should be properly reinforced.

48. Warm Air Furnaces—It is recommended that all such furnaces, whether for gravity or mechanical type systems, be made of welded, or riveted and welded, steel instead of cast iron so as to prevent smoke, coal dust, ashes, etc., from escaping from the furnace and being carried throughout the house. A gravity warm air heating system should preferably be of a type that will allow it to be converted into a mechanical system at a later date if so desired.

49. Boilers — Boilers (furnaces) *should be of sufficient size to heat the house without being overloaded or "forced"*. Boilers designed for a particular fuel are more efficient when used with that fuel than when used with another type of fuel. There are boilers on the market, however, that will give good efficiency when used with either coal or oil. Prospective home owners who think that they may have reasons to change from oil to coal (or vice versa) should consider the use of such a boiler as mentioned above.

Where practicable, it is advisable to select a type of boiler (or furnace) that is provided with suitable built-in heating coils for supplying domestic hot water during the heating season, at least, and preferably during the entire year.

50. Oil Burners—A "gun-type" atomizing burner, of a reputable make, is recommended for the average installation.

51. Material for Piping—See Table 1, P. 75.

52. Selection of Equipment—Only reputable brands of equipment should be considered, and then the names of various local people who are using such equipment should be secured so that a careful check may be made in regard to the following important questions: (1) Does the equipment operate satisfactorily? (2) What are the operating costs? (3) Does the local dealer render prompt service at a reasonable cost?

53. Specifying Equipment—It is recommended that several *alternate* brands of heating equipment (possibly of different types) be included in the specifications of your home, for such a procedure may result in a lower bid. The local dealers representing the brands of equipment selected usually will be glad to go over the requirements with prospective home owners, and furnish them with the necessary data for specifying the various parts of the system. Care should be exercised, however, to prevent the omission of important details and the inclusion of *unnecessary* gadgets.

GETTING THE HOUSE BUILT

OBTAINING BIDS AND AWARDING CONTRACT

1. Check Contract Documents—All contract documents, especially the working drawings and specifications, should be checked carefully. (Review Sec. 7, P. 29.)

2. Select Contract Bidders — The contractors who are to be allowed to submit bids should be selected (review Sec. 3, Pars. 8 to 10, P. 14). The number of bidders may range from three (minimum) to six or more (four is a good average). In fairness to the contractors, only contractors who are entirely eligible (from every standpoint) to perform the work should be selected, as each contractor who bids on the job must spend a certain amount of his time in preparing his estimate.

3. Instructions to Bidders—Included with each set of drawings and specifications that are issued to the contractors for their use when estimating, there should be instructions as to the time and place for receiving the bids. About two weeks of time is usually allowed the contractors. The bids should be in written form, and may be received at your home, or the contractors' homes or offices. All bids may be opened and inspected by you in privacy.

4. If Bids Are Too High—If even the lowest bid is excessively high, the contractors should be interviewed to ascertain the cause. It may be possible to eliminate a few "luxury" type of items, and then obtain another set of bids that are more in line with the maximum amount that you have decided to spend for a home. However, if it becomes necessary to "cut corners" on good construction in order to reduce the building costs sufficiently, you are advised to select a smaller, or less costly, type of house.

5. Awarding the Contract—The bids should be examined carefully, especially the list of subcontractors. (This list should be required of each bidder by the General Conditions.) If the lowest bid is based on subcontracts from undesirable subcontractors or lumber mills, and the contractor refuses to replace them with acceptable subcontractors or mills, the next highest bid should be considered. In other words, the contract should not necessarily be awarded on the basis of the lowest bid, but rather on the basis of obtaining the *best* house for the *least* money. This can be accomplished only by awarding the contract to a reputable contractor who subcontracts work to reputable subcontractors, only. Your lawyer should examine the contract documents *before* you sign them.

6. After the Contract Is Signed — After the contract is signed, and before the work is begun, you should take care of the following:

(a) Have a survey made of the lot to establish lot lines and bench marks for the contractor (Par. 1, P. 76).

(b) Take out Owner's contingent liability insurance; and take out, and maintain, fire insurance on the job. (These requirements are listed in the General Conditions recommended in Pars. 12 and 13, P. 30.)

(c) Arrange with Utility Companies for electric power, service pipes, and meters.

(d) Decide upon location of: (1) Electric meter and main switch, (2) hose faucets, (3) telephone outlets, (4) radio outlets, (5) tile bathroom accessories, etc.

(e) Decide upon samples of: (1) Brickwork, (2) stucco, (3) interior plaster, etc.

(f) Select: (1) Paint colors, varnish and stain finishes, etc., (2) finish hardware, (3) linoleum, (4) electrical fixtures, etc.

INSPECTION AND ACCEPTANCE OF WORK

7. Need for Careful Inspection — Good drawings and specifications are necessary for the purpose of showing and specifying good construction; but careful inspection, and a determination to see that the requirements of the contract are fulfilled, are often necessary to assure that such good construction is actually obtained.

8. Responsible Superintendent Necessary—It is of the utmost importance to make sure that the contractor, himself, or a competent and responsible superintendent is on the job at all times during the construction. Also, no change in supervision should be allowed, except in special cases. (The prospective

me owner will be protected in this respect if he
ses the General Conditions recommended by Pars.
2 or 13, P. 30.)

9. Start Right—Inspection should be started at the
me the lot is surveyed, and stopped only after the
mpleted job is accepted. All defective material
ould be condemned and replaced before it has been
sed, in so far as it is possible and advisable, so as to
revent the necessity of "tearing" it out later. The
me to make the contractor re-execute any work con-
ining defective material or workmanship is as soon
ter the discovery of such defective material and
orkmanship as possible. Naturally, a spirit of
riendly co-operation should exist between every
wner and contractor, and the contractor should be

treated with all fairness. Such fair treatment, however, should be combined with the necessary amount
of firmness.

10. Checking List — The Drawings and Specifications should be used as a checking list when inspecting. A review of the various Sections of this Guide,
especially those portions dealing with "Usual Defects", should also prove helpful.

11. Acceptance of Job—The final payment for the
work (Par. 10, P. 30), should be made only after the
house has been *completed* in accordance with the
Drawings and Specifications, and the contractor has
fullfilled the requirements of the General Conditions
as to liens.

BUYING A READY-BUILT HOUSE

1. Examining the Ready-Built House—Any ready-built house that you may consider buying should embody, as nearly as possible, all of the features and quality that you would insist upon having in any home that you should build.

The Building Lot—The location, size of lot, etc., should be appraised just as carefully as though you intended to *build* on the lot (make use of the information presented in Sec. 5). It would be unwise to consider a house that is located in a depreciating or unrestricted neighborhood.

The Exterior Appearance—If your house is to be a source of pride to you, and is to have a reasonable amount of resale value, it should have a pleasing exterior appearance that embodies *good* architecture (review the information given in Sec. 6). If the exterior of the house in question incorporates any important architectural defects, it will be advisable for you to remove this house from your list.

Type of Construction—Each type of construction, such as wood construction, brick veneer construction, stucco construction, etc., has its faults. Study carefully the information given in regard to "Types of House Construction" in Sec. 6, and try to decide upon the type of construction that you prefer. If the ready-built house is of a type of construction that is acceptable to you, study this particular type of construction carefully. Then, when you examine the house in detail, you can make sure that it incorporates the proper material, workmanship, and construction methods that are necessary to make its particular type of construction acceptable.

What Contractor Built the House—This is an important question. Find out the name of the contractor, and investigate him thoroughly (review Sec. 3, Pars. 8 to 10). If he has a poor reputation, you should look for another house. The odds against this particular house will be too great.

2. Depreciation and Obsolescence in an U s e d House—A home loses its economic or monetary value with age just as surely as does an automobile, a radio, a suit of clothes, or any other commodity. This is due to depreciation and obsolescence. (See Fig. 1 and Tables 1 and 2).

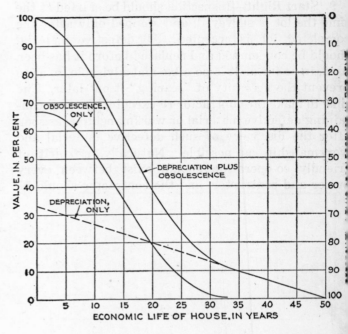

FIG. 1.—*Depreciation, Obsolescence, and Value in a Used Frame House.*

Obsolescence is responsible for 67% of the decline in value of the structure, while depreciation is responsible for only 33% of the decline in value. Such a low depreciation value is based on the structure being kept in good physical repair, however.

(Courtesy of the National Real Estate Magazine)

Depreciation—Depreciation, in its narrow sense, is physical. It is the constant wearing away of the house by the many agents of nature, whose functions are to reduce all dead or inert matter to a "state of dust". For a poorly built house this wearing away process will be extremely rapid, while for a properly built house, it may be relatively slow. Fig. 1 shows that 33% of the original value of the *average* frame house will eventually be lost due to depreciation.

Obsolescence—Obsolescence is a man-made, economic factor, and may be defined as a "going out of style". A house may become obsolete due to outmoded design, rundown neighborhood, lack of modern equipment, or due to any other cause that might make it undesirable as a home; and it should be noted that many houses are "obsolete" the day they are built.

Although developments in home construction come gradually, at the *present* trend of obsolescence the *average* frame house of today will very probably be considered "old" at 10 years of age, and obsolete and undesirable at 33 years; and, as shown by Fig. 1, 67% of the original value of the house will eventually be lost due to *obsolescence*.

Depreciation and Obsolescence Data—Although it is obviously impossible to obtain exact data to cover every case of obsolescence and depreciation, it is believed that the following data (based on information contained in "Boeckh's Manual of Appraisals,"[1] through the courtesy of the publishers) will serve as an useful guide to prospective home owners in estimating the probable useful life of residences and residential equipment. It is apparent that good judgment must be used in regard to determining the obsolescence of a house, for some new homes may be twenty years "out of style", both inside and out, the day they are completed; while other homes may be "ahead of the times", in both style and equipment, at the time of their completion.

[1]Published by the Rough Notes Co., Inc., Indianapolis, Ind.

TABLE 1.—*Probable Useful Life of Residences*
(Table is based on such residences being kept in the usual state of repair during their life).

1-FAMILY RESIDENCE	EXPENSIVE[1]		GOOD[2]		AVERAGE[3]		CHEAP[4]	
	Life in Years	Depreciation Rate, %	Life in Years	Depreciation Rate, %	Life in Years	Depreciation Rate, %	Life in Years	Depreciation Rate, %
Frame	50	2	40	2½	33	3	25	4
Brick Veneer	50	2	45	2¼	36	2¾	28	3½
Masonry	75	1⅓	50	2	40	2½	33	3

[1]"Expensive" denotes residences in which the highest grade of materials have been used and where such materials have, usually, been designed and made specially for the job. Also, such buildings have been constructed by the highest type of contractor, and under complete, competent architectural supervision.

[2]"Good" denotes residences in which standard materials of the best grade have been used throughout, and workmanship meets all architectural requirements. Such buildings have been built by a reputable general contractor and reputable subcontractors.

[3]"Average" denotes residences which meet Building Code requirements but in which less expensive materials have been used. Such buildings have been built by reputable contractors using architect's plans, but without architectural supervision.

[4]"Cheap" denotes residences in which sub-standard construction, cheap or second grade materials, and poor workmanship have been used. Such buildings usually have been built by the so-called "promotional" type of contractor (Jerry-builder) from either stock plans or plans of his own making, and without architectural supervision or guidance.

TABLE 2.—*Probable Useful Life of Residential Equipment*

TYPE OF EQUIPMENT	ESTIMATED LIFE, IN YEARS	DEPRECIATION RATE, IN %	TYPE OF EQUIPMENT	ESTIMATED LIFE, IN YEARS	DEPRECIATION RATE, IN %
Heating Systems:			**Plumbing (contd.):**		
Boilers and Furnaces	20	5.0	Valves—		
Burner Equipment (Gas)	16	6.3	Brass Body, Water or Steam	*	*
Burner Equipment (Oil)	10	10.0	Iron Body, Water or Steam	20	5.0
Radiators	25	4.0	**Roofs:**		
Lighting Systems:			Asbestos	25	4.0
Conduits and Fittings	*	*	Asphalt (Prepared)	15	6.7
Wiring	20	5.0	Galvanized Iron—		
Fixtures	15	6.7	Light or Cold Dipped	15	6.7
			Heavy or Hot Dipped	20	5.0
Plumbing:			Tar and Gravel (5-Ply)	20	5.0
Faucets and Flushing Valves	15	6.7	Tarred Felt	10	10.0
Fixtures (Bath Tubs, Lavatories, Etc.)	25	4.0	Copper	*	*
Pipes—			Slate	*	*
Brass or Copper	*	*	Tile	*	*
Iron, Cold Water	25	4.0			
Iron, Hot-Water or Steam	20	5.0			
Sewer, Cast-Iron or Vitrified	*	*			

*Life of Building.

3. Amount to Pay for a Ready-Built House—This amount should be the value of the building lot *plus* the "sound" value (actual, present-day worth) of the house.

Ascertaining the Value of Building Lot—A fair valuation of the building lot may be arrived at by ascertaining the price asked for neighboring lots of similar value. You may also have a disinterested Building and Loan Association appraise the lot for you. A rough check on your findings may be made by checking the assessed values of the lot at the courthouse. (In this case, it will be necessary for you to ascertain what per cent of the *true value* of the lot that the *assessed* value represents.)

Determining the Sound Value of a House—The "sound value" (actual present-day worth) of a house may be obtained by simply deducting from the present-day *cost of reproducing the house* (Par. 4), its *"net depreciation"* (Par. 5).

4. Ascertaining the Cost of Reproducing House—This figure may be obtained by one of the following methods:

Contractor's Appraisal — A contractor may be hired to examine the house as to quality of material and construction, and to then make a fairly close estimate of the cost of reproducing the house at present costs of material and workmanship. To be of the most value, this estimate must be made just as painstakingly as if the contractor were actually submitting a bid to reproduce the house. Needless to say, the contractor selected should be thoroughly reliable, competent, and *disinterested in the sale of the house.*

This type of appraisal has several advantages, provided you select a competent contractor: (1) You will ascertain how much it would cost to reproduce the house at present prices. (2) You will have the benefit of an inspection by a person who can point out defects.

Expert Appraiser—Another method is to secure the services of an "expert appraiser". This appraiser should preferably be the agent of an appraisal company, but may be employed in the capacity of an appraiser by a Building and Loan Company, Insurance Company, Bank, etc.

5. Determining the Net Depreciation of a House—The following data and instructions (based on information contained in "Boeckh's Manual of Appraisals", through the courtesy of the publishers) are applicable to Table 1, and indicate the manner in which Table 1 may be used for determining the *net depreciation* of a house.

"Observed Condition" Corrective Factors for Table 1

OBSERVED CONDITION OF BUILDING[1]	CORRECTIVE FACTORS[2]	
	Exterior	Interior
Excellent	—10%	—10%
Good	— 5%	— 5%
Normal for Age	0	0
Fair, Only	+ 5%	+ 5%
Poor	+10%	+10%

[1]Buildings that are expected to reach only their normal life span rate as *Normal*. Buildings that may be expected to extend their life expectancy by 10% rate as *Good*. Buildings that may be expected to extend their normal life expectancy by 20%, or more, rate as *Excellent*. Similarly, buildings that may be expected to fall short of their life expectancy by 10% rate as *Fair*, and if by 20%, or more, as *Poor*.

[2]Since maintenance plays such an important part in the life of a structure, the factor of "condition" must be considered, both as to the exterior and interior of the building. Therefore, corrective factors are used either to extend or retard the normal life expectancy of the building, depending on conditions found at the time of the appraisal.

Typical Examples—The following examples will indicate how the net depreciation of a building may be found. When using the corrective factors, the total amount of depreciation (based on the yearly rate given in Table 1) should be limited to 80% (see "Example 2").

EXAMPLE 1. Let us assume a brick residence, *Good* classification, twenty years of age; observed condition excellent, both interior and exterior. Table 1 sets a depreciation rate of 2% per year, or a total of 40%. Because the "observed condition" of the structure shows that it has been well maintained both as to interior and exterior, and the shorter-lived mechanical equipment has been replaced recently, we would be justified in giving the *Excellent* corrections of 10% and 10% (20% total), which would give a final result as follows:

Total depreciation 40%
"Observed Condition" credit (20% of 40%) . . . −8%

    Net depreciation 32%

In the foregoing example, had the exterior of the house been otherwise sound but needed a coat of paint, the probable corrections would have been 5% and 10% (15% total), which would give the following result:

Total depreciation 40%
"Observed Condition" credit (15% of 40%) . . . −6%

    Net depreciation 34%

EXAMPLE 2. Let us assume a frame residence, *Cheap* classification, age 22 years. Observed condition: Exterior sound and well painted; interior sound and in good condition. Considering its general condition, we would expect this building to last another eight to ten years. Because the actual life expectancy is greater than that given in Table 1 by more than 20% for its class, this building's condition would be rated as *Excellent* under "Corrective Factors".

Total depreciation (22 years @ 4% is 88%, but 80%
   is maximum allowed) 80%

"Observed Condition" credit (10% and 10%, or 20% of
   80%) . . . . −16%

Net depreciation 64%

6. Protecting Your Interests—Regardless of all the inspections you may make when buying a ready-built house, you are still, to some extent, buying blindly. This is due, in part, to the fact that so many vital parts are hidden from view. Therefore, when buying a ready-built house, you are advised to have your lawyer draw up a sales contract form that will fully protect *your* interests. Such a form should contain all of the protective clauses of Form No. 1, below, plus the following warranties, and such other warranties and agreements as your lawyer may deem advisable (see Par. 7 of Form No. 1):

(a) A warranty against defective material and workmanship for a specified length of time.

(b) A warranty that certain concealed portions of the building (such as plumbing, building paper, flashing, etc.) are of a specified material and workmanship.

7. Renting Before Buying—Where possible, you are advised to *rent* a house, with an option to buy, before deciding to buy it. This has many advantages, as you will not only have more opportunity to study the house carefully, but will also be better able to decide as to whether or not you like the neighborhood. (See Form No. 2, P. 176.)

FORM NO. 1

SAMPLE CONTRACT FOR THE SALE OF REAL ESTATE

THIS AGREEMENT of Sale made this .... day of ...., 19........, between.............................. ...., hereinafter known as the Buyer, and ...., hereinafter known as the Seller.

WITNESSETH: That for and in consideration of the sum of .... Dollars ($.........................) by $\frac{cash}{check}$ in hand paid, receipt of which is hereby acknowledged, the Buyer agrees to buy, and the Seller agrees to sell, for the sum of.......................................Dollars ($.........................) all that certain piece, parcel, or lot of land, with the buildings and improvements thereon, described as follows, to-wit:

....

....

The purchase price to be paid as follows:

....

....

IT IS AGREED:

1. This Agreement is conditional upon the Buyer obtaining a ....*(FHA, etc.)*......loan of..............................Dollars ($.........................) upon the above described property from the ......*(First National Bank, etc.)*......by......*(Time and date)*......, 19.......... Failure of the Buyer to obtain the above described loan will make this Agreement voidable at the option of the Buyer.

2. The Seller shall convey the above described property with a General Warranty Deed with the usual covenants of title, same to be prepared at the expense of the Seller.

3. All taxes, insurance, rents, and interest shall be prorated as of ...., 19........, and final settlement shall be made and deed delivered on or before ...., 19........, or as soon thereafter as title can be examined and papers prepared, allowing a reasonable time to correct any defects reported by the title examiner.

4. The title shall be free and clear of all liens and encumbrances of every kind, except the following: ....*(Description of any mortgages, or other liens or encumbrances, subject to which the property is sold)*.........

5. The property shall be conveyed subject to all recorded lawful restrictions now thereon; but the incorporation of said restrictions in the deed conveying the property herein above referred to, by fully setting forth therein such restrictions or by reference thereto, shall in nowise extend the life of said restrictions heretofore placed on said property.

6. The Seller shall assume the risk of loss or damage to said premises by fire or other casualty, prior to the delivery of the deed, not caused by the negligence of the Buyer, his family, guests, servants, or agents.

7. The Seller shall, and does, hereby warrant this property as follows, to-wit: ....*(The building lot contains no fill; house is constructed in accordance with attached drawings and specifications; etc.)*................

WITNESS the following signatures and seals made this............... day of.................................., 19........

....(Seal)

....(Seal)

....(Seal)

....(Seal)

FORM No. 2

SAMPLE OPTION FOR THE PURCHASE OF
REAL ESTATE

WITNESSETH: That for and in consideration of the sum of .... ($........................) by

$\frac{cash}{check}$ in hand paid, receipt of which is hereby acknowledged, ..., hereinafter known as the Vendor, agrees for himself, his heirs, executors and administrators, to sell and convey to.., hereinafter known as the Vendee, or to his assigns, for the sum of.. ($........................), all that certain piece, parcel, or lot of land, with the buildings and improvements thereon, described as follows, to-wit:....................

....

....

....

The terms of payment, in the event of the exercise of this option by the Vendee, shall be as follows:................................

....

....

....

IT IS AGREED:

1. This option begins as of............day of............................, 19............, and expires 11:59 p.m. of the....................day of ...., 19.........

2. The Vendee shall notify the Vendor in writing if he decides to exercise this option, such notification to be signed by the Vendee, or his assigns.

3. Within .... days after exercise of this option by the Vendee, the Vendor shall convey to the Vendee the above described property with a General Warranty Deed with the usual covenants of title, same to be prepared at the expense of the Vendor.

4. The Vendor shall assume the risk of loss or damage to said premises by fire or other casualty, prior to the delivery of the deed, not caused by the negligence of the Vendee, his family, guests, servants, or agents.

WITNESS the following signatures and seals made this................ day of.., 19.........

....(Seal)

....(Seal)

....(Seal)

....(Seal)

LIST OF PUBLICATIONS FOR THE HOME BUILDER

1. How to Use the Tables 1 and 2—The following information may prove helpful when using this Section:

Reference Numbers—The purpose of the "Ref. No." opposite each publication listed in Table 1 is merely to make it easier to refer to these publications throughout this Guide.

Source Numbers—The "Source No." opposite each publication listed in Table 1 is a "key" to the name and address of the publisher, who is listed in Table 2, opposite the *same* "Source No."

Free Publications—All publications listed as "free" in Table 1 may be obtained by requesting same on a penny postcard addressed to the publisher listed in Table 2.

Government Publications — These publications, *where prices are shown,* may be obtained by sending the necessary sum to the Superintendent of Documents, Government Printing Office, Washington, D. C. (Do not remit in stamps or foreign money, as these are not acceptable.)

Libraries—Some of the more expensive publications listed in Table 1 may be borrowed from the larger libraries.

INDEX TO PUBLICATIONS LISTED IN TABLE 1

REFERENCE NUMBER (See Table 1)	TITLE	REFERENCE NUMBER (See Table 1)	TITLE
R 1	Architectural	R15	Miscellaneous
R 2	Brick and Mortar	R16	Painting and Decorating
R 3	Chimneys and Fireplaces	R17	Plaster and Lath (Interior)
R 4	Concrete	R18	Plumbing
R 5	Contract Documents	R19	Roofing and Sheet Metal
R 6	Electrical	R20	Specifications[1]
R 7	Financial	R21	Stucco
R 8	Fire Prevention	R22	Termite Prevention
R 9	Floors (Wood)	R23	Tile (Ceramic)
R10	Heating, Ventilating, and Air Conditioning	R24	Wood and Lumber (General)
R11	House Construction (General)	R25	Wood Walls (Interior and Exterior)
R12	Insulating and Sound Proofing		
R13	Landscaping		
R14	Lists of Publications (Miscellaneous)		

[1]Specifications are also contained in References R3-4, R4-6, R4-8, R6-1, R94-, R10-6, R10-7, R10-8, R11-2, R16-14, R18-2, R19-14, R24-8, and R25-3. (See Table 1.)

TABLE 1—*Selected List of Publications for the Home Builder*

Ref. No.	Title	Source No. (See Table 2)	Price
ARCHITECTURAL			
R1-1	List of Documents published by The American Institute of Architects	S3	Free
R1-2	Principles of Professional Practice (A. I. A. Document No. 225)	S3	$ .02
R1-3	Schedule of Proper Charges (A. I. A. Document No. 177)	S3	.02
R1-4	How to Select an Architect by Direct Selection	S3	.02
R1-5	Modern Design (Tech. Bulletin No. 2)	S51	.05
R1-6	Principles of Planning Small Houses (Tech. Bulletin No. 4)	S51	.10
R1-7	List of House Plan Services (LC-801)	S14	Free
R1-8	Planning Neighborhoods for Small Houses (FHA Form No. 2242)	S51	.10
R1-9	Planning the Kitchen (Circular No. C5,3)	S45	Free
R1-10	Shelter for Living	S21	3.75
R1-11	Building or Buying a House	S23	2.75
R1-12	Tomorrow's House	S44	3.00
R1-13	Architectural Graphic Standards	S21	6.00
BRICK AND MORTAR			
R2-1	Brick Structures—How to Build Them	S50	.25
R2-2	Water Permeability of Masonry Walls (BMS7)	S51	.10
R2-3	Practical Bricklaying	S23	1.75
R2-4	Face Brick, Rough and Smooth; Common Brick (R7)	S51	.05
R2-5	Construction of Weather Resistant Masonry Walls	S50	.10
R2-6	Masonry Mortar	S29	Free
CHIMNEYS AND FIREPLACES			
R3-1	Construction of Chimneys and Fireplaces (Farmers' Bulletin No. 1649)	S51	.05
R3-2	Make Your Chimney Safe	S28	Free
R3-3	Chimneys, Flues and Fireplaces; and How to Build Them	S28	Free
R3-4	A Standard Ordinance for Chimney Construction	S27	Free
R3-5	Fireplaces and Chimneys (Farmers' Bulletin No. 1889)	S51	.10
R3-6	The Heart of the Home (Fireplaces)	S50	.20
CONCRETE			
R4-1	Use of Concrete on the Farm (Farmers' Bulletin No. 1772)	S51	.10
R4-2	Foundation Walls and Basements of Concrete	S41	Free
R4-3	Integral Waterproofing for Concrete (TIBM6)	S14	Free
R4-4	Facts About Concrete Masonry	S41	Free
R4-5	Concrete Floors for Residences	S41	Free
R4-6	Concrete Floor Finishes	S41	Free
R4-7	Finishes for Concrete Floors (LC-758)	S14	Free
R4-8	Concrete Sidewalks	S41	Free
R4-9	Making Cellars Dry (Farmers' Bulletin No. 1572)	S51	.05
R4-10	Reinforced Concrete: A Manual of Standard Practice	S10	Free
CONTRACT DOCUMENTS			
R5-1	Contract Documents for Small House Construction (Tech. Bulletin No. 3)	S51	.05
R5-2	The A. I. A. Short Form for Small Construction Contracts	S3	.40
R5-3	A. I. A. General Conditions of the Contract for the Construction of Buildings (Form A2)	S3	.35
R5-4	A. I. A. Agreement Form (Owner and Contractor—Stipulated Sum—Form A1)	S3	.15
R5-5	A. I. A. Owner's Protective Bond (Form B1)	S3	.10
ELECTRICAL			
R6-1	Handbook of Residential Wiring Design	S26	.25
R6-2	Better Lighting	S16	Free
R6-3	Fluorescent Lamps (LC-652)	S14	Free
R6-4	Good Lighting in Houses (Home Information No. 30)	S8	.15
R6-5	Safety Rules for Radio Installations (H35)	S51	.10
R6-6	Electric Light for the Farmstead (Farmers' Bulletin No. 1838)	S51	.10
R6-7	Planning Your Farmstead Wiring and Lighting (Miscellaneous Pub. No. 597)	S43	Free
FINANCIAL			
R7-1	Present Home Financing Methods	S51	.05
R7-2	How to Own Your Home (BH17)	S51	.05
R7-3	Illustrative Case (FHA Form No. 2042)	S51	.20
R7-4	The Best Way to Achieve Low-Cost Housing is to Build Low-Cost Homes	S30	.10
R7-5	How to Acquire a New Home—At Less Than One Dollar Per Day	S30	.10
R7-6	The FHA Plan of Home Ownership (FHA 2098)	S17	Free
R7-7	Financial Aspects of Home Ownership (Home Information No. 1)	S8	.15
R7-8	Financing the Home (Circular A1-3)	S45	Free
FIRE PREVENTION			
R8-1	Safeguarding the Home Against Fire	S27	Free
R8-2	Keep Your Home From Burning	S28	Free
R8-3	Protect Your Property Against Lightning	S28	Free
R8-4	Nature's Artillery (Lightning Protection)	S27	Free
R8-5	Protection of Buildings and Farm Property from Lightning (Farmers' Bulletin No. 1512)	S51	.05
R8-6	Fire Retardant Roofing	S28	.10
FLOORS (Wood)			
R9-1	Selection, Installation, Finish, and Maintenance of Wood Floors for Dwellings (Circular No. 489)	S51	.05
R9-2	Preventing Cracks in New Wood Floors (Leaflet No. 56)	S51	.05
R9-3	Northern Hard Maple, Beech and Birch Floorings	S22	Free
R9-4	How to Lay, Finish and Care for NOFMA Oak Floors	S32	Free
R9-5	Southern Pine Floors	S48	Free
HEATING, VENTILATING AND AIR CONDITIONING			
R10-1	List of Publications and Articles Relating to Home Heating Problems (LC-284)	S14	Free
R10-2	Why Conditioned Air in Houses Improves Human Comfort (Home Information No. 25)	S8	.15
R10-3	How Air in Houses is Conditioned by Modern Equipment (Home Information No. 26)	S8	.15
R10-4	Heating, Ventilating, Air-Conditioning Guide (Annual)	S5	5.00
R10-5	Air-Conditioning in Summer and Winter	S23	3.00
R10-6	Technical Code for the Design and Installation of Mechanical Warm Air Heating Systems	S34	.50
R10-7	Non-Technical Code for the Installation of Mechanical Warm Air Furnace Heating Systems in Residences	S34	.25
R10-8	The Standard Code Regulating the Installation of Gravity Warm Air Heating Systems in Residences	S34	.25
R10-9	A Study of the Oil Burner as Applied to Domestic Heating (Tech. Bulletin No. 109)	S51	.10
R10-10	Choosing a Heating Plant Wisely	S40	.05
R10-11	Mechanical Equipment for the Home (Tech. Bulletin No. 6)	S51	.05
R10-12	Questions and Answers for the Home Fireman	S51	.10
R10-13	Fuels and Burners (Circular G3.5)	S45	Free

TABLE 1 (Cont.)—*Selected List of Publications for the Home Builder*

Ref. No.	Title	Source No. (See Table 2)	Price
R10-14	Oil Burners for Home Heating (Department Circular No. 406)	S51	.05
R10-15	Oil Heat	S39	Free
R10-16	Heating the Home (Circular G3.1)	S45	Free
R10-17	Copper Tube	S11	Free

HOUSE CONSTRUCTION (General)

Ref. No.	Title	Source No. (See Table 2)	Price
R11-1	How to Judge a House	S51	.10
R11-2	Recommended Minimum Requirements for Small Dwelling Construction (BH18)	S51	.15
R11-3	Practical Suggestions on Frame House Construction (No. R991)	S12	Free
R11-4	Use and Abuse of Wood in House Construction (Miscellaneous Pub. No. 358)	S51	.10
R11-5	Recent Developments in Dwelling Construction (Tech. Bulletin No. 1)	S51	.05
R11-6	Light Frame House Construction (Bulletin No. 145)	S51	.40
R11-7	Recent Progress on Housing Research at the Forest Products Laboratory (No. R1193)	S12	Free
R11-8	Pictured Good and Poor Practice in Frame House Construction Details (Tech. Note No. 242)	S12	Free
R11-9	Care and Repair of the House	S51	.20
R11-10	Professional Pointers for Home Makers	S55	Free
R11-11	Prefabricated Homes (CS 125-45)	S51	.05
R11-12	Minimum Construction Requirements for New Dwellings; by States (Obtainable from FHA insuring office in each state)	......	Free

INSULATING AND SOUND PROOFING

Ref. No.	Title	Source No. (See Table 2)	Price
R12-1	Thermal Insulation of Houses (Home Information No. 4)	S8	.15
R12-2	Thermal Insulation: Summary and Conclusions (TIBM 16)	S14	Free
R12-3	Aluminum Foil Insulation (LC 535)	S14	Free
R12-4	Home Insulation With Mineral Products (Information Circular 7220)	S15	Free
R12-5	Condensation Problems in Modern Buildings	S12	Free
R12-6	Accumulation of Moisture in Walls of Frame Construction During Winter Exposure (Report BMS93)	S51	.10
R12-7	Story of Insulation Board	S20	Free
R12-8	Theory and Use of Architectural Accoustical Materials	S1	Free
R12-9	Sound Insulation of Wall and Floor Constructions (BMS 17)	S51	.10
R12-10	Acoustics: Publications by the Staff of the National Bureau of Standards (LC 778)	S14	Free
R12-11	Sound Insulation	S49	Free

LANDSCAPING

Ref. No.	Title	Source No. (See Table 2)	Price
R13-1	Beautifying the Farmstead (Farmers' Bulletin No. 1087)	S51	.05
R13-2	Planting and Care of Lawns (Farmers' Bulletin No. 1677)	S51	.05
R13-3	Beautifying the Home Grounds (A Plan Book)	S48	.25
R13-4	Extend Your Home to All You Own	S9	Free

LISTS OF PUBLICATIONS (Miscellaneous)

Ref. No.	Title	Source No. (See Table 2)	Price
R14-1	List of Published Material Relating to Home Building and Maintenance (LC 805)	S14	Free
R14-2	List of Publications Relating to Building Codes and Construction Practice—Home Building—Building Material Specifications—Home Maintenance (LC 811)	S14	Free
R14-3	Services of the National Bureau of Standards to the Home Building Industry and to the Household (SHBI)	S14	Free

Ref. No.	Title	Source No. (See Table 2)	Price
R14-4	List of FHA Publications	S17	Free
R14-5	Miscellaneous Lists of Publications for Home Builders	S1 to S56	Free

MISCELLANEOUS

Ref. No.	Title	Source No. (See Table 2)	Price
R15-1	Let's Build a Wood Fence	S30	.05
R15-2	Bird-House Book	S47	.15
R15-3	Back-Yard Playgrounds (Home Information No. 5)	S8	.15
R15-4	Material List and Working Details for Lawn Furniture	S47	.15

PAINTING AND DECORATING

Ref. No.	Title	Source No. (See Table 2)	Price
R16-1	Painting Instructions (Leaflet)	S47	Free
R16-2	Aluminum Paints (TIBM 43)	S14	Free
R16-3	Painting on the Farm (Farmers' Bulletin No. 1452)	S51	.05
R16-4	Why Some Wood Surfaces Hold Paint Longer Than Others (Leaflet No. 62)	S51	.05
R16-5	Whitewash and Cold Water Paints	S29	Free
R16-6	When and How to Paint Homes and Farm Buildings (Mimeograph R962)	S12	Free
R16-7	Some Causes of Blistering and Peeling of Paint on House Siding (Mimeograph R6)	S12	Free
R16-8	Paint, Varnish, and Bituminous Materials; List of National Bureau of Standards Publications and Federal Specifications (LC 795)	S14	Free
R16-9	List of Books on Paints and Varnishes and Wood Finishing (Tech. Note No. 195)	S12	Free
R16-10	Painting Exterior Woodwork (Mimeograph R1029)	S12	Free
R16-11	Behavior of House Paints on Different Woods (Mimeograph R1053)	S12	Free
R16-12	Outside House Painting (LC 603)	S14	Free
R16-13	Painting of Steam and Hot Water Radiators (LC 445)	S14	Free
R16-14	Paint Manual: With Particular Reference to Federal Specifications (BMS 105)	S51	1.00

PLASTER AND LATH (Interior)

Ref. No.	Title	Source No. (See Table 2)	Price
R17-1	Metal Lath for Homes	S25	Free
R17-2	Gypsum Lath	S19	Free
R17-3	Suitability of Fiber Insulating Lath as a Plaster Base (BMS 3)	S51	.10
R17-4	The A B C's of Plastering	S19	Free
R17-5	Brief on Gypsum Plaster	S19	Free
R17-6	Adhesion of Gypsum Plaster to Various Backings	S19	Free
R17-7	The Fire Resistance of Gypsum Plaster	S19	Free

PLUMBING

Ref. No.	Title	Source No. (See Table 2)	Price
R18-1	Recommended Minimum Requirements for Plumbing (BH13)	S51	.50
R18-2	Plumbing Manual (BMS 66)	S51	.20
R18-3	Farm Plumbing (Farmers' Bulletin No. 1426)	S51	.05
R18-4	What You Should Know About Plumbing	S40	.05
R18-5	Brass Pipe	S11	Free
R18-6	Sewage Disposal for Suburban and Country Homes (Supplement No. 58 to P. H. Reports)	S18	Free
R18-7	Safe Sewage Disposal for Rural Homes (Home Information No. 28)	S8	.15
R18-8	Farmstead Water Supply (Farmers' Bulletin No. 1448)	S51	.05
R18-9	Good Water for Farm Homes (P. H. Bulletin No. 70)	S51	.05
R18-10	Water-Distributing Systems for Buildings (BMS 79)	S51	.15

TABLE 1 (Cont.)—*Selected List of Publications for the Home Builder*

Ref. No.	Title	Source No. (See Table 2)	Price
	ROOFING AND SHEET METAL		
R19-1	Roofings in the United States—Results of a Questionnaire (BMS 57)	S51	.10
R19-2	Survey of Roofing Materials in the Southeastern States (BMS 6)	S51	.15
R19-3	Survey of Roofing Materials in the Northeastern States (BMS 29)	S51	.10
R19-4	Survey of Roofing Materials in the North Central States (BMS 75)	S51	.15
R19-5	Survey of Roofing Materials in the South Central States (BMS 84)	S51	.15
R19-6	Roofing Slate (R14-28)	S51	.05
R19-7	Shingles: Mineral-Surfaced Asphalt (TIBM 51)	S14	Free
R19-8	Materials Used in Bituminous Built-up Roofing (TIBM 40)	S14	Free
R19-9	Metallic Roofing for Low-Cost House Construction (BMS 49)	S51	.10
R19-10	Roof Coverings for Farm Buildings and Their Repair (Farmers' Bulletin No. 1751)	S51	.05
R19-11	The Life of Your Roof Hangs by a Nail	S11	Free
R19-12	Safeguard Your Home With Copper, Brass and Bronze	S11	Free
R19-13	Monographs on Copper Roofing	S11	Free
R19-14	Sheet Copper (Handbook)	S11	Free
R19-15	Facts About Galvanized Sheets	S7	Free
	SPECIFICATIONS		
R20-1	List of Standards and Specifications for Building and Construction Materials, Fixtures, Supplies, and Equipment (LC 808)	S14	Free
R20-2	List of A. S. T. M. Standards	S5	Free
R20-3	Index and Price List of the New York Building Congress Standard Specifications	S35	Free
R20-4	Standard Metal Lath Specifications for Better Plastering and Concrete Stucco	S25	.05
R20-5	Standard Specifications for Gypsum Plastering	S19	Free
R20-6	Specifications for Lime Plastering	S29	Free
R20-7	Basic Specifications for Tile Work, No. K-300	S52	Free
R20-8	Specifications Manual for Certified Oak Floors	S32	Free
	STUCCO		
R21-1	Investigations of Portland Cement Stucco Construction (TIBM 19)	S14	
R21-2	Recommendations for Portland Cement Stucco Construction (TIBM 20)	S14	Free
R21-3	Finishes and Maintenance of Portland Cement Stucco Construction (TIBM 21)	S14	Free
R21-4	Portland Cement Stucco	S41	Free
R21-5	Plasterer's Manual	S41	Free

Ref. No.	Title	Source No. (See Table 2)	Price
	TERMITE PREVENTION		
R22-1	Exposing the Termite	S30	Free
R22-2	Injury to Buildings by Termites (Leaflet No. 101)	S51	.05
R22-3	Subterranean Termites and Their Control (Farmers' Bulletin No. 1911)	S51	.10
R22-4	Prevention of Termite Damage to Buildings	S56	Free
R22-5	Protection Against Termites (Tech. Circular No. 2)	S17	Free
R22-6	Termite Shields	S11	Free
R22-7	Tidewater Red Cypress Repels Termite Attack	S47	Free
	TILE (Ceramic)		
R23-1	Facts About Tile	S52	Free
	WOOD AND LUMBER (General)		
R24-1	Wood Handbook	S51	.35
R24-2	Suitability of Woods for Use in the Frame House (Tech. Note No. 245)	S12	Free
R24-3	Correct Moisture Content of Lumber (Tech. Note No. D-5)	S12	Free
R24-4	Seasoning, Handling and Care of Lumber (Consumers' Edition)	S51	.15
R24-5	Selection of Lumber for Farm and Home Buildings (Farmers' Bulletin No. 1756)	S51	.05
R24-6	Lumber Grade-Use Guide for Softwood and Hardwood Lumber in Building and General Construction	S30	1.50
R24-7	Prevention and Control of Decay in Dwellings (Tech. Note No. 251)	S12	Free
R24-8	Architect's Specification Manual for Residences (Grade-Use Guide)	S48	Free
R24-9	Grade Marking of Lumber for the Consumer's Protection	S51	.10
R24-10	Reducing the Hazards of Inadequately Dried Lumber in Postwar Housing (No. R1600)	S12	Free
R24-11	Weathering and Decay (Tech. Note No. 221)	S12	Free
R24-12	Treated Lumber—Its Use and Economies	S51	.05
R24-13	The Preservative Treatment of Farm Timbers (Farmers' Bulletin No. 744)	S51	.05
	WOOD WALLS (Interior and Exterior)		
R25-1	Wood Walls Produce the Best Houses for the Least Money	S30	.10
R25-2	Wood Shingles (CS 31-38)	S51	.05
R25-3	Certigrade Handbook of Red Cedar Shingles	S42	Free
R25-4	An Inside Story of Tidewater Red Cypress for Interiors of Beauty and Stability	S47	Free
R25-5	Paneling Old or New Interiors With Real Pine	S54	.10
R25-6	Modern Home Interiors	S30	.10
R25-7	Beautiful and Practical Knotty Pine	S54	Free
R25-8	All Woodwork Tidewater Red Cypress (About Williamsburg Lodge, Williamsburg, Virginia)	S47	Free
R25-9	Make Your Attic Livable	S54	Free

TABLE 2—*Sources of Home-Building Information*

Source No.	Names and Addresses
S1	Acoustical Materials Association, 350 Fifth Ave., New York 1, N. Y.
S2	American Concrete Institute, New Center Bldg., Detroit, Mich.
S3	American Institute of Architects, The Octagon, 1741 New York Ave., N. W., Washington 6, D. C.
S4	American Institute of Steel Construction, Inc., 101 Park Ave., New York 17, N. Y.
S5	American Society of Heating and Ventilating Engineers, 51 Madison Ave., New York 10, N. Y.
S6	American Society for Testing Materials, 260 S. Broad St., Philadelphia 2, Pa.
S7	American Zinc Institute, Inc., 35 E. Wacker Drive, Chicago 1, Ill.
S8	Better Homes in America, Purdue Research Foundation, West Lafayette, Ind.
S9	California Redwood Association, 405 Montgomery St., San Francisco 4, Cal.
S10	Concrete Reinforcing Steel Institute, Builders Bldg., Chicago 1, Ill.
S11	Copper and Brass Research Association, 420 Lexington Ave., New York 17, N. Y.
S12	Department of Agriculture (Forest Products Laboratory), Madison, Wis.
S13	Department of Commerce (Bureau of Foreign and Domestic Commerce), Washington 25, D. C.
S14	Department of Commerce (National Bureau of Standards), Washington 25, D. C.
S15	Department of the Interior (Bureau of Mines), Washington 25, D. C.
S16	Edison Electric Institute, 420 Lexington Ave., New York 17, N. Y.
S17	Federal Housing Administration, Washington 25, D. C.
S18	Federal Security Agency (Public Health Service), Washington 25, D. C.
S19	Gypsum Association, 211 W. Wacker Drive, Chicago 6, Ill.
S20	Insulation Board Institute, 111 W. Washington St., Chicago 2, Ill.
S21	John Wiley and Sons, Inc., 440 Fourth Ave., New York 16, N. Y.
S22	Maple Flooring Manufacturers Association, 1740 McCormick Bldg., Chicago, Ill.
S23	McGraw-Hill Book Co., Inc., 330 West 42nd St., New York 18, N. Y.
S24	Meredith Publishing Co., Des Moines, Iowa.
S25	Metal Lath Manufacturers Association, Engineers Bldg., Cleveland 14, Ohio.
S26	National Adequate Wiring Bureau, 155 E. 44th St., New York, N. Y.
S27	National Board of Fire Underwriters, 85 John St., New York 7, N. Y.
S28	National Fire Protection Association, 60 Batterymarch St., Boston, Mass.
S29	National Lime Association, 927-15th St., N. W., Washington 5, D. C.
S30	National Lumber Manufacturers Association, 1319-18th St., N. W., Washington 5, D. C.
S31	National Mineral Wool Association, 1270 Sixth Ave., New York 20, N. Y.
S32	National Oak Flooring Manufacturers Association, Inc., 830 Dermon Bldg., Memphis, Tenn.
S33	National Terrazzo and Mosaic Association, Inc., 1420 New York Ave., N. W., Washington 5, D. C.
S34	National Warm-Air Heating and Air-Conditioning Association, 145 Public Square, Cleveland 14, Ohio.
S35	New York Building Congress, The, 101 Park Ave., New York, N. Y.
S36	Northern Hemlock and Hardwood Manufacturers Association, Oshkosh, Wis.
S37	Northern Pine Manufacturers Association, 4438 Wentworth Ave., Minneapolis, Minn.
S38	Northeastern Lumber Manufacturers Association, Inc., 271 Madison Ave., New York, N. Y.
S39	Oil-Heat Institute of America, Inc., 30 Rockfeller Plaza, New York 20, N. Y.
S40	Plumbing and Heating Industries Bureau, 35 E. Wacker Drive, Chicago 1, Ill.
S41	Portland Cement Association, 33 W. Grand Ave., Chicago 10, Ill.
S42	Red Cedar Shingle Bureau, 5508 White Bldg., Seattle, Wash.
S43	Rural Electrification Administration, Washington 25, D. C.
S44	Simon and Schuster, Inc., 1230 Sixth Ave., New York, N. Y.
S45	Small Homes Council, Mumford House, University of Illinois, Urbana, Ill.
S46	Small Homes Guide, 82 W. Washington St., Chicago 2, Ill.
S47	Southern Cypress Manufacturers Association, Jacksonville, Fla.
S48	Southern Pine Association, Canal Bldg., New Orleans, La.
S49	Steel Joist Institute, 201 N. Wells St., Chicago, Ill.
S50	Structural Clay Products Institute, 1756 K. St., N. W., Washington 6, D. C.
S51	Superintendent of Documents, Government Printing Office, Washington 25, D. C.
S52	Tile Manufacturers Association, Inc., The, 50 E. 42nd St., New York 17, N. Y.
S53	West Coast Lumbermen's Association, 364 Stuart Bldg., Seattle, Wash.
S54	Western Pine Association, 510 Yeon Bldg., Portland, Oregon.
S55	Weyerhaeuser Sales Company, St. Paul, Minn.
S56	Wood Preserving Corporation, The, Koppers Bldg., Pittsburgh, Pa.

INDEX